Digital TV, Satellite & Multimedia

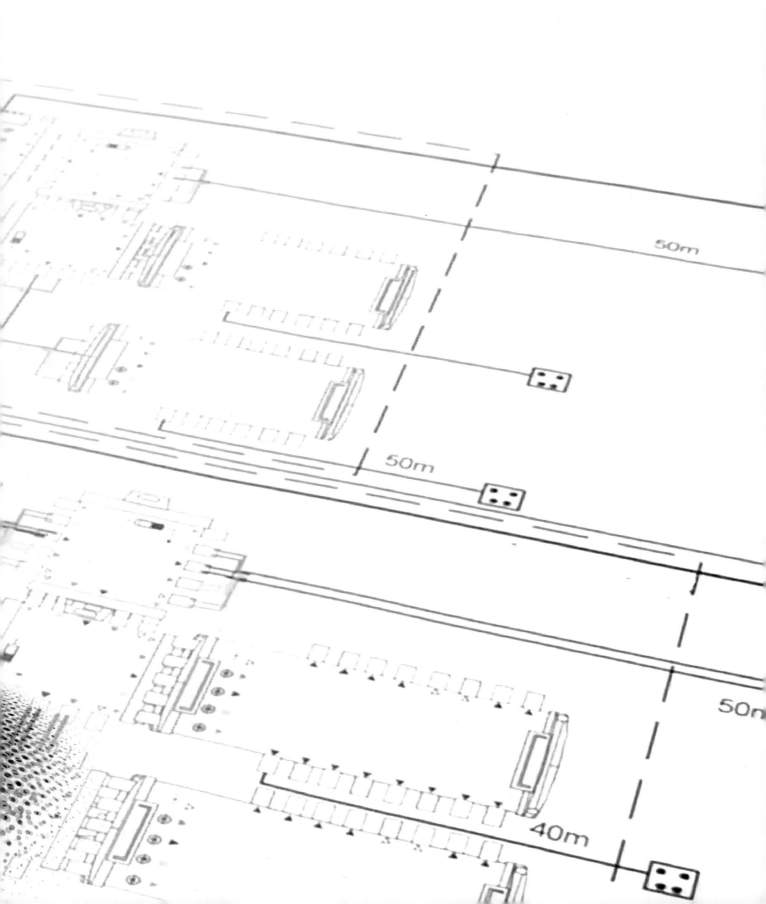

Digital TV, Satellite & Multimedia

by

R A Calaz
C Eng, B Sc(Eng), MIET, ACGI, MSCTE

Copyright notice

Published by Vision Products (Europe) Ltd
Units 1-2 Redbourne Park
Liliput Road
Brackmills
Northampton
NN4 7DT
Telephone: 0845 017 1010
Fax: 0845 017 1011
Website: www.vision-products.co.uk

Produced by the marketing department at Vision
Text Design: Lisa Tweed
Cover Design: Gareth Wraight
Production Editor: Pete French

ISBN: 978-0-9562748-0-9
Copyright © 2009 Vision Products (Europe) Ltd

About the Author

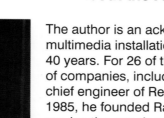

The author is an acknowledged expert in the field of TV, satellite and multimedia installations having been a Chartered Engineer for more than 40 years. For 26 of those years, Bob was with the Rediffusion group of companies, including a secondment in South Africa for 15 years as chief engineer of Rediffusion South Africa. Returning home to the UK in 1985, he founded Race Communications Ltd - based in Berkshire – to service the growing TV industry. The company thrives to this day with Bob planning, specifying and supplying Digital Switchover equipment to professional installers countrywide.

Bob has written and presented numerous technical articles and papers throughout the world and is always in demand as an advisor to a variety of commercial, industry and governmental bodies. In addition, he spends several days a week running technical training courses for military and civilian personnel at the Career Transition Partnership in Aldershot.

Bob is married with two children, is a keen Rotarian and spends his weekends at his house in Kent.

Acknowledgements and Thanks

A lot of people helped to create this book.

I am particularly indebted to Les Hampson of TV & Satellite Ltd who spent many hours proofreading the draft copy and came up with many suggestions on how to improve the document.

Many other individuals and companies gave me help and assistance including the following:-
Keith Bail; Mark Bartlett; Dr C Bewick; Dr J Boccaccio; Stuart Calaz; Richard Clarke; Ron Etheridge, Brian Horobin; Ivan Horrocks; Simon Humphries; Roger Miles; Matt Presdee; Barry Simpson; Richard Stallworthy; Jeff Tyler; Kevin Wright.

Information, logos and images from the organisations below were also used. Copyright remains with the respective copyright holders.

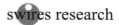

Disclaimer
All statements made and opinions given in this publication are interpretations made by the author from the information available to him, and should not be relied upon as statements of fact.

Contents

PART ONE - FUNDAMENTALS OF ELECTRICITY   Page

1.1   Electricity   13
1.2   Voltage   14
1.3   Current   14
1.4   Resistance   15
1.5   Ohm's law   16
1.6   Power   16
1.7   Prefixes   16
1.8   Voltages   17
1.9   UHF and satellite TV signal levels   18

PART TWO - DIGITAL TELEVISION

2.1   Analogue picture formats   21
2.2   Digital picture formats   23
2.3   Analogue to digital conversion   25
2.4   Digital compression   26
2.5   Programme multiplexing   28
2.6   System overload   30
2.7   Noise removal and error correction   32

PART THREE – DIGITAL TV DISPLAYS

3.1   The home cinema   35
3.2   Picture displays   36
3.3   The cathode ray tube   37
3.4   Flat panel TV displays   38
3.5   High Definition TV   41
3.6   Analogue Interconnections   43
3.7   Digital interconnections   45
3.8   HDMI cables and connectors   46

PART FOUR – MODULATION TECHNIQUES

4.1   Radio waves   51
4.2   Types of modulation   58

PART FIVE – UHF BROADCASTING AND RECEPTION

5.1   Broadcasting formats   65
5.2   Principles of radio and TV aerials   67
5.3   UHF signal measurements   73
5.4   TV amplifiers   77
5.5   Splitters, combiners, diplexers and filters   81
5.6   Mounting hardware   84
5.7   Installation techniques   89
5.8   Typical domestic systems   100
5.9   Troubleshooting   102

Page

PART SIX – UHF SIGNAL DISTRIBUTION
6.1   Coaxial cables and connectors   109
6.2   Distribution within the home   116
6.3   Multi-dwelling units   119
6.4   MATV network planning   127
6.5   Choice of SMATV relay channels   133
6.6   Gap fillers   136

PART SEVEN – SATELLITE TV RECEPTION
7.1   Satellite locations   139
7.2   Satellite footprints and frequency bands   140
7.3   Dish antennas   143
7.4   Feedhorns and LNBs   147
7.5   Signal measurements   154
7.6   Satellite receivers   155
7.7   BSkyB installations   156
7.8   Multi-satellite reception   165
7.9   Motorised systems   172

PART EIGHT – SATELLITE TV DISTRIBUTION
8.1   System concepts   181
8.2   Multiple Sky installations   184
8.3   System concepts   190
8.4   System electrical safety   194
8.5   Network planning   196
8.6   Installation techniques   212

PART NINE – TEST EQUIPMENT FOR TV AND SATELLITE RECEPTION
9.1   The frequency spectrum   219
9.2   Analogue TV measurement parameters   221
9.3   Digital TV measurement parameters   222
9.4   Signal level meters   227
9.5   Spectrum analysers   228

PART TEN – FIBRE OPTIC DISTRIBUTION
10.1   Why fibre?   233
10.2   The propagation of light   234
10.3   Wavelengths and types of propagation   235
10.4   Fibre construction   236
10.5   Fibre connectors   237
10.6   Fibre jointing techniques   237
10.7   Fibre hardware   246
10.8   System planning   247
10.9   Installation and commissioning   248

Page

PART ELEVEN – THE DISTRIBUTION OF VOICE AND DATA SIGNALS
11.1   An introduction to telephony   251
11.2   Telephone installations   252
11.3   Data switching and routing   256
11.4   The internet   258
11.5   Broadband internet connections   261
11.6   VoIP   263
11.7   IPTV   264

PART TWELVE – STRUCTURED CABLE NETWORKS
12.1   Network concepts   267
12.2   Network cables and connectors   269
12.3   Installation techniques   271

APPENDICES
A   Health and Safety   281
B   References and websites   289
C   Abbreviations and glossary of terms   291

Part One - Fundamentals of Electricity

1.1 Electricity

Electricity can be compared to the water distribution system in your house. With everything turned off, the water pressure exists, but no water is used. When a tap is turned on, water flows in the pipe, the quantity depending on the pressure in the mains, the size (or resistance) of the pipe and the amount the tap is turned on. As more taps are opened, more water is used. If too many taps are turned on at the same time, the pressure drops and there is very little water coming from each tap.

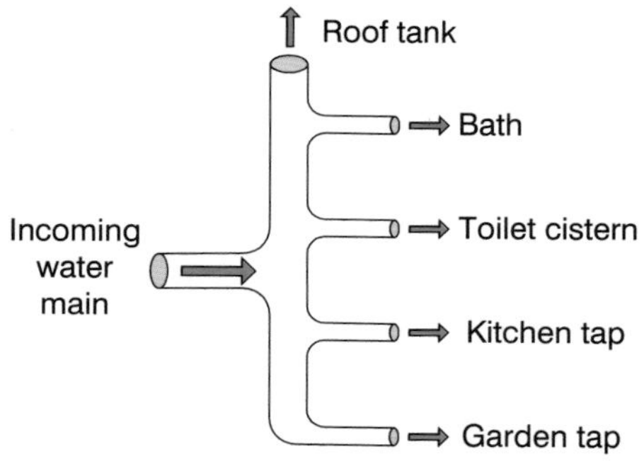

A domestic electricity supply works in much the same way.

The equivalent of water pressure is the mains "voltage". With all the switches turned off, no energy flows through the cables. When a switch is turned on, "current" flows through them, the amount depending on the voltage applied, the size of the cables and the "resistance" of the load. As more switches are turned on, more current is used.

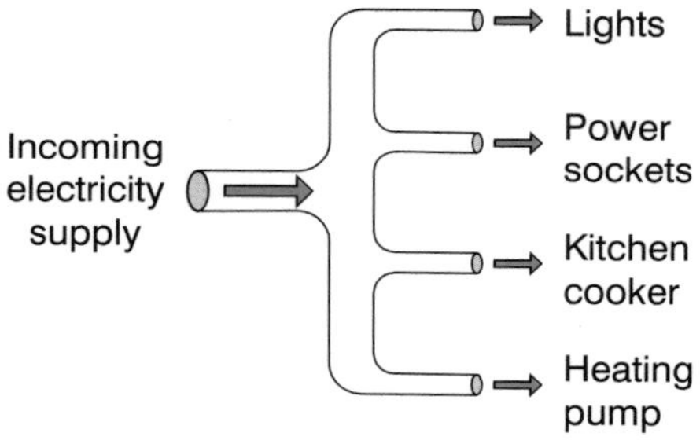

In a domestic environment, lighting cables are relatively thin (typical cross sectional area (CSA) of $1mm^2$) because the current requirements are small and a circuit breaker limits the maximum current to six amps. Power cables to wall sockets are thicker ($2.5mm^2$) and the total current consumption is limited to thirty amps. A kitchen cooker utilises $4mm^2$ cables to cater for currents of up to forty amps. This is why your electricity consumer unit incorporates circuit breakers of different values.

Keywords

- Voltage
- Current
- Resistance

[Diagram: Incoming water main branching to Roof tank, Bath, Toilet cistern, Kitchen tap, Garden tap]

[Diagram: Incoming electricity supply branching to Lights, Power sockets, Kitchen cooker, Heating pump]

Keywords

Voltage •

Multimeter •

1.2 Voltage

Voltage (V) can be regarded as the source of energy and is measured in Volts. The mains supply in Britain is nominally 230 Volts. Radio transmitters often radiate at much higher voltages whilst TV aerials receive small voltages – tiny fractions of a volt. Voltage is usually the most important characteristic and all signal level meters measure voltages. A "multimeter" can be used to measure low voltages such as those generated by a torch battery, for higher voltages use an electricians multimeter with properly shrouded leads conforming to the relevent British Standard.

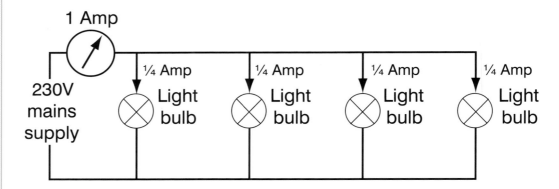

1.3 Current

Amps •

Current (I) is the energy flowing through a cable and is measured in Amperes or Amps. All active electronic circuits use current provided by a power supply unit (PSU) and the total current requirement can be calculated by adding together all the individual current requirements. Current can also be measured using a multimeter:

Note that the current consumed by a light bulb will vary, depending on its wattage.

1.4 Resistance

Resistance (R) is defined in Ohms and by the symbol Ω on a circuit diagram. A "resistor" is usually the most common component in electronic circuits and its value can be determined from the coloured stripes on its body as shown alongside:

The first and second stripes indicate the first and second digits of the value in Ohms, and the third stripe indicates the number of subsequent zeros.

For example: Red Red Orange

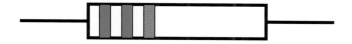

The value of this resistor is 22 000Ω.
The only resistor value likely to be encountered by installers is 75Ω. Such a resistor would have stripes coloured violet/green/black:

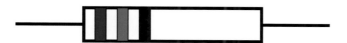

0	Black	■
1	Brown	■
2	Red	■
3	Orange	■
4	Yellow	■
5	Green	■
6	Blue	■
7	Violet	■
8	Grey	■
9	White	□

There is sometimes a fourth stripe to indicate its tolerance (or how close it is to the stated value):

Gold	+/- 5%
Silver	+/- 10%
No fourth stripe	+/- 20%

Some connectors have 75Ω resistors built into them – they are known as 75Ω terminations and are used at the end of a system line or on an unused high output of a distribution amplifier.

Resistance values can also be measured with a multimeter

Keywords

- Ohms

- Resistance colour code

- Terminations

1.5 Ohm's Law

Ohm's Law •

This states the relationship between these three values:

Voltage = Current x Resistance   or   **V = I x R**

If two of these values are known, the third one can be calculated. The formula is often written as follows to illustrate these relationships:

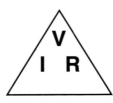

Thus,   **V = I x R**   **I = V/R R = V/I**

For instance, if a light bulb is connected to the 230V mains power supply and consumes 0.5 Amps of current, its resistance can be calculated as follows:

Resistance = Voltage / Current   = 230 / 0.5   = 460Ω

1.6 Power

Power •

Power (P) is measured in Watts. Its relationship to Volts and Amps is as follows:

Power = Current x Voltage   or   **P = I x V**

Or, inside a triangle:

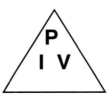

The power of the lamp in the above example can therefore be calculated as follows:

P = I x V   = 0.5 x 230   = 115 watts

1.7 Prefixes

Voltage Prefixes •

In order to simplify the recording of high and low voltages, prefixes are used, as follows:

One millionth of a Volt	= 1 microvolt	(μV)
One thousandth of a Volt	= 1 millivolt	(mV)
One Volt	= 1 volt	(V)
One thousand Volts	= 1 kilovolt	(kV)
One million Volts	= 1 megavolt	(MV)

Keywords

The same prefixes are used for amps, ohms and watts (and also for other parameters, as will be seen later). For example:

One thousandth of a Volt	= 1 millivolt	(mV)
One thousandth of an Amp	= 1 milliamp	(mA)
One thousandth of an Ohm	= 1 milliohm	(mΩ)
One thousandth of a Watt	= 1 milliwatt	(mW)

1.8   Voltages

Since the voltage levels at the output of a TV or satellite amplifier can be up to one thousand times higher than the input level, our industry uses a more convenient unit of measurement, called a decibel or dB.

Most signal meters display levels in dB with reference to 1µV (abbreviated to dBµV) and the conversion from Volts to dBµV is as follows:

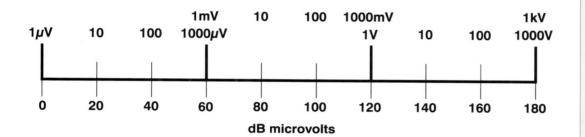

dB microvolts

• Decibel (dB)

• dB Microvolts

Other meters display levels in dBmV (dBs with reference to 1mV) as shown below:

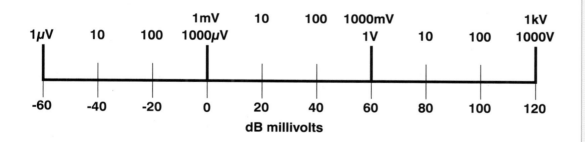

dB millivolts

• dB Millivolts

Note that, to convert from dBmV to dBµV, one simply adds 60 to the reading.

Keywords

dB Signal Levels •

1.9   UHF and Satellite TV Signal Levels

Domestic aerial and satellite installers always measure signal levels in dBµV or dBmV because the mathematics is limited to simple addition and subtraction. Losses in a system are subtracted and amplifier gains are added. For instance, if the signal level from an aerial is 65dBµV and the loss on the coaxial cable between the aerial and TV receiver is 10dB, the signal level at the TV is 65 − 10 = 55dBµV:

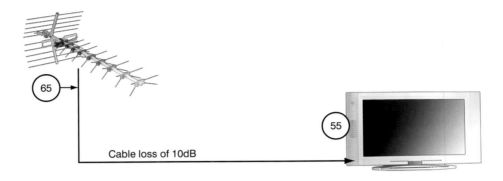

If an amplifier with a gain (or amplification) of 13dB is added at the receiver location, the signal will be increased by 13dB to 68dBµV:

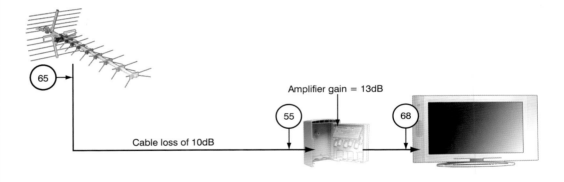

Note: *The figures inside the circles represent the signal levels in dBµV, a convention that will be used throughout this document.*

Amplifier Location •

If the amplifier were fitted at the aerial location instead of being adjacent to the TV receiver, the signal levels on the cable would be different but the signal level into the TV receiver would be the same (this would actually give better results, as described later in the document).

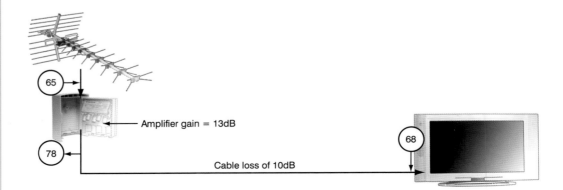

Keywords

• Splitter Loses

If the signal is split to feed two outlet locations, the splitter would reduce the signal to each leg by 4dB and the levels would be as follows:

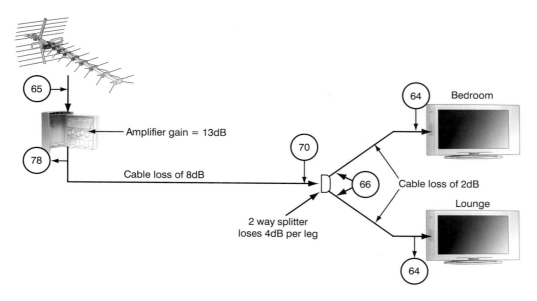

These examples show that the use of dB makes the calculation of signal levels on a system very easy!

The same principles apply to satellite signals. If the signal level from the LNB is 65dBμV and the cable loss is 15dB, the level at the input to the satellite receiver is 50dBμV:

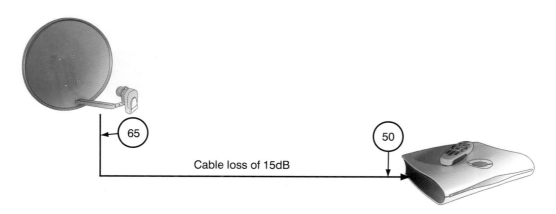

It is important to be able to measure signal levels because these will determine the reliability of the system. If the levels are too high or too low, the overall performance will be adversely affected.

Connectors & Adapters

VISION®

Crimp Fitting

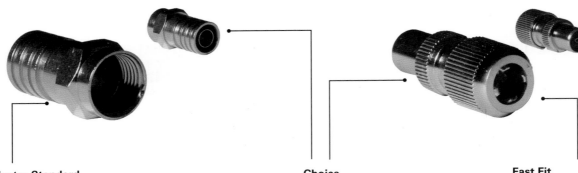

Twist Fitting

Industry Standard
Connection for everyday use

Choice
Material to suit budget. Options include
Brass, Zinc, Nickel & Aluminium

Fast Fit
Connection for low
stress environments

Compression Fitting

Adapters & Terminators

Ulra Secure
Cable connection for
demanding situations

Wide Variety
Models available to change
gender, space plugs and
extend cables. Options
include F type, BNC, IEC TV
& Quick Links.

Features will vary across the range from model to model

Specialist Tools Available In The Vision Range

| Compression Tool | 3-Jaw Crimping Tool | F Connector Spanner | F Connector Grip Tool |

Part Two - Digital Technology

2.1 Analogue Picture Formats

A UK analogue picture is made up of 625 horizontal lines which are scanned in sequence from left to right, from the top of the screen working downwards.

All the odd-numbered lines are scanned first, in one fiftieth of a second – this is called a field. The even numbered lines are scanned during the next fiftieth of a second, so a whole picture (or frame) takes two fiftieths or one twenty fifth of a second. This process (called **"interlaced scanning"**) reduces the perceived flicker on the screen – the human eye thinks that it is seeing fifty pictures per second, whereas it is only seeing fifty "half pictures" each second. It takes a finite time for the beam to return from the bottom left of the picture to the top right (to start the next field) – this time interval is used to transmit several pages of **teletext**. DVD players work differently. They sequence each picture line-by-line – a technique known as **"progressive scanning"**.

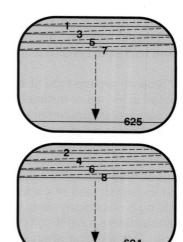

An analogue **"video"** signal is the electrical waveform representing one or more lines of a picture. A single line of the video waveform for a test signal is shown below:

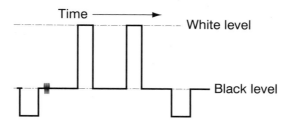

For a picture that changes from black to white across the screen, the video waveform would look as follows:

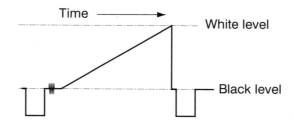

Keywords

- Analogue Formats
- Interlaced Scanning
- Teletext
- Progressive Scanning
- Video Test Signal
- Video Waveform

21

Keywords

For a normal picture, the corresponding video waveform would look as shown in the diagram alongside, the deviations between black and white representing the brightness of that part of the scene.

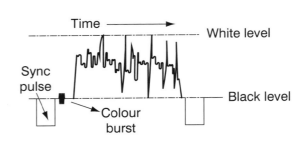

Sync Pulse •

A line "synchronising pulse" (abbreviated to "sync pulse") is transmitted at the end of each line. This is "blacker-than-black" and not seen by the viewer – it is used to synchronise the line scanning circuit in each TV receiver. A wider field sync pulse performs the same function for

Oscilloscope •

the field scan circuit. An "oscilloscope" is needed to display a video waveform, although some makes of spectrum analyser can show a line sync pulse.

TV receiver picture tube sizes are quoted in inches or millimetres using the diagonal measurement between opposite corners of the screen. The ratio between the width and height of a picture is called the

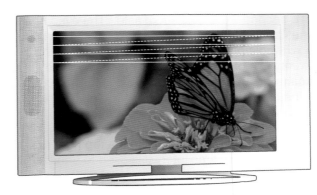

Aspect Ratio •

aspect ratio. Early TV receivers had an aspect ratio of 4 x 3 (4 units wide by 3 units high) although some manufacturers have modified this to 5 x 4. This was fine when all films were made with an aspect ratio of 4 x

Cinemascope •
Widescreen •

3, but these days, films are made in **cinemascope** which has an aspect ratio of 16 x 9. For this reason, most people now purchase **widescreen** TV receivers with a 16 x 9 aspect ratio.

This creates a problem for viewers watching a cinemascope transmission on a TV receiver with a 4 x 3 aspect ratio. They must either watch the full 16 x 9 picture with a black stripe at the top and

Letterbox •

bottom (this is called a **letterbox** format) or watch only the centre of the cinemascope picture. Terrestrial broadcasters sometimes make this decision on behalf of the viewer when they transmit a cinemascope

film in the 4 x 3 format. BSkyB satellite receivers allow a viewer with a 4 x 3 TV receiver to choose which option they prefer when watching a cinemascope transmission.

Widescreen •
Formats

Viewers with widescreen receivers can normally choose how they wish to view a 4 x 3 transmission. The options include:
• Watching in 4 x 3 format with a black stripe either side of the picture
• Allowing the picture to fill the screen width and losing the top and bottom of the picture
• Stretching the picture in the horizontal direction to fill the screen
• Stretching just the horizontal edges of the picture to fill the screen

SCART •

Some broadcasters transmit information as to the aspect ratio being used. The set top box then controls the aspect ratio of a widescreen TV receiver using pin 8 of the SCART. This feature is not available unless a SCART lead is being used.

2.2 Digital Picture Formats

Digital pictures are scanned out in the same way as analogue pictures, but they are made up of individual elements (pixels) which are relayed in blocks or slices. Each pixel has a luminance (brightness) value, chrominance (colour) value and information as to its position on the screen.

Pixels are processed in groups of 64 (ie in the form of a square on the tube face, 8 pixels wide and 8 pixels high). Several such squares in sequence are referred to as a slice.

Groups of 8x8 pixels form a slice

Digital signals can have the following advantages over analogue signals:
- More channels can be accommodated in the same frequency band. A single UHF TV channel can accommodate one analogue programme or (typically) up to eight or nine digital programmes.
- It is easier to provide features such as interactivity.
- Digital TV uses much of the same technology as computers, resulting in the same benefits as computer performance improves.
- Better picture and sound quality can be achieved.

Analogue and digital can be compared in basic terms as follows:

Analogue TV
- Picture resolution is about 396 x 529 = 210,000 pixels
- Digital NICAM stereo sound has FM-like quality. Analogue sound (non NICAM) is often poor
- Picture snow and ghosting can occur
- PAL artefacts such as dot crawl and cross colouration may become visible
- The picture degrades gracefully
- No Electronic Programme Guide is available
- Teletext has limited resolution and colours, and lacks features

Digital Terrestrial TV
- Picture resolution is about 720 x 576 = 414,720 pixels
- Digital MPEG2 stereo sound has near-CD quality
- Much better immunity to interference, with no evidence of ghosting / snow
- Digital artefacts may become visible with rapidly moving objects
- The picture freezes suddenly
- Electronic Programme Guide (EPG) available

Keywords

- Pixels

- Luminance
- Chrominance

- Pixel Blocks

- Pixel Slices

- Advantages of Digital

Keywords

- Teletext has modern feel and many features
- Has potential for further development

Binary Numbers •

Binary Data •

Digital information is carried as "0"s and "1"s – these are called **binary numbers**. The simplest electrical circuit is a switch, that can be either off (0) or on (1), so a series of switches can represent a sequence of "0"s and "1"s, or binary data. The switches can be either "daisy-chained" (serial data) or in parallel (parallel data). Because the switches hold this information, they can be regarded as a data store, or memory.

Bits and Bytes •

Binary data can also be represented by two different voltage levels. By convention, 0V represents a "0" and +5V represents a "1". The "pulses" in the drawing are called **"bits"**; a group of 8 such bits is known as a **"byte"**:

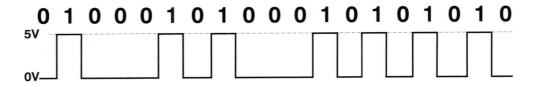

If a digital signal is affected by noise, say by dropping from 5V to 4.5V, a "conditioning" circuit can restore the wrong voltage to the right one. Noisy digital signals can therefore be "cleaned" to be exactly as they were before they were affected by the noise.

A single bit can have only two states – a "0" or a "1".
Two such bits can have four states: 00 01 10 11
Three bits can have eight states: 000 001 010 011 100 101 110 111 and so on.
It can therefore be seen that, every time the number of bits increases by one, the number of states doubles, as shown below:

Binary States •

No of bits	1	2	3	4	5	6	7	8
No of states	2	4	8	16	32	62	128	256

As previously stated, analogue signals are made up of lines of information, whereas digital signals are made up of picture elements, or "pixels". The characteristics of each pixel can be defined by a series of binary numbers, representing its brightness (luminance), colour (chrominance) and position on the screen (co-ordinates). A digital picture is therefore represented by a continuous stream of binary digits.

Keywords

- Analogue to Digital Conversion

- Sawtooth Waveform

- Sampling

- Brightness Levels

- Bit Rates

2.3   Analogue to Digital Conversion

The following diagram shows a "sawtooth" display with the picture changing from black to white across the screen. Also shown is the equivalent analogue video signal for one line of the picture.

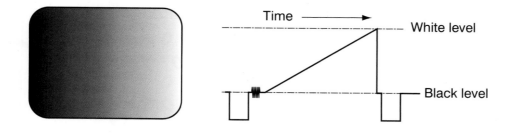

In the next drawing, **"A"** represents the same video waveform. The signal level is sampled at regular intervals. The resultant samples are shown in **"B"**.

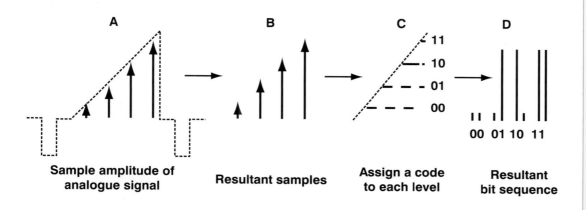

| Sample amplitude of analogue signal | Resultant samples | Assign a code to each level | Resultant bit sequence |

A binary code is then assigned to each amplitude level. Four such levels are shown in drawing **"C"** and these can be represented using two digits as shown. The resultant encoded digital signals are shown in "D", the amplitudes simply representing a **"0"** or **"1"** as appropriate.

A detailed picture cannot be reproduced using only four discrete levels. In practice, 256 levels are used and these can be individually identified using only 8 bits ($2^8 = 256$) as outlined on the previous page. Each group of 8 bits (or 1 byte) corresponds to a different brightness level between black and white. We therefore need 8 bits of binary information to represent the brightness of each pixel. We also need another 8 bits of information to represent the chrominance and position co-ordinates – a total of 16 bits for each sample. The sample rate needs to be much higher than 4 samples per line. In practice, we use sample rate of 13.2MHz ie 13.2 million samples per second. In theory the required bandwidth for one programme is therefore 16 x 13.2 million samples per second, or 211.2MHz. Since digital signals consist of data bits, we change the terminology and refer to **bit rates**, in this case 211.2 million bits per second, or 211.2Mb/sec.

Keywords

Since the information is transmitted at discrete time intervals (see drawing "D"), it is possible to interleave two or more video signals into the same pulse train. ie.

2 multiplexed PAL programmes require 2 x 211.2 = 422.4Mbits/sec
3 multiplexed PAL programmes require 3 x 211.2 = 633.6Mbits/sec etc.

Time Division •
Multiplexing

This is called **T**ime **D**ivision **M**ultiplexing **(TDM)**. For more than one programme, it is necessary to transmit synchronising information in the form of clock pulses so that the programmes can be separated at the receiver location.

A multiplex containing 6 programmes therefore requires bandwidth of 6 x 211.2 = 1267.2MHz! The bandwidth of a terrestrial multiplex is 8MHz, and that of a satellite multiplex is typically 30MHz, much too small to accommodate all this data.

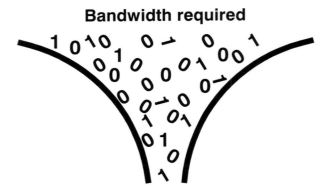

Bandwidth required

Bandwidth available

Digital •
Compression

2.4   Digital Compression

A TV signal contains a large amount of repetitive and redundant information, especially if there is little or no movement in the scene being televised.

Moving Picture •
Experts Group
(MPEG)

A body called THE MOVING PICTURE EXPERTS GROUP **(MPEG)** have examined this problem and issued standards for the coding and decoding of digital signals. These standards have been adopted for terrestrial and satellite TV broadcasting.

MPEG •
Compression

MPEG standards define the methods used to compress large amounts of data into a smaller bandwidth without reducing the visible picture quality. They are video compression or "image coding" techniques.

We have already seen that each picture element (or pixel) is represented by a series of "bits". For a PAL picture, there are normally 720 pixels in each line.
For each pixel, we actually create a coded message describing its luminance (brightness), colour (chrominance) and horizontal/vertical position in the picture. The receiver then builds up the picture, pixel by pixel, starting in the top left-hand corner and working across and downwards.

This picture contains a lot of repetition. When a TV picture has large areas of the same colour and brightness (eg. sky), it is only necessary to transmit the first pixel followed by a code to say how many times to duplicate this pixel along the TV line. This is called **spatial**

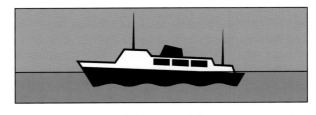

Spatial •
(Intraframe)
Compression

or "intraframe" compression and takes place within a single TV frame. A large amount of redundant information can be removed in this way without affecting the resultant picture quality at all. Spatial compression looks for repetitions in a single field.

The changes between adjacent TV frames are often small and a major bandwidth saving can be achieved by transmitting only these changes instead of the whole picture:

In the three frames shown above, the only major differences are the position of the javelin and the athlete's right arm. If the first frame is transmitted in full, it is only necessary to transmit the <u>changes</u> to frames two and three in order to reconstruct all three frames in full at the receiver. This is called **temporal** or "interframe" compression, which takes place between frames, again without affecting the resultant picture quality. Temporal compression compares two successive fields for similarities.

Since successive frames of a TV picture contain a large amount of regularly repeated information, the changes between frames are, to some extent, predictable. Exploitation of this to reduce the amount of data transmitted is called **statistical** compression and takes place between consecutive frames. Such predictions can be verified by looking backwards from the later frames.

The example shown above is a case where the position of the javelin is predictable in the frames following the three shown.

These are the main ways of compressing data. Other techniques are also used, including the following:
- Removal of blanking periods and synchronizing pulses – these can be replaced by simple data codes;
- Run length coding – long repetitions of ones and zeros can be grouped together. For example, the sequence 1111100000000000001111 can be relayed as 1,5:0,12:1,4.
- Variable length coding – as in Morse Code, the most commonly occurring data sequences are given the shortest codes.

MPEG video compression utilises all these techniques to reduce the required frequency bandwidth. If the missing information is of the type not noticed by the human eye and brain, the picture quality will appear to be the same as the original.

Successive frames are transmitted in groups:

Direction of prediction

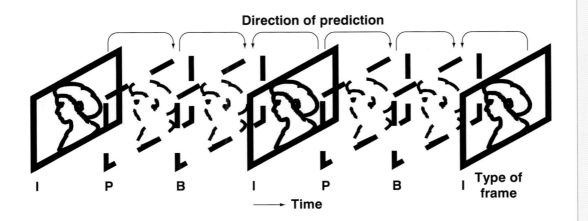

Keywords

I Frames •

P Frames •

B Frames •

- **I Frames**
  These "intraframes" are the starting point and act as a reference point for the other types of frame. They are individually compressed using spatial compression before transmission, with no account being taken of what is happening in adjacent frames. The amount of compression achievable is less than for other types of frame. Typically, every twelfth frame is an I frame.

- **P Frames**
  Starting with a single previously reconstructed frame, P frames use forward prediction (statistical compression) and temporal redundancy, resulting in much greater compression. The P frame uses the nearest previous I or P frame on which to base its predictions. They act as a reference for future P or B frames but errors will be carried forward to succeeding P or B frames.

- **B Frames**
  B frames look both ways (forwards and backwards) to predict motion and allow the decoder to rebuild a frame that is between I and/or P frames. They are not used as reference frames for further predictions. Whilst they give a large amount of video compression, they require several frames of video storage, thus increasing the cost of the decoder.
  The system encoder defines the sequence of I, P and B frames, depending on the type of material being transmitted.

A static scene often contains much repetitive information. Pictures of quiz games or a newscaster reading the news contain few differences between successive frames. These signals can be compressed using the MPEG techniques described in the previous paragraphs. On the other hand, high-action scenes such as a football match or a Formula 1 Grand Prix contain many changes between frames and cannot be compressed to the same extent. Digital signals representing such pictures therefore require a greater frequency bandwidth. Researchers are studying the characteristics of the human eye to produce ways of removing detail without affecting the subjective picture quality, in order to reduce the bandwidth required.
Using the MPEG 2 standards, it is now possible to obtain pictures of PAL quality using a bit rate of only 2-6 Mbits per programme per second - quite a reduction from the theoretical requirement of 211.2Mbits/sec! The new MPEG 4 standards will reduce the bandwidth requirements even further, with a target of 0.5Mbits/sec. These improvements will take place at the transmission end of the chain so current digital receivers will benefit without modification.

Programme •
Multiplexing

2.5 Programme Multiplexing

The main advantage of digital TV is to obtain more channels within a given frequency band. This is achieved by relaying several programmes in a single multiplex. At the start of digital broadcasting, each multiplex contained 4 or 5 programmes but this has since been increased. Problems arise when several of the programmes contain high action at the same time, each requiring a greater frequency bandwidth than the amount available.

Statistical •
Compression

This can be minimised to a certain extent using a technique called "statistical compression". Within a single multiplex, a larger frequency bandwidth can be allocated to channels with high action. This can be changed dynamically as the programme content of each channel changes.

Keywords

transponder bandwidth

High action channels
can have more bandwidth

1.5Mbits/sec is
sufficient for interviews
quiz games etc

Channel bandwidths can be adjusted in accordance with instantaneous picture movement demands

The multiplexing process combines each channel of compressed digital data into "packets", together with information to identify which programme the data belongs to. The receiver uses this information to sort out all the programme data for the programme required, which is then decompressed and converted back to the analogue format:

• Data Packets

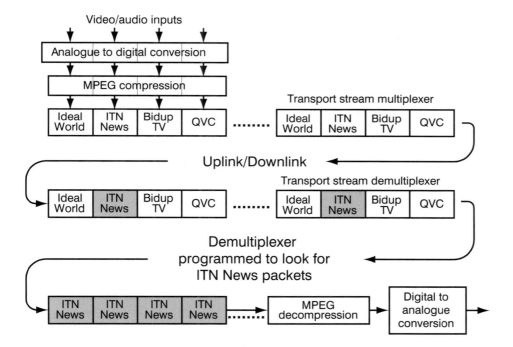

Keywords

Discrete Cosine •
Transform

Pixel Blocks •

Macro Block •

2.6 System Overload

Intraframe compression (getting rid of repetition) is achieved using a process called Discrete Cosine Transform **(DCT)**. The luminance pixels are grouped into **blocks**, each eight high by eight wide. Four such blocks then make up one **macro block** as shown.

This grouping is called **4:2:0** which includes 16 x 16 luminance pixels plus two 8 x 8 blocks of chrominance pixels – one R-Y block and one B-Y block.

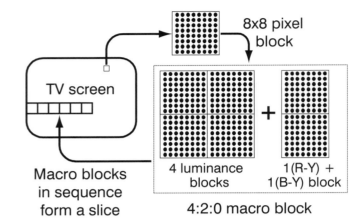

Macro blocks in sequence form a slice

4:2:0 macro block

4:2:0 grouping is used for domestic applications - other groupings are used for high-definition TV but these require a larger bandwidth.

DCT converts the values of the pixels in a block from the time domain to the frequency domain and takes advantage of the correlation between pixel values in the block.

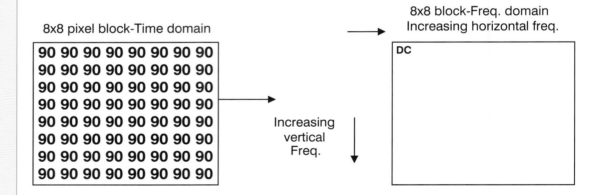

The resultant matrix block consists of the coefficients of the frequency components, each relating to the amplitude of a pattern within the block. The only absolute number will be in the top left hand corner (ie. Zero frequency or DC), the others being positive or negative difference values.

For a block with high spatial redundancy (ie. blue sky), the frequency components will be zero and the only substantial coefficient will be DC. Blocks containing lots of detail will have high frequency components and therefore high coefficients.

The coefficients are then "quantised" ie.rounded up or down to the nearest whole number. The number of quantising levels can be varied by the system encoder, according to the type of programme material being transmitted and the bandwidth available. The quantising scale is not linear, being weighted to give smaller steps (ie. greater definition) at lower frequencies where the perception of the human eye is more efficient. **Quantising is the key factor in minimising the bit rate.**

Quantiising •

Since the numbers in the top left hand corner of the quantized matrix are the most important (their importance diminishing the farther they are from this corner), they are scanned in order of increasing frequency in a zig zag fashion from top left to bottom right. Many blocks contain only zeros towards their ends, which can all be replaced by a single "end of block" (EOB) code.

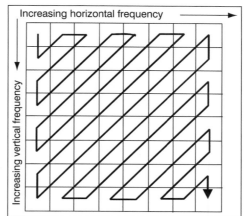

The following example shows how the luminance values of a whole block of 64 pixels can often be represented by just a few digits, especially when the pixels are all the same colour:

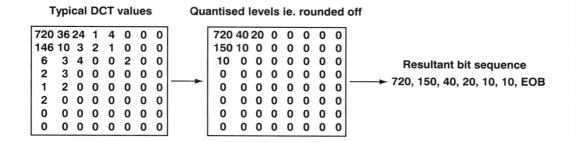

Typical DCT values

720	36	24	1	4	0	0	0
146	10	3	2	1	0	0	0
6	3	4	0	0	2	0	0
2	3	0	0	0	0	0	0
1	2	0	0	0	0	0	0
2	0	0	0	0	0	0	0
0	0	0	0	0	0	0	0
0	0	0	0	0	0	0	0

Quantised levels ie. rounded off

720	40	20	0	0	0	0	0
150	10	0	0	0	0	0	0
10	0	0	0	0	0	0	0
0	0	0	0	0	0	0	0
0	0	0	0	0	0	0	0
0	0	0	0	0	0	0	0
0	0	0	0	0	0	0	0
0	0	0	0	0	0	0	0

Resultant bit sequence
720, 150, 40, 20, 10, 10, EOB

DCT is applied to all "I" frames. For "P" frames and "B" frames, the encoder decides on a block-by-block basis whether to utilize spatial (DCT) or temporal (interframe) compression methods. Interframe coding is normally used unless there is a lot of movement in the picture in which case spatial techniques will provide more compression. A "data rate controller" continuously controls the DCT quantizing threshold level to ensure that the available bandwidth is fully utilized without exceeding the capacity of the channel.

Several macro blocks are grouped into slices, a series of which make up a whole frame or picture. The slices are used for error detection – a "0" coming through as a "1" or a "1" coming through as a "0". If an error is detected, the whole slice is ignored. This is why a digital picture first goes "blocky" before it freezes, whenever uncorrected errors occur.

• Data Errors

A summary of MPEG2 compression techniques is shown in the diagram below:

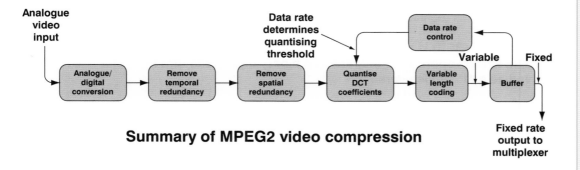

Summary of MPEG2 video compression

Keywords

When the buffer is full, the data rate control coarsens the quantising levels, thereby reducing the amount of data being transmitted and reducing the picture quality accordingly. This manifests itself as a loss of detail around areas of high action. If the quantity of data continues to increase, the buffer overloads and the picture first blocks and then freezes.

Picture Blocking •

A picture blocks because data is corrupted and system can no longer interpolate the data stream. Whilst this may be due to data overload, it can also be caused by weak signals or interference. This can happen quite suddenly – one moment the picture is fine, and then it suddenly freezes.

Cliff Effect •

This is known in the trade as the **"cliff effect"**. One can be walking quite safely along the top of a cliff and, all of a sudden, you fall over the edge.
It is therefore most important to ensure that one is well away from cliff edge. The system can work perfectly when installed, but the moment the signal is degraded (for whatever reason, such as poor weather conditions), the picture disappears.

The only way to tell how far you are from the edge of the cliff is by measuring signal parameters with the correct digital test equipment. The overall performance of the system is determined by the number of uncorrected errors (the **B**it **E**rror **R**atio or **BER**) reaching the decoder.

Bit Error Ratio • (BER)

Noise Removal •

2.7 Noise Removal and Error Correction

Noise on an analogue signal degrades the picture quality and cannot easily be removed.
Noise on a stream of binary information can corrupt the data, causing errors to be received. However, since the noise appears on the flat levels of the binary data, much of it can be removed by slicing off the tops and bottoms of the signals without corrupting the data. The signal can then be amplified to its original level without any noise being present. The actual slicing levels can be adapted to minimise the level of noise - this technique is known as "adaptive slicing".

Slicing •

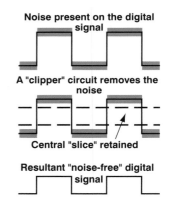

Noise present on the digital signal

A "clipper" circuit removes the noise

Central "slice" retained

Resultant "noise-free" digital signal

Bit Error Ratio (BER) is a measurement of signal quality after demodulation. It simply indicates what proportion of the received binary digits (bits) are incorrect – "0" received as a "1" or vice-versa.

A digital receiver is able to correct some of the errors in the binary data received using a technique known as error correction. The maximum number of errors that can be corrected in this way is usually quoted as 2 errors in every 10 000 bits of binary data.

Error Correction • Parity Bits

Error correction is achieved by adding additional data, called **parity bits**. A parity bit is added to each block of data and is either a 0 or 1 so as to make the total always equal to an odd number when they are all added together. The following example illustrates this principle when parity bits are added prior to transmission:

Keywords

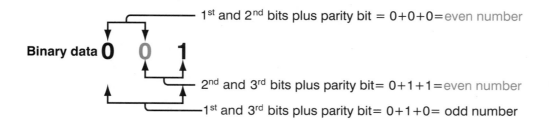

1st and 2nd bits = 0 + 1 = 1   1 + 0 = odd number

Binary data 0 1 1   **Parity bits**

2nd and 3rd bits = 1 + 1 = 2   2 + 1 = odd number

1st and 3rd bits = 0 + 1 = 1   1 + 0 = odd number

The parity bits are transmitted along with the data.
If the middle "bit" is corrupted and received as a 0 instead of a 1, the received data would be as follows:

1st and 2nd bits plus parity bit = 0+0+0=even number

Binary data 0 0 1

2nd and 3rd bits plus parity bit= 0+1+1=even number

1st and 3rd bits plus parity bit= 0+1+0= odd number

The receiver knows that the bits must always add up to an odd number. It knows from the top total that there is an error in either the first or second bit, and from the second total that there is an error in either the second or third bit. It can therefore determine that the second bit is wrong, and put it right.

Parity bits can eliminate single bit errors caused by noise. The more parity bits that are transmitted, the more chance the receiver has of correcting any errors that occur in the transmission chain.

Impulse interference can cause longer bursts of errors. To minimise this, bytes of data are resequenced. The datastream is split into 12 different paths, each with a different delay, and then remultiplexed together. Each path takes a multiple of 17 bytes as shown. The sync byte has no delay and is used to synchronise the reverse effect at the receiver end of the chain to put the bytes back into their correct order.

Transmitted data   Sync byte path
1
2   17 bytes
3   2x17 bytes
4   3x17 bytes
Received data
12   11x17 bytes

- Resequencing

The bit stream is then further scrambled or "randomised" in a defined way with every eighth sync byte being inverted to provide a reference point.

These error correction techniques are applied in three stages:

1. **Outer Coding** to minimise burst errors. Each MPEG2 bitstream packet of 188 bytes (consisting of 187 bytes of data followed by 1 sync. byte) is followed by 16 bytes of error correction data, thus increasing the packet size to 204 bytes. This is known as **Reed Solomon (RS)** 204:188 coding.
2. **Interleaving and Scrambling.** The bytes of data are then resequenced to minimise the effects of longer bursts of errors.
3. **Inner Coding.** Further **Forward Error Correction (FEC)** is applied to the input data, the exact amount being under the control of each individual broadcaster. This is known as "Convolutional Error Correction" or **Viterbi** correction.

- Outer Coding

- Reed Solomon (RS)
- Interleaving

- Forward Error Correction (FEC)
- Viterbi

Keywords

FEC modifies the bit stream in a controlled fashion before transmission and also sends information on how it was modified. Based on this information, the receiver will expect a specific bit sequence and can correct a bit stream if the sequence is different to that expected.

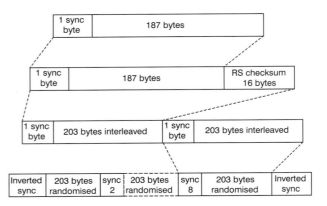

FEC • The FEC is quoted as a fraction eg. 3/4, which means that, for every 3 bits transmitted, one parity bit will be added, so the final number of bits will be 4, not 3. The highest FEC would be 1/2 ie. one parity bit for each symbol bit. This would make the system very rugged (ie. more immune to interference) but at the expense of greatly increased bandwidth requirements. The terrestrial TV channels use a FEC of 2/3 or 3/4. Most satellite broadcasters currently use a FEC of 3/4 but BSkyB use 2/3, the additional error correction allowing for the use of smaller satellite dishes.
It is necessary to specify the symbol rate (the speed at which the data is being transmitted) and the FEC before downloading channels, so that system can correctly distinguish between the error correction bits and the actual data being loaded in.

To summarize, the more error correction that is applied, the more rugged the signal becomes (at the expense of signal bandwidth, of course), and this in turn affects the required dish size.

The procedures for measuring BER are outlined in section nine.

Part Three - Digital TV Displays

Keywords

• Home Cinema

3.1 The Home Cinema

Since watching TV is the most popular pastime in the UK, many people dedicate a room in the home just for watching TV programmes. This could be the lounge with a widescreen TV in one corner, or a complete Home Cinema with a large viewing screen and Hi Fi sound system.

Most films are made for the cinema where the image is projected on to a huge screen in a darkened environment with black walls. It is possible to recreate this big-screen experience in the home if you have the luxury of a room dedicated to this purpose. For most homes, a compromise has to be made – the room needs to be comfortable and attractive to serve as a family room, yet provide the best conditions when watching movies. The provision of an overhead projector with a motorised screen or a flat wall-mounted TV display with moveable curtains can help to create such an environment. Wireless remote control devices are now available to turn the room into a cinema at the touch of a button. Lighting is most important. The ambient light level should be low with the minimum of light falling on the front of the screen. There should be no bright light sources within the viewer's field of view and especially behind or close to the screen.

The room acoustics must also be correct. The reverberation time can sometimes be optimised by covering the walls with heavy curtains.

The audio system must be equally impressive, being capable of faithfully reproducing sounds throughout the required frequency range, even at high volume levels. The human voice has a typical frequency range of 50Hz to 12KHz for males and is somewhat higher for females. Musical instruments range from the bass devices below 100Hz to high pitched wind instruments (up to 15KHz) and some generate harmonics at even higher frequencies. Our range of hearing is typically 50Hz to 15 - 20KHz although one's ability to hear the higher frequencies diminishes as one gets older. A typical inexpensive Hi Fi system can reproduce sounds over the range 50Hz – 15KHz, whilst a good quality Home Cinema receiver/amplifier would typically handle the range 30Hz - 20KHz.

• Hi-Fi

Facilities may be required to reproduce programmes from some or all of the following:

Audio only
FM radio
DVD audio player
DAB receiver
Record player
CD player
iPod, or other data storage device

• Audio Sources

Audio plus video
Analogue or digital TV receiver, possibly with NICAM stereo
Analogue or digital satellite receiver
Cable TV
DVD video player and / or VCR
Personal computer (for internet downloads, streaming video, data etc) or media centre,
IPTV source, via a broadband data input

• AV Sources

Keywords

Picture Displays •

TV Projector •

Projector Screen •

3.2 Picture Displays

Computer screens must be viewed from a close distance, whereas a TV display is normally viewed from much further away. The optimum size of the TV viewing screen depends on the number of people watching at any time and their positions in the room. Those sitting too close will see the line structure of the picture, whilst those too far away will not perceive the detail. The optimum viewing distance in front of the screen for viewing a normal interlaced TV picture is between four and twelve times the picture width. High definition displays can be viewed from much closer without seeing the line structure.

The perceived brightness of a picture reduces as the viewer moves sideways away from a line perpendicular to the screen. For a conventional 4:3 or 16:9 TV set, or a flat TV display, the typical horizontal coverage angle is about 120°.

For really big screens, it will be necessary to use a TV projector. Front projection with the projector mounted on the ceiling gives the best cinema "feel" but the room must be dark for the best results – any ambient light falling on the screen will be reflected and make the blacks look less black. Rear projection is less affected by ambient light and some such screens can be viewed in daylight conditions.

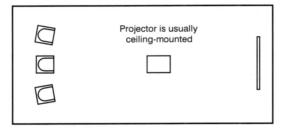

Front projection

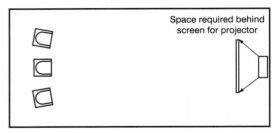

Rear projection

The choice of projector screen is most important. Light striking a screen is scattered in all directions some of it towards the viewer, the exact amount depending on the "gain" of the screen. The higher the gain, the brighter the image appears to be. In the same way that a high gain TV aerial has a narrow beamwidth, a high gain screen has a narrow viewing angle. Wherever possible, choose a low gain screen for front projection and a high gain version for rear projection.

Some rear projectors incorporate Fresnel lenses to limit the vertical projection angle, concentrating the light in the horizontal plane to give bright pictures over a horizontal viewing angle of almost 180°.

For multi-purpose rooms, the screen and projector can be motorised so that they disappear from sight when not in use.

Keywords

• Cathode Ray
  Tube (CRT)

3.3   The Cathode Ray Tube

The majority of television receivers utilise a **C**athode **R**ay **T**ube **(CRT)** as the means of displaying the picture to the viewer. This consists of an evacuated glass tube incorporating an electron "gun" and a screen coated with phosphorus on the inside. The side view of a CRT is shown alongside.

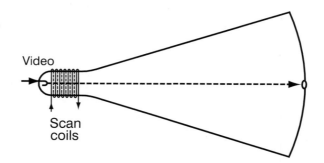

The electron gun incorporates a heater to generate "electrons" that are accelerated by a very high voltage (typically 26 000 Volts) and collide with the phosphorus coating. Since it is a basic law of physics that energy cannot be destroyed, this energy appears as light, forming a luminous spot on the screen, which can be seen from the front through the glass. Current is passed through a coil of wire (called a scan coil), that creates a magnetic field, causing the spot to move left and right. A second scan coil simultaneously causes the spot to move up and down, tracing out the whole picture. The gun is turned off for a black picture, and on for a white one. A "video" signal is applied to the gun, turning it on and off as the spot scans across the screen.

To produce colour pictures, a metal screen, called a "shadow mask", with a hole in the middle, is placed behind the phosphorus coating. An impurity is added to the phosphorus to make the spot glow red instead of white. The beam from a second gun looks through the same hole to see a different part of the screen coated with another impurity to make that spot glow green; similarly, a third gun produces a blue spot on the screen.

• Shadow Mask

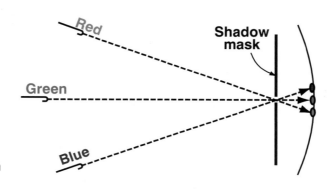

The red, green and blue spots are known as a "Triad" and appear as a single white spot when viewed from a distance.

• Triad

There is not just one hole is the shadow mask, but about 80 000 of them. There are some 240 000 phosphor dots on the screen, one third of each of the three colours, all so carefully placed that each of the three guns can only "see" the appropriately coloured spots. One can therefore produce a picture of any colour by turning the appropriate guns on and off. It is therefore necessary to have three separate video signals, red green and blue (or RGB) to produce a colour picture.

• Red / Green /
  Blue (RGB)

Keywords

Flat Panel •
Displays

HDTV •

Pixels •

Light Emitters •

Light Modulators •

Plasma •

Plasma Display •
Panel (PDP)

Liquid Crystal •
Display (LCD)

3

3.4   Flat Panel TV Displays

The basic disadvantage of a Cathode Ray Tube is that it is heavy and bulky.
High Definition Television (HDTV) only makes sense if the viewer uses a larger than normal display screen, which eliminates the possibility of using CRTs. These requirements have lead to the development of flat television displays, both for the computer laptop market and for the domestic TV market.

Such displays are relatively thin and can be hung on the wall, although the furniture layout may have to be changed to accommodate this. Also, flat screen displays are quite heavy, and care must be taken that the wall and fixings are strong enough to take the load.

A flat panel display comprises red, green and blue picture elements or **"pixels"**. On a computer screen, the pixels are usually square, whereas they are normally rectangular in shape on a TV screen.

There are two basic technologies available for flat screen displays:
- **Light emitters.** Each pixel consists of a red, green and blue plasma light source which is switched on and off, as required.
- **Light modulators.** The illumination is provided by a backlight, which is modulated as it passes through LCD "bubbles"

A **plasma** screen is a type of light emitter, having a flat, lightweight surface covered with some two million tiny glass bubbles, each containing a gas-like substance (plasma) and having a coloured phosphorus coating that is either red, green or blue. The functions of light generation and modulation are combined to produce variable amounts of ultra-violet illumination, which stimulate red, green and blue phosphors to produce visible light. The "**P**lasma **D**isplay **P**anel" **(PDP)** is now widely available, with a viewing angle and colour purity almost as good as that of a CRT.

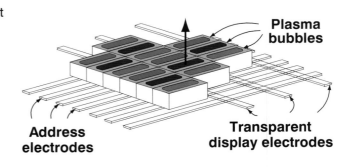

Plasma bubbles

Address electrodes

Transparent display electrodes

The alternative **L**iquid **C**rystal **D**isplay **(LCD)** panel uses light modulation. The illumination is provided by a backlight and modulated by a voltage controlled change in the polarisation of light passing through a liquid crystal, which is then passed through red, green and blue colour filters. Active Matrix Liquid Crystal Displays (AMLCDs) are extensively used for laptop computers – they are virtually flicker-free but have a limited viewing angle and tend to degrade the resolution of moving images. Plasma-Addressed Liquid Crystal (PALC) displays have higher brightness and contrast, but are more costly to produce.

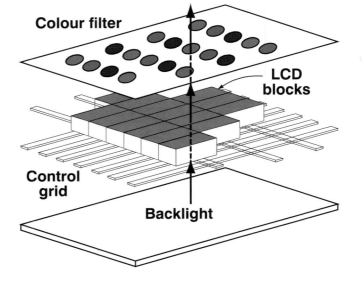

Colour filter

LCD blocks

Control grid

Backlight

Overhead projectors often use a different technology, called **D**igital **L**ight **P**rocessing **(DLP)**. This concept also uses a backlight that shines through some 2.1 million tiny mirrors, each one-fifth the size of a human hair. These mirrors form part of an optical semiconductor chip (called a Digital Micro-mirror Device or DMD), whose control electronics direct each mirror to tilt in turn, thus varying the brightness of that particular "pixel". Colour is produced using a rotating colour filter.

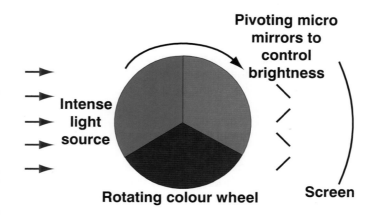

The relative advantages and disadvantages of each type of display are as follows:

Plasma
Better contrast and blacker "blacks"
Wider viewing angle
Can be made with very small depth (for hang-on-the-wall applications)
Relatively high power consumption
Most prone to screen burn-in
Not affected by magnetic fields

LCD
Greatest colour saturation
Very bright
"Comet-tail" effect on areas with high movement
Lighter weight and cooler running
The contrast and colour of the image can change when viewed from different angles

DLP
Greatest contrast ratio
Can be used in high ambient light
Wide viewing angle
Because it is a projection device, the screen can be any size (depending on the lamp brightness).

Another type of display becoming available uses **O**rganic **L**ight **E**mitting **D**iode **(OLED)** technology. Each pixel consists of a group of RGB LEDs which can be switched on and off as required. Their biggest advantage is that they do not need a backlight and such panels can therefore be very thin. The electroluminescent layer is made up of a film of carbon based compounds which are deposited by a printing process. The resultant display panel can even be flexible if required. The only problem with the early models is that their brightness deteriorates over time.

Wall Mounts

Flat panel displays are often hung on a wall. The larger models are heavy and care must be taken when mounting them, particularly on dry walls (usually plasterboard panels nailed to a wooden frame). In such cases, the following precautions should be taken:

Keywords

• Digital Light Processing (DLP)

• Organic Light Emitting Diode (OLED)

• Wall Mounts

Keywords

Do not position the display over a heat source such as a working fireplace.
Use the appropriate wall mounting bracket. The face of the display should be perpendicular to the viewer(s) so a bracket with tilt and / or swing adjustment may be required.
The display should be positioned so that sunlight or strong internal lighting does not fall on it.

150mm

Mains power socket

Wall

Wall

Use a spirit level to ensure that the display face will be horizontal when mounted.
Ensure that the plasterboard is firmly fixed to the wooden battens.

Metallic Stud • Locator

Take great care not to locate fixings holes where there are hidden mains power cables under the plasterboard. Use a metallic stud locator/cable detector for this purpose, bearing in mind that power cables are normally run horizontally or vertically from an outlet socket, and in corners or just below the ceiling as indicated alongside.

Cavity Fixings •

Drill a pilot hole to assess the depth of the void between the plasterboard and the brickwork behind. For small depths, consider drilling into the bricks and using Rawlplugs and coachscrews. Otherwise use cavity fixings, depending on the available depth behind the plasterboard.

Spread the fixings apart as much as possible. The top row of fixings is the most important, since these will take most of the load.

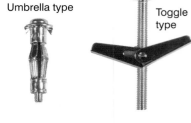

Umbrella type

Toggle type

Spring Toggle • Fixings

Umbrella Fixings •

Two of the popular types of cavity fixing are shown alongside. The spring toggle or butterfly type is not preferred because it can more easily pull through the plasterboard, especially if the fixing is not central in the hole. The umbrella type usually provides a much safer fixing – the Rawlplug M5 version is rated for a load of 12kg or 14kg per fixing, for 9.5mm and 12.5mm plasterboard respectively. The total load can be calculated by adding together the weight of the display plus wall bracket, then adding a 50% safety factor. Additional fixings will be required for swing or cantilever arms.

To fit cavity fixings of the umbrella type, drill a hole of the appropriate diameter, insert the fixing and tap it gently until the anti-rotation lugs penetrate the face of the plasterboard. Then, applying a firm forward pressure, tighten the screw to set the fixing in position. Remove the screw, position the wall bracket, reinsert the screw and tighten until secure.

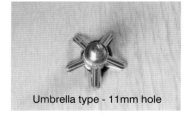

Umbrella type - 11mm hole

It is important to check the ability of the wall bracket to carry the weight of the display before it is mounted on the wall. Apply a downwards load of 50% more than the weight to be carried, to ensure that the bracket will not pull off the wall.

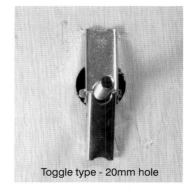

Toggle type - 20mm hole

3.5   High Definition TV (HDTV)

Computers have 4:3 screens and use progressive scan. The original format was called VGA which utilised 307 200 pixels (in 480 rows, each with 640 pixels). Subsequent formats offer better resolution:

Width x Height (pixels)	Video Display
640 x 480	VGA
800 x 600	SVGA
1024 x 768	XGA
1280 x 1024	SXGA
1600 x 1200	UGXA

The TV broadcasting industry followed the computer world, using the widescreen XGA format. Because these TV displays have more pixels, they produce pictures with more detail and are referred to as High Definition TV **(HDTV)** displays. This is particularly important for large screen displays where the line structure would otherwise be visible on the screen:

The increased number of pixels means that the scanning is conducted at a higher speed and therefore requires a higher frequency bandwidth or digital bit rate.

HDTV utilises both interlaced and progressive scanning. Interlaced scanning loses about 30% of the vertical resolution (this is accentuated by fast moving objects) and is fine for movies and general entertainment. Progressive scanning is better for viewing high action sports. Also, since flat screen displays are based on progressive scanning, less electronics is required in the receiver.

The most common high definition TV scanning standards used in the UK are as follows:
    720p   1280 x 720 pixels @ 50 Hz with progressive scanning
    1080i   1920 x 1080 pixels @ 25Hz with interlaced scanning

Some broadcasters have chosen to use both scanning standards, leaving the viewers to choose which standard suits them best.

41

Keywords

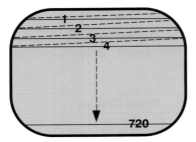

720 progressive scanning

All digital picture displays have a natural or "native" display resolution, and can rescale inputs from sources on other formats.

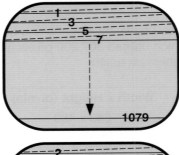

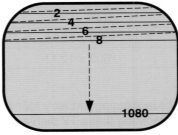

1080 interlaced scanning

Full HD •

BluRay •

There is also a **"Full HD"** standard called **1080p** which uses 1080 lines with progressive scanning. This uses a 1920 x 1080 pixel format to produce even greater picture resolution. BluRay DVDs are now available in the 1080p format, which produces quite stunning pictures.

HD Ready •

To assist the general public, the retail industry has introduced an "HD ready" logo. All display devices using such a logo must comply with the following requirements:
• A widescreen 16 x 9 format
• A minimum resolution of 1280 x 720 pixels (720p)
• DVI or HDMI connectivity, with HDCP (see section 3.7)

An enhanced "Full HD" logo is also available for devices that can display 1080p pictures. The original version of HDMI (version 1.0) supports 1080p, whilst version 1.3 refers to even higher quality formats such as WQXGA (2560 x 1200) and beyond.

Recent developments in high definition DVDs have conditioned viewers to expect the very best technical quality on their TV screens. But is HD worth the extra cost? Will they be able to see the increased detail?

Resolution •

The human eye can distinguish an angular resolution of about 1 minute of arc. At a viewing distance of 2,7m from the TV receiver, the average viewer will therefore benefit if his TV is bigger than about 69cm (27 inches), so those with large flat screen displays will certainly benefit from HDTV.

Minimum angular resolution is 1 minute of arc

2.7m

The following are all required in order to view HD pictures:
• An HD source
• An HD display
• HD interconnections, and possibly also
• HD de-encryption

HD material is currently available from the following sources in the UK:
- Satellite – Sky offer a choice of more than 30 HD channels, and some European broadcasters relay HD on the Astra satellites at 19°E. Freesat also offers a choice of HD channels for UK viewers.
- Cable TV – Virgin Media offer a choice of HD programmes
- DVD – Blu-ray players
- The internet

3.6   Analogue Interconnections

Terrestrial TV signals are demodulated to produce a composite video signal and two separate audio outputs. The composite video signal is then used to derive the black-and-white (luminance - symbol Y) and colour (chrominance - symbol C) signals. VCRs record colour signals in this format, which is known as Y/C or S-VHS.

The chrominance signal is then used to derive two "colour-difference" signals (R-Y) and (B-Y) which (together with the luminance signal) are known as the Component Video signals – DVD players reproduce signals in this format.

The three component video signals are then derived to produce the Red, Green and Blue (RGB) waveforms required by a colour TV display device.

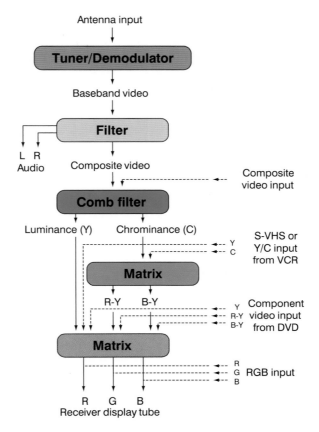

Some TV receivers can accept signals in any of the above formats, having SCART socket(s) for the composite video and RGB inputs, a DIN connector for S-VHS and separate connectors for component video.
The conversion of a video signal into its luminance and chrominance components introduces degradations to the picture, and this process should be avoided wherever possible. Since a VCR processes an analogue signal in the S-VHS format, the best results would be obtained using the receiver's S-VHS input. Similarly, a DVD player reproduces signals in the component video format so the component video input should be used.

Analogue audio signals can be interconnected using SCART or phono (RCA) connections to produce monaural, stereo or Dolby Pro-Logic surround sound. Dolby Digital data requires either a single coaxial cable or an optical link and is backwards compatible, being able to produce either a two-channel stereo mix for regular stereo playback, or a mono mix for playback through a monaural system.

Most of the above options are catered for by the SCART connector.
"SCART" stands for 'Syndicat des Constructeurs d'Appareils Radio Recepteurs et

Keywords

- Analogue Interconnections
- Composite Video
- S-VHS
- Component Video DVD Players
- RGB
- SCART
- Dolby Pro-Logic

Keywords

Televisieurs", and was developed by the French in 1980 - its use became mandatory in French equipment. Most other European countries have adopted the SCART connector as standard. It is also known as the Peritel or Euro-connector.

There are 20 pins (plus an outer screen) as shown alongside.

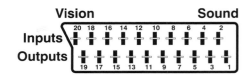

The normal use of each pin is as follows with the most important pins highlighted:

SCART •
Connections

1. **Audio right output**
2. **Audio right input**
3. **Audio left output**
4. **Audio earth**
5. Blue earth
6. **Audio left input**
7. Blue input
8. Source switching
9. Green earth
10. Intercom. line
11. Green input
12. Intercom line
13. Red earth
14. Intercom earth
15. Red input
16. RGB blanking
17. **Video earth**
18. Blanking earth
19. **Composite video output**
20. **Composite video input**

Crossover Cable •

The video and audio pins of a SCART lead are cross connected so that the inputs at one end are connected to the outputs at the other end ie pin 19 at one end is connected to pin 20 at the other end and vice versa. This is why it is known as a "crossover" cable Some SCART leads are supplied with only the nine highlighted pins connected. If units are to be interlinked using RGB, it is necessary to use a fully wired SCART lead. Cheaper SCART leads incorporate a single overall screen, whereas quality versions have individually screened wires.
Pin 8 (source switching) is normally used to automatically switch the input of a TV receiver from the aerial socket to the SCART socket whenever the source unit is switched on – this is achieved by applying 12V to pin 8 of the receiver SCART socket.

The choice of interconnection format will depend on the following:
• What formats can the source equipment provide
• What formats can the display equipment accept
• How long are the interconnecting leads
• How many pieces of equipment are to be interconnected

RGB SCART •

A colour TV display needs separate red, green and blue video signals, and if the picture origination equipment can supply these (and if the display device can accept RGB), then the best picture quality will be obtained using RGB interconnections. This can be achieved using a composite SCART cable or three separate coax leads, depending on the sockets available. Such leads should preferably be less than 10m long.
Most displays will also accept composite video signals on a single coaxial cable (or via a SCART connector). However, the signals have now been converted twice (from RGB to composite video and then back again), which may degrade the video picture quality. For

Keywords

the same reasons, it is preferable to connect VCRs using S-VHS (if available), and DVDs using component video. However, for any of the above solutions, the audio must be relayed separately, although a SCART caters for this as well.

3.7   Digital Interconnections

Most computers utilise a multicore cable with 15 pin D-Sub (VGA) connectors to relay analogue data to the adjacent display monitor. This requires three wires for RGB and two for synchronising pulses. Larger wall-mounted plasma or LCD computer displays can be connected in the same way.

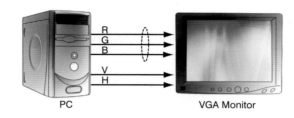

• D-Sub
  Connectors
• VGA

In 1999, a standard "DVI" digital interface was introduced, to simplify the connection between such devices. This transfers uncompressed real-time digital video at various resolutions, including those used for HDTV.

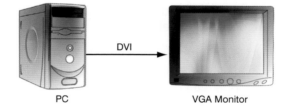

• DVI

This standard was adopted by the home entertainment industry for interconnections between units. Three serial data streams are relayed (one each for red, green and blue) and such a link can support all the common resolution standards, including 720p and 1080i. Separate circuits are required for the audio connections. Several types of DVI connector are available, depending on whether or not analogue signals are also required.

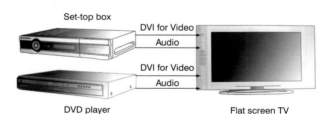

Although DVI handles the transfer of uncompressed real-time RGB video to a display, the consumer electronics industry has adopted a simpler and more versatile form of DVI connector, called **H**igh-**D**efinition-**M**ultimedia-**I**nterface **(HDMI)**. HDMI replaces five video cables and up to eight audio cables with a single cable, as illustrated alongside. It can also relay control commands between items of equipment.

HDMI connectors are not unlike USB connectors, and have 19 pins. HDMI is backwards compatible with equipment using DVI by using a suitable adaptor cable.

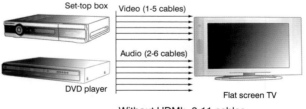

Without HDMI: 3-11 cables

• HDMI

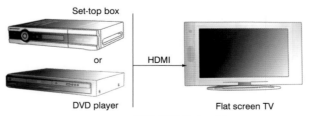

With HDMI: 1 cable

45

Keywords

HDCP •

TMDS •

DDC •

CEC •

HDTV connectors are shown in the picture alongside,
with an HDMI connector at the top, and a DVI connector at the bottom.

HD interconnections use an encryption technique called **H**igh **D**efinition **C**ontent **P**rotection **(HDCP)** to ensure that HD material cannot be copied by unauthorised personnel. Data "keys" are used to allow only permissible display devices to display the HD transmissions.

3.8   HDMI Cables and Connectors

HDMI cables carry the following services:

- 3 uncompressed video data streams on separate twisted pairs of wires, using a technique known as **T**ransition **M**inimised **D**igital **S**ignalling **(TMDS)**, with the audio information multiplexed on to the video data stream in the blanking interval periods.

Red   0 1 1 1 0 0 1 1 0 1 0 1 0 0

Blue   0 1 0 1 1 0 0 1 1 0 1 0 0 0

Green 0 0 1 1 0 0 1 1 1 0 1 0 0 0

- A Clock pulse data stream, also on a twisted pair of wires. This always runs at 10% of the video data rate and is used to synchronise the receiver with the incoming data.

- A **D**ata **D**isplay **C**ontrol channel **(DDC)**. When the system starts up, this channel sends and receives serial data to set the system for its best overall operational video and audio performance. It also supplies all the HDCP content protection keys – in most cases, these have a two second life span and the system continuously requires fresh keys for continuous operation.

- A **C**onsumer **E**lectronics **C**ontrol **(CEC)** channel to provide for integrated control functions such as the automatic switching of display formats (16:9 v 4:3) or HDMI standards (720p v 1080i), and display activation.

- A 5V supply voltage to supply the display's DDC communication circuitry, even when the display itself is turned off.

- A reverse "hot plug detect" circuit, to confirm that the display's DDC circuitry is powered up.

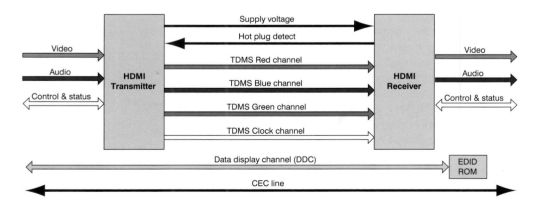

Keywords

• HDMI
  Connections

• EDID

• I2C Bus

• HDMI Data
  Speeds

• Deep Colour

• HDMI
  Standards

An HDMI cable normally comprises 100 Ohm screened twisted pair cables inside a screened outer sheath. This drawing shows the pin connections for a male plug, into which the female socket on the end of an HDMI cable is connected.

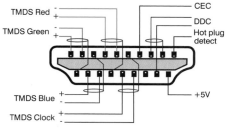

Pin 18 (+5V) is set back about 50% in the connector to ensure all the other connections are made before power is applied on the supply voltage line to the display device. When the HDMI transmitter is first switched on, this voltage is relayed to the HDMI receiver (it must be in the range 4.7-5.4V at the receiving end) which confirms receipt of the voltage via the "hot plug detect" line. The transmitter then communicates with the receiver on the DDC line using Extended Display Identification for Display (EDID) coding to set up the communication parameters. The transmitter sends an HDCP key to the receiver, which must respond within two seconds for transmission to begin. These communications are regularly repeated throughout the transmission. The serial data is relayed on a 100 kHz square wave using the I2C bus specification.

HDMI Data Speeds

The following table shows the speed of the uncompressed video data being relayed over each of the three video pairs in an HDMI cable:

Standard	Pixels	Scan Rate	Clock Speed	Bit Rate
480p (SD)	640 x 480	50Hz	27.0 MHz	270 Mb/sec
720p (HD)	1280 x 720	50Hz	74.25 MHz	742.5 Mb/sec
1080i (HD)	1920 x 1080	25Hz	74.25 MHz	742.5 Mb/sec
1080p (Full HD)	1920 x 1080	50Hz	148.5 MHz	1485 Mb/sec

These are truly phenomenal frequencies, especially as the cable losses increase with frequency. These bit rates are for a standard colour depth of 8 data bits per colour channel per pixel, giving a range of 256 different values. A recent enhancement for "deep colour" uses up to 20 bits per colour component, thus requiring an even greater frequency bandwidth.

The original HDMI standard (Rev 1.1) allowed for a bit rate of 1650 Mb/sec for each colour channel. A subsequent revision (Rev 1.3) has increased the required bandwidth to 3400 Mb/sec, to allow for future improvements. Both standards allow for the inclusion of high resolution audio formats such as Dolby Digital and DTS.

The original HDMI cable standards (category 1) were specified for a clock speed of up to 74 MHz whereas the latest high speed standard (category 2) can handle 340 MHz – necessary for 1080p transmissions.

It is most important that HDMI cable networks can be tested to ensure that they can operate reliably with these extreme bandwidth requirements.

HDMI System Testing

Data is relayed as a binary "1" or "0", depending on the phase angle of the carrier wave. If all this data is superimposed, the result would be in the shape of a human eye, as shown alongside. The vertical axis

represents the signal amplitude and the horizontal axis represents time. This is known as "eye pattern testing".

Keywords

Eye Pattern •
Testing

Eye Mask •

The display unit must be able to recognise this data and therefore has a limited range of operation as shown by the "eye mask". If the mask touches any of the signal traces, the receiver will lose its ability to recognise the data, and errors are likely to occur.

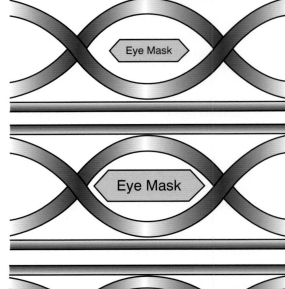

Full HD systems (1080p) have a bigger mask area and there is therefore a greater risk of errors occurring.

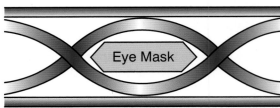

Signal attenuation occurs as the data travels along the cable, thus increasing the chance of errors.

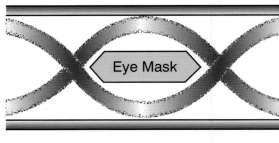

Electrical noise picked up by the HDMI cable will decrease the size of the eye window and also increasing the risk of errors.

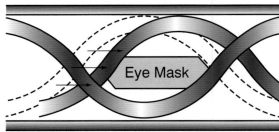

These diagrams show one cycle of a carrier wave. Such a wave with a frequency of 1500MHz has a wavelength of only 20cm. A difference in cable lengths of the RGB data pairs of only 1cm will cause a significant timing error, as shown in this diagram, further reducing the size of the eye window.

HDMI Timing •
Error

This can be caused by a number of factors:

• Jitter on the data being relayed.

• Unequal cable lengths of the red, green and blue data cables (known as "inter-pair skew"), possibly caused by overtwisting or undertwisting the cable pairs during manufacture or when fitting a connector.

• Unequal wire lengths within a single twisted pair (known as "intra-pair skew").

• The use of higher data rates, as required for 1080p transmissions. Cable losses increase with frequency and this can cause delays in the data transmission path, especially on long cable runs.

HDMI Distribution

HDMI switches have multiple inputs and outputs. The more elaborate versions have a receiver / transmitter pair which can improve the quality of a datatream by reclocking the data and restoring the original output levels and integrity.

The HDMI cables linking a switch to multiple displays could all have different lengths and therefore different losses. It may therefore be beneficial to fit an HDMI equaliser at the display end of each of the longer cable runs. It is recommended that mains powered units are used – versions that use the 5V supply rail in an HDMI cable will increase the current drawn and therefore the voltage at the display end of the cable may not be enough to power the DDC communication circuitry.

Alternatives to HDMI Cables:

- **Structured cable networks.** Two CAT5e or CAT6 cables are required to provide for the entire HDMI interface. Products are available for cable lengths of up to 65 metres.
- **Coaxial cables.** Multiple coax circuits can extend the system reach to 100 metres.
- **Fibre.** These systems are more costly but can provide HD services over even longer distances.
- **Wireless HD.** Definitely tomorrow's technology for use in the home. Most of the current technologies use some form of video compression, which may limit the performance resolution.

HDMI Remote Control

The CEC option (pin 13 on an HDMI connector) allows suppliers to provide control options using an AV link protocol known as IEEE1394 (sometimes known as "FireWire" or "i.LINK"). Manufacturers using such options include Samsung (Anynet), Pioneer (Kuro Link) and Panasonic (Viera Link). Alternatively, an additional cable can be installed to provide remote control of source selection and control functions from a remote viewing location, as follows:

- **Coax cable.** This is often run alongside the HDMI cable to provide terrestrial TV services to a flat panel display, and can also be used to relay infra-red commands in the reverse direction. Several manufacturers offer products for this purpose. For instance, a remote eye can be attached to the display to receive commands from a Sky handset and control a Sky receiver at the source location (see part 8.1).
- **CAT5 cable.** Some manufacturers offering HD distribution over two CAT5e or CAT6 cables also include a remote control option in the reverse direction. Alternatively, an additional CAT5 cable can be installed to provide the additional remote control facilities.

HDMI Troubleshooting

A lack of picture on the display at the receiving end of an HDMI network may be due to any of the following:

- The transmitter HDMI connector is not pushed in properly. The +5V pin is recessed more than the others.
- The +5V voltage at the display end is less than 4.7V, causing the handshaking to fail. This may be because too many devices are connected, each drawing current, resulting in insufficient voltage at the display input.
- The HDMI cable is too long, causing data errors to occur. This often causes sparkles to appear on the picture, especially in black areas. An inferior 3m cable will always perform better than a 15m superior version.
- The HDMI cable is of poor quality, causing errors. This often results in the picture disappearing intermittently.
- Network timing errors, especially on CAT5e or CAT6 networks. This may be because the installer altered the amount of twist on one of the cable pairs when fitting a connector.
- The display does not recognise the HDCP key. This may be due to data corruption on the DDC line, again due to the use of poor quality cable.
- The HDMI transmitter does not have enough HDCP data keys for all the display devices connected.

Keywords

- HDMI Distribution

- HDMI Equaliser

3

- HDMI Alternatives
- HDMI over CAT5

- HDMI Remote Control
- Firewire

- Viera Link

- HDMI Troubleshooting

- Long HDMI Cables

Gold Masthead Signal Processing

VISION®

Super Low Noise
New generation ultra-low noise electronics for the UK TV reception of even the weakest signals

Interference Blocking Technology
Unique compartmentalised design is almost impervious to interference under normal conditions

Variable Gain
Optimise performance on selected models

Clear Labeling
Shows Important specifications on product without the need for a data sheet

Weather Resistant Housing
CAD design includes drip trays, wind traps and ABS construction to keep out unwanted moisture under adverse weather conditions

Tip Up Electronics Module
Improved pivot range assists easy cabling

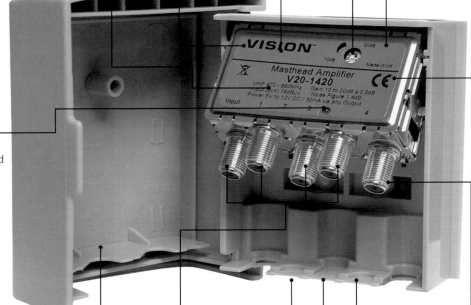

LED Indicator
Shows Masthead is active once cable and power supply are connected

CE Compliant
CE compliant for safety and peace of mind

Moisture Venting
Allows any trapped moisture to evaporatesafely away and prolong electronics module life

Flexible Powering
For simple installs can be powered on any leg

Cable Break-Outs
Allows housing to remain sealed with 2-5 cables of varying sizes

Gold F-Connectors
Superb connection quality for top performance

Features will vary across the range from model to model

Also Available In The Vision Masthead Range

VHF/UHF Masthead

UHF/FM/ DAB

UHF Masthead

Masthead PSU

Masthead Kit

www.vision-products.co.uk

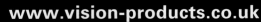

Keywords

• Radio Waves

• Rotating Vector

• Phase

• Wavelength

• Frequency
• Hertz
• Prefixes

• Carrier Wave

• Modulation

4.1 Radio Waves

Whilst a battery produces a constant voltage, radio waves have a voltage that varies with time.

Imagine a voltage (or **"vector"**) V that is rotating about a fixed point in an anticlockwise direction as shown in the accompanying diagram. The angle α varies from zero (at the start point) to 360° and is called the **"phase"**. If the output is plotted against time as shown on the right hand side of the diagram, the output voltage will vary between positive and negative – this is called a sine wave.

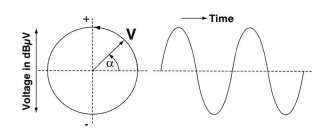

The distance between two adjacent peaks is called the **"wavelength"**:

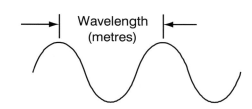

One revolution of the vector is called a cycle. The number of cycles that take place each second ie. the **frequency (f)**, is called **"Hertz"** (abbreviated **Hz**).

The prefixes given in section 1.7 are also applicable to Hz. Thus

    1 000Hz = 1kHz (Kilohertz)
    1 000 000Hz = 1MHz (Megahertz)
    1 000 000 000Hz = 1GHz (Gigahertz).

The next diagram shows the variation in voltage over time for a low frequency and a higher one.

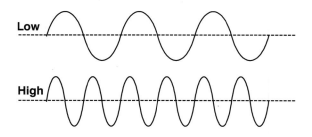

All radio waves are generated in this manner and the basic sine wave is called a carrier wave. This can be modified to carry information (pictures, sound or data, for instance) by varying the vector size (V), the phase (α) or frequency (f). This process is called **"modulation"**.

Keywords

The frequencies used for broadcasting and commercial communications include the following:

30kHz to 300kHz	- Low frequency band (LF)
300kHz to 3MHz	- Medium frequency band (MF)
3 to 30MHz	- High frequency band (HF)
30 to 300MHz	- Very high frequency band (VHF)
300MHz to 3GHz	- Ultra high frequency band (UHF)
3 to 30GHz	- Super high frequency band (SHF)

Frequency Bands •

The following frequency bands are commonly used for broadcasting and commercial communications:

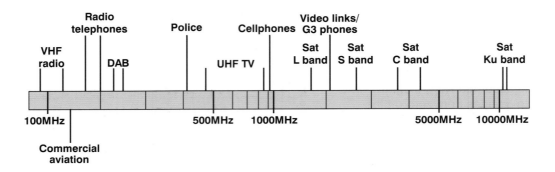

The broadcasting frequency bands of particular interest are as follows:

FM radio	87.5 to 108MHz
Digital Audio Broadcasting (DAB)	215 to 230MHz
UHF TV	470 to 854MHz
Satellite Ku band	10700 to12750MHz

Radio Waves •

Radio waves behave in a similar fashion to waves on water. Imagine a lake with an island in the middle. You stand on the side and throw a stone into the water, causing waves that emanate outwards, getting smaller as they get farther away. Do you get any waves on the far side of the island?

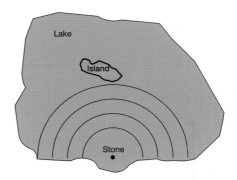

Wavefront •

The answer is – well yes but much smaller – just ripples perhaps. This is because the "wavefront" acts as a series of individual radiators, pushing the water in front of it and sending out its own "wavelets" which are of smaller amplitude.

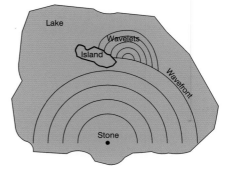

Wavelets •

The same is true for a radio wave. The energy has a wavefront with the transmitting aerial at its centre. The wavefront can be regarded as an infinite number of smaller transmitters, each one sending out wavelets in front of it. These combine with all the other wavelets to form a new wavefront at points further away in the direction of propagation.

Keywords

This is why it is possible to receive radio signals at locations that are shielded by high buildings, although the signal strength is very much weaker. Radio waves always travel in straight lines but they do manage to go round obstacles!

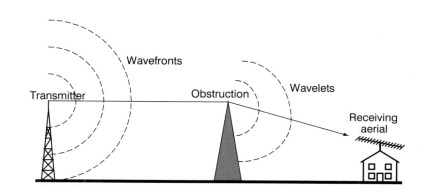

A receiving aerial will therefore receive signals from a transmitter via a variety of paths (depending on the characteristics of the aerials) as shown alongside. The direct signal will have a distance "L". The other signals will arrive later, since they had further to travel.

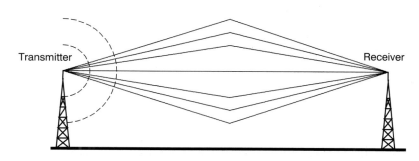

• Radio Paths

Consider a signal propagated along a path of length "L plus one wavelength" (or L plus a number of whole wavelengths). When the two signals are added together, the peaks and troughs of the signals coincide and the signals add other. together in amplitude. The two signals are said to be "in phase" with each other.

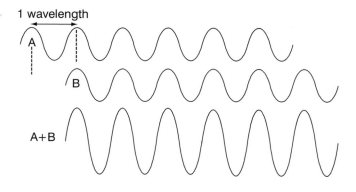

• In-Phase

Now consider a signal travelling along a path length of "L plus half a wavelength" (or an odd multiple thereof). The second signal is now **"out of phase"** and will therefore subtract from the direct signal.

• Out-of-Phase

Freznel Zones •

If you were to look at a received signal "end on" (ie. looking back towards the transmitter), you could imagine a series of concentric rings (called **Freznel zones**), alternately in phase and out of phase with the direct signal L depending on the path lengths as explained above.

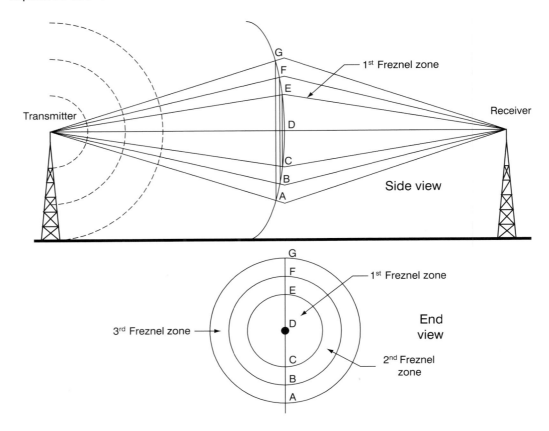

About one quarter of the total energy is contained in the first Freznel zone and it is important to site the receiving aerial with no blockage within this area. The size of the Freznel zones vary with frequency (and therefore with the programme being watched). This is why TV aerial siting is often called a black art – maybe an aerial works well on one side of a chimney but not on the other, or some of the channels are satisfactory but others are not. In practice, one must often try the aerial in a variety of locations before deciding on its exact position.

Electric Field •
Magnetic Field •
Electromagnetic •
Wave

Radio signals are created by varying the current in a transmitting aerial. This creates an **electric** field and also a **magnetic** field at right angles to it. This is why radio signals are called **electromagnetic waves**. These waves propagate away from the transmitting aerial at the speed of light which is 300 million metres per second ($3 \times 10^8 ms^{-1}$).

The way the transmitting aerial is mounted establishes the polarisation. A vertically mounted transmitting aerial will produce an electrical field in the vertical plane and is said to be **vertically polarised** and it is necessary to mount the receiving aerial with its elements vertical to receive these transmissions. For **horizontal polarisation**, the transmitting and receiving aerials are mounted horizontally. Most UK high power TV transmitters are

Polarisation •

Vertical polarity

Horizontal polarity

horizontally polarised, and most low power gap fillers are vertically polarised, to minimise the interference between transmitting sites.

When an electromagnetic wave passes through a mass of air that is denser than the air surrounding it (such as a rain cloud), some of the energy will be changed in direction or **refracted**:

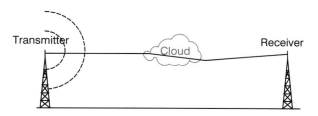

The earth's outer atmosphere is called the **ionosphere**. This has layers of air of different densities that change with time of day. Radio waves can be refracted as they pass through these layers and some can be reflected back to earth, often many hundreds of miles away from the transmitter due to a "ducting" effect.

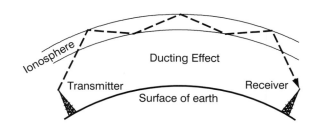

This is why some TV viewers in southern England sometimes experience interference from TV signals on the same channels from France – this is called **co-channel interference**. The author actually used this phenomenon to feed a relay transmitter at Orangemund in Namibia from the TV transmitter in Cape Town more than 800 miles away – during the day, there was no signal at all but after dark a perfect picture was received as long as there was no rainfall along the intervening route!

Electromagnetic waves can also be reflected from nearby buildings:

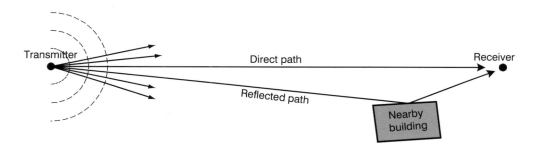

Since the reflected signal has further to travel, it will be delayed in time and therefore appear to the right of the directly received signal, causing a **ghost** or reflection. The amount of displacement to the right depends on the additional path length.
Ghosting can be very objectionable on analogue pictures, especially in built up areas with lots of high rise buildings, and it may be desirable to orientate the aerial for minimum ghosting instead of maximum signal. Digital signals are largely immune to reflected signals – indeed, the ghost can actually increase the level of the signal received!

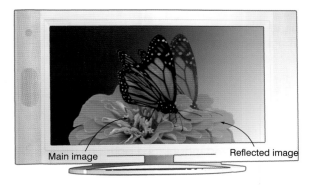

Keywords

- Refraction

- Ionosphere

- Co-channel Interference

- Reflection

- Ghosting

Keywords

Wavelengths •

Wavelengths

Consider an electromagnetic wave with a frequency of 300MHz. This means that there are 300 000 000 peaks (ie. wavecrests) each second. Since it is propagating forwards at the speed of light which is 300 000 000 metres per second, then its wavelength must be 1 metre.

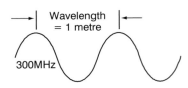

If the frequency is halved to 150MHz, there will only be one cycle where previously there were two and the wavelength is doubled to 2 metres. Conversely, if the frequency is doubled to 600MHz, the wavelength will be halved to 0.5 metres.

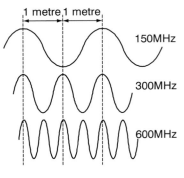

Therefore, for any frequency "f" in MHz, the wavelength will be 300/f metres:

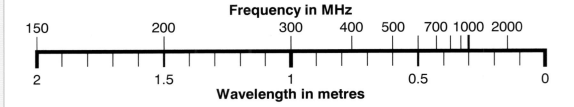

Frequency •

Filters •

Filters

Electronic circuits consist of three basic components. The resistor has already been described (see section 1.4). The others are a **Capacitor** and an **Inductor**.

Capacitor •
Inductor •

A capacitor is a device that can store and release electrical energy. Its symbol in an electronic circuit is "C" and its value is measured in "Farads". In a circuit diagram, it is shown:

Farads •

An inductor normally comprises a coil of wire. A current flowing in the wire produces a magnetic "flux" which is called inductance. Its symbol is "L" and it is measured in "Henries". In a circuit diagram, it is shown thus:

Henries •

Capacitance and inductance both use the same prefixes as given previously. For instance, one thousandth of a Henry is called a millihenry (mH) and one millionth of a Farad is called a microfarad (μF).

Tuned Circuit •
Q Factor •

A capacitor and an inductor together create a **tuned circuit** that has the property of passing one frequency (or band of frequencies, depending on its sharpness or "Q" factor) and rejecting all others, or vice versa depending on whether they are wired in series or parallel:

Keywords

• Resonant
  Circuit

• Characteristic
  Impedance

• Filter Types

• Transformer

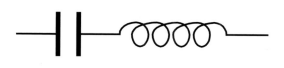

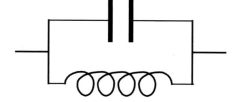

Series Resonant-passes one frequency   **Parallel resonant-rejects one frequency**

These series and parallel resonant circuits can be combined together to produce various types of **filter** ie. low pass, band pass, high pass, notch, band stop etc. The resonant frequency "f" of a tuned circuit can be calculated using the formula

$$f = \frac{1}{2\pi \sqrt{LC}}$$

Where L is the inductance in henries and C is the capacitance in farads.

A tuned circuit is purely resistive at its resonant frequency. This is called its **characteristic impedance** (z_o):

$$z_o = \sqrt{\frac{L}{C}}$$

At lower frequencies, the effect of the inductance predominates and the circuit is said to be inductive; at higher frequencies than the resonant frequency, the effect of the capacitance predominates and the circuit is said to be capacitive.

Various types of filters used in the TV industry are shown below:

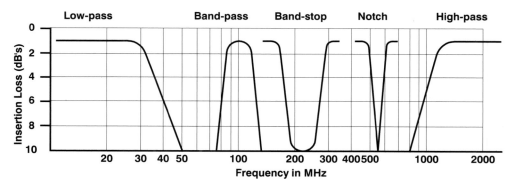

Frequency responses of various types of filters

An inductor is often wound on a metal or carbon (Ferrox) core, or "former", to increase its value. Two such coils of wire on the same former are called a **transformer** which can be used to link two radio frequency (rf) circuits together whilst creating dc isolation between them. Transformers can also be used to change rf voltages and impedances according to the formulae:

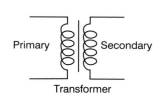

Transformer

Keywords

$$\frac{N_1}{N_2} = \frac{V_1}{V_2} \qquad\qquad \frac{N_1}{N_2} = \sqrt{\frac{Z_1}{Z_2}}$$

Where N_1 = No of turns on primary winding
N_2 = No of turns on secondary winding
V_1 = Primary voltage
V_2 = Secondary voltage
Z_1 = Primary impedance
Z_2 = Secondary impedance

4.2   Types of Modulation

The previous section described
how a carrier wave is generated.
The wave can be modified to carry
picture, sound or data information
by **modulating** the signal in any of
the following ways:

* By varying the length of the vector
V as it rotates – this is called
amplitude modulation or "AM".

Amplitude •
Modulation

Frequency •
Modulation

Phase •
Modulation

* By varying the speed of rotation of the vector (thereby changing its frequency) – this is
called **frequency modulation** or "FM".
* By varying the phase angle α to represent different discrete values – this is called
phase modulation.

The following paragraphs give examples of each type of modulation.

Amplitude Modulation (AM) is
used by some radio stations
and all the original TV broadcasters.

Analogue TV pictures are originated
as a video signal as described in
part 2.1 – one line of a typical video
waveform is shown alongside.

Video •
Frequencies

A composite video signal of normal
domestic quality is comprised of
frequencies in the band 50Hz -
5.5MHz. It is not possible to transmit
these signals through the air – these
frequencies are allocated for other
services and you would not
be able to have more than one
programme at a time. Instead, the
video signal is amplitude-modulated
on to a carrier frequency in the
appropriate broadcasting band – the
example alongside shows a UHF
carrier wave (UHF channel 21 in this
case) modulated with the same
video signal.

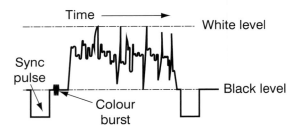

Original video signal

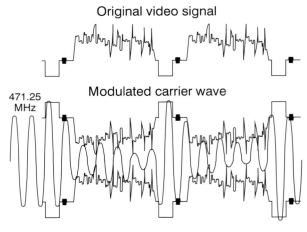

Modulated carrier wave

471.25 MHz

In practice, the carrier frequency is nearly one hundred times higher than the highest frequency component of the video signal and the modulated signal therefore contains enough detail to represent the video signal in its entirety.

At the receiver location, the modulated UHF signal is amplified and passed to a "detector" which removes the high carrier frequencies, leaving the original composite video signal.

Frequency Modulation (FM) is used for FM radio and analogue satellite applications. The frequency of the carrier wave is varied in accordance with the information to be relayed. In this case the various frequencies represent different brightness levels of the video signal.

FM transmitters require considerably less power than AM, to produce the same coverage.

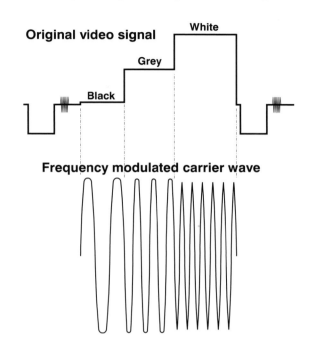

Original video signal

White

Grey

Black

Frequency modulated carrier wave

Keywords

• AM/FM Comparisons

For both AM and FM, the associated sound information can be relayed on a separate sub-carrier frequency.

AM has the disadvantage that any noise, interference or other extraneous signals that is superimposed on the modulated carrier wave will cause distortion of the video signal. FM is much more immune to such disturbances because the information is carried by the frequency, not the amplitude. Such disturbances will have much less effect on the picture quality – this is called the FM improvement ratio. The amount of improvement depends on the depth of modulation (in effect, the maximum change in carrier frequency compared to the unmodulated frequency itself), but it can be more than 15dB. Therefore, whilst the signal to noise ratio (S/N) at the output of an AM receiver is approximately the same as its input carrier to noise ratio (C/N) (dependant of course on the satisfactory design of the receiver), the output S/N ratio of an FM receiver can be much better than its input C/N ratio. This can be further improved by pre-emphasising the higher frequencies during the modulation process with corresponding de-emphasis being applied by the FM receiver.

On the other hand, the energy of an AM signal is centred around a single frequency, whereas FM frequencies are changing, so more bandwidth is required.

To summarise, FM signals are more immune to interference whilst AM signals require less bandwidth. FM is used for VHF radio broadcasts which are of better quality than the short, medium and long wave AM radio transmissions. The original analogue PAL TV standards for terrestrial broadcasting utilised AM for picture information and FM for sound. Because analogue satellite TV signals are very weak, FM was always used to provide more immunity to noise and interference, together with a saving in satellite battery power.

Keywords

Phase • Modulation

Symbol •

MPEG •

PSK •

Constellation • Diagram

Digital Terrestrial TV Modulation

Digital TV is all about the relay of binary data. The characteristics of each picture element are represented by binary numbers (called bits) and a standard definition picture consists of some 200 million such bits per second (200Mb/sec). This could be relayed on a carrier wave using a technique called **phase modulation**, where each cycle or **"symbol"** represents a binary bit as shown alongside. In this case we would

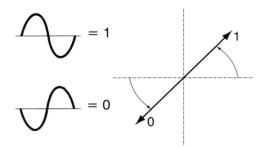

need 200 million cycles per second, or a bandwidth of 200MHz – and that's just for one programme! High Definition TV has even more detail and therefore requires more data to represent it, and the bandwidth required is in excess of 1000Mb/sec.

Imagine trying to fit all this data into the 8MHz bandwidth of a UHF channel. It's clearly not possible. For this reason, the **M**oving **P**icture **E**xperts **G**roup **(MPEG)** has defined standards to compress data into a more manageable bandwidth. **Using MPEG2 compression, the required bandwidths are 2Mb/sec and 16Mb/sec for each standard definition and high definition programme respectively.** The broadcasters then have the task of squeezing as many programmes as possible into each digital multiplex or "mux".

Phase modulation (also known as **P**hase **S**hift **K**eying or **PSK**) is used to relay digital signals on a <u>single</u> frequency by altering the phase of the vector (α), depending on whether a "0" or "1" is being transmitted:

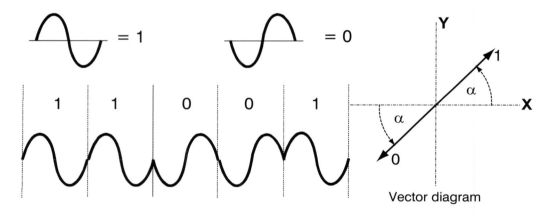

Vector diagram

In this example, a symbol or cycle starting in the positive direction represents a data 1, and a cycle starting in the negative direction represents a data 0. Therefore, each cycle of the carrier wave relays one data bit. The bit rate is therefore said to be equal to the symbol rate.

By having four different phase angles (or "states") instead of two, it would be possible to double the data capacity to two bits per cycle, since there are four ways of arranging two bits as shown in the drawing alongside.

This drawing is known as a **constellation diagram.**

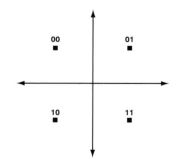

Keywords

• DTT
• QAM

• 16QAM

• 64QAM

• 256QAM

• QSPK

The **D**igital **T**errestrial **T**elevision **(DTT)** broadcasters use a technique called **Q**uadrature **A**mplitude **M**odulation **(QAM)** to increase the bandwidth of each channel even more. QAM varies both the amplitude and the phase of the carrier wave in order to relay more information. The BBC currently uses **16QAM**, where each cycle has 16 different states. Since there are 16 different ways of arranging four binary bits, each cycle relays four bits instead of one, thus increasing the capacity of each multiplex by a factor of four.

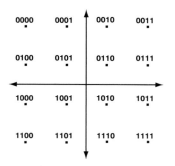

16 QAM - 4 bits per cycle

ITV have chosen to use **64QAM**. Because there are 64 ways of arranging 6 binary bits, each cycle relays six bits.

This is why the ITV multiplex carries more programmes than the BBC multiplex. However the various states are closer together, so any distortion or noise on the waveform may cause the demodulator to interpret the symbol wrongly, thus creating an error. For this reason, 64QAM is less robust than 16QAM, and therefore requires a "cleaner" signal and additional error correction using the techniques described in section 2.7. This is why the ITV pictures are the first to freeze under poor signal conditions.

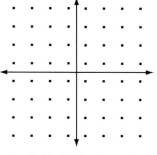

64 QAM - 6 bits per cycle

It is possible to extend this concept even further. This drawing illustrates a **256QAM** signal, where the bit rate is eight times the symbol rate (since there are 256 ways of arranging eight bits).

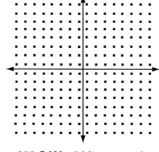

256 QAM - 8 bits per cycle

Digital Satellite TV Modulation

Satellite transmissions are subject to the following constraints:
• Power levels from the satellite are very limited
• Non linear amplification in the satellite transponder
• Enormous free space path losses
• Risk of terrestrial interference
• Significant signal degradation due to rainfall.

Since the received signals are so weak, it is not possible to use amplitude modulation techniques at all. Instead, satellite broadcasters use a version of phase shift keying with two carriers "I" and "Q" at the same frequency, phased 90° apart. This is called "**Q**uadrature **P**hase **S**hift **K**eying" or **QPSK**.

These four states can represent two digits:

00   01   10   11

Therefore, the bit rate is double the symbol rate.

QPSK is very rugged, since distortions of the signal envelope (or amplitude) caused by interference or amplifier non-linearity do not affect the picture quality as long as the phase of the vector can be detected.

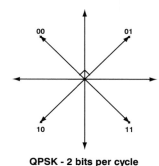

QPSK - 2 bits per cycle

Keywords

Transponder •
Bandwidth

A typical satellite transponder has a bandwidth of 30 MHz (much more than the 8 MHz of a terrestrial TV channel) and can accommodate 10 or more channels of PAL quality. When periods of high action occur simultaneously on several channels on the same transponder, the buffer coarsens the quantising levels (with a consequent loss of picture quality) until the system eventually overloads, resulting in "blocky" pictures.

TV Broadcasting Standards

Analogue •
Reference

Terrestrial analogue and digital TV broadcasts in the UK utilise UHF channels 21 – 68 in the frequency band 470 – 854 MHz, as detailed in the next section. Analogue services are prone to interference, particularly due to multipath reflections, which cause ghostimg. Digital signals can be broadcast at much lower power (typically 1/1000th) than analogue and can therefore use channels that would otherwise not be available.

DVB •

DVB-T •
DVB-S •
COFDM •

The actual method of digital broadcasting is specified by a set of standards produced by the **D**igital **V**ideo **B**roadcasting **(DVB)** Group, a European consortium for broadcasting transmissions. These DVB standards define such things as the type of modulation, error correction and guard bands between channels. They are known as **DVB-T** and **DVB-S** for terrestrial and satellite broadcasts respectively.

DVB-T specifies the use of **C**oded **O**rthogonal **F**requency **D**ivision **M**ultiplex **(COFDM).** Instead of transmitting the data on a single frequency carrier wave, COFDM splits the data into a large number of slower digital streams, each of which modulate a set of closely spaced adjacent carrier frequencies. This gives much more efficient use of the 8MHz channel bandwidth, and provides greater immunity to the effects of reflections on the received signal. There are two such standards as follows:

- 1705 carriers, spaced 4kHz apart (known as 2K)
- 6817 carriers, spaced 1kHz apart (known as 8K)

Increasing the number of carriers does not alter the payload bit rate, which remains constant. Britain currently uses the 2K standard and the rest of Europe uses the 8K standard which provides a more stable signal. 8K DTT receivers are backwards compatible with the 2K standard and all UK receivers manufactured since 2002 will operate on either standard.

Current DTT transmissions in the UK have the following data capacities:

Multiplex	Programmes	Modulation	FEC	Capacity (Mb/Sec
1	BBC	16QAM	3/4	18
2	ITV/Ch4	64QAM	2/3	24
A	Ch4SC/Ch5	64QAM	2/3	24
B	BBC	16QAM	3/4	18
C	Commercial	16AQM	3/4	18
D	Commercial	16QAM	3/4	18

Multiplex •
Bandwidths

This shows that the current total capacity for all six multiplexes is 120Mb/sec, or some 60 channels of standard definition (assuming 2Mb/sec per channel). It is therefore clear that there is no room left for any high definition channels.

Following the completion of the analogue switch-off programme in 2012, the following changes are being considered:

DTT Power •
Levels

- The power of each DTT multiplex (which is currently restricted so as not to interfere with adjacent analogue channels) will be increased, probably by about 13dB.

Keywords

- Because these increased signal levels will be more rugged, all multiplexes will switch to 64QAM, thus giving an immediate increase of 30% in the data payload available. Some may even change to 256QAM, giving an even greater capacity.
- Some HD channels will use a more efficient compression technique called MPEG4, which will require a reduced data bandwidth of 10Mb/sec.
- The UK will change from the 2K standard to the 8K standard (thus making the early 2K receivers obsolete).

• MPEG4

The main implication of these changes is that room may then be available for some DTT high definition channels. UK viewers will also be able to access HDTV (one such channel at a time) from the internet, as long as their broadband connection speed is at least 10Mb/sec.

These changes are defined by a new set of standards, called **DVB-T2**. Not all channels will change and it is expected that DVB-T2 will exist alongside DVB-T for some years. The improved satellite standards **(DVB-S2)** have already been implemented and BSkyB now offer more than 30 HD programmes, with bit rates in excess of 15Mb/sec for each channel – clearly not possible using a TV aerial.

• DVB-T2

• DVB-S2

4

It is also expected that the channels will be reallocated between the DTT multiplexes (which will all have increased bandwidths as a result of the changes) leaving multiplex B clear for HD channels using DVB-T2 standards. The following four channels may be available in HD as the analogue switch-off progresses):

• HD by DTT

- BBC
- ITV/STV/UTV (depending on the region)
- Channel 4/S4C
- Channel 5

Of course, anyone wanting these HD channels will need a new set top box.

TV & Radio Reception

VISION®

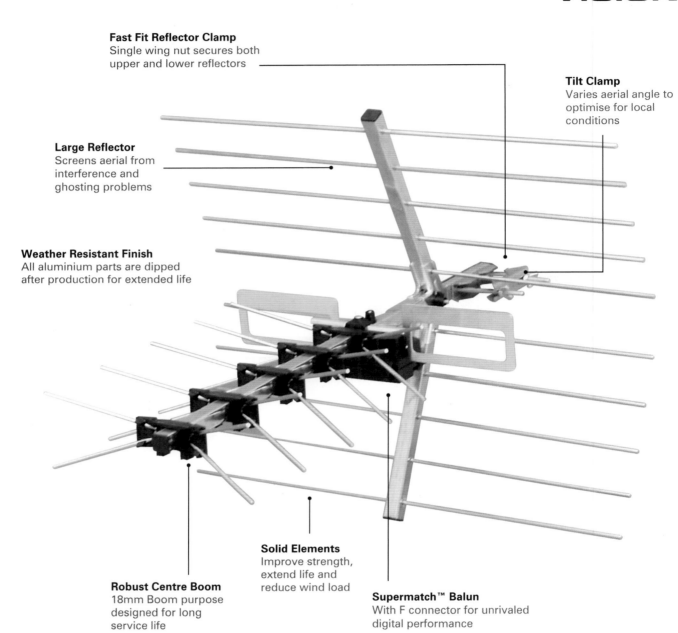

Fast Fit Reflector Clamp
Single wing nut secures both
upper and lower reflectors

Tilt Clamp
Varies aerial angle to
optimise for local
conditions

Large Reflector
Screens aerial from
interference and
ghosting problems

Weather Resistant Finish
All aluminium parts are dipped
after production for extended life

Solid Elements
Improve strength,
extend life and
reduce wind load

Robust Centre Boom
18mm Boom purpose
designed for long
service life

Supermatch™ Balun
With F connector for unrivaled
digital performance

Features will vary across the range from model to model

Also Available In The Vision Aerial Range

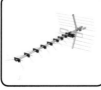

FM and
DAB Radio

High Gain
UHF TV

Log Periodic
UHF TV

Super High
Gain UHF TV

Yagi UHF TV

www.vision-products.co.uk

Keywords

• UHF Spectrum
  PAL I

• UHF Channel
  Bandwidth

• UHF Channel
  Frequencies

5.1 Broadcasting Formats

The TV spectrum between 470-860MHz is divided into 48 channels, each 8MHz wide, numbered 21 to 68. Britain adopted the "PAL I" standard for analogue TV broadcasts, where the 8MHz bandwidth of each channel is utilised as shown alongside.

This display illustrates how a single UHF analogue channel looks when viewed on a spectrum analyser. Most signal measurements are taken using the vision or luminance carrier, which is 1.25MHz above the bottom of the 8MHz bandwidth.

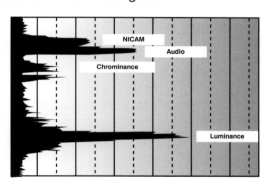

Since it is still often necessary to measure analogue TV signal levels, the TV channels and vision carrier frequencies are listed on the following chart:

CHANNEL	RANGE (MHz)	VISION FREQ. (MHz)	CHANNEL	RANGE (MHz)	VISION FREQ. (MHz)
21	470-478	471.25	45	662-670	663.25
22	478-486	479.25	46	670-678	671.25
23	486-494	487.25	47	678-686	679.25
24	494-502	495.25	48	686-694	687.25
25	502-510	503.25	49	694-702	695.25
26	510-518	511.25	50	702-710	703.25
27	518-526	519.25	51	710-718	711.25
28	526-534	527.25	52	718-726	719.25
29	534-542	535.25	53	726-734	727.25
30	542-550	543.25	54	734-742	735.25
31	550-558	551.25	55	742-750	743.25
32	558-566	559.25	56	750-758	751.25
33	566-574	567.25	57	758-766	759.25
34	574-582	575.25	58	766-774	767.25
35	582-590	583.25	59	774-782	775.25
36	590-598	591.25	60	782-790	783.25
37	598-606	599.25	61	790-798	791.25
38	606-614	607.25	62	798-806	799.25
39	614-622	615.25	63	806-814	807.25
40	622-630	623.25	64	814-822	815.25
41	630-638	631.25	65	822-830	823.25
42	638-646	639.25	66	830-838	831.25
43	646-654	647.25	67	838-846	839.25
44	654-662	655.25	68	846-854	847.25

Keywords

DTT •

Guard Band •

DTT •
Multiplex

Digital **T**errestrial **T**elevision **(DTT)** utilises the same UHF channel numbers, but the 8MHz bandwidth of each channel is used in a different way. Instead of being composed of discrete frequencies, the digital energy is spread across most of the band (7.61MHz) leaving just a "guard band" between adjacent channels. This energy is called a **multiplex** (abbreviated to "mux") and contains not one but several TV programmes that have been multiplexed together. This is why the principle advantage of changing from analogue to digital television is that we can get more programmes into the same bandwidth.

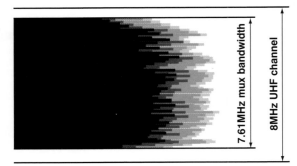

The following analogue programmes have been generally available in the UK:

BBC 1   BBC 2   ITV   Channel 4   Channel 5

These are being replaced by six digital multiplexes carrying the public service channels (PSB multiplexes) and other channels (COM multiplexes) as follows:

Original Multiplex Name	Post-Switchover Name	Operator
1	BBC A	BBC
2	D3 & 4	Digital 3 & 4
A	SDN	SDN
B	BBC B	BBC
C	NGW A	National Grid Wireless
D	NGW B	National Grid Wireless

Post •
Switchover
Channels

The actual UHF channels used by each UK transmitter are available from the Ofcom website (www.ofcom.org.uk). For example, the current Crystal Palace channel allocations are as follows:

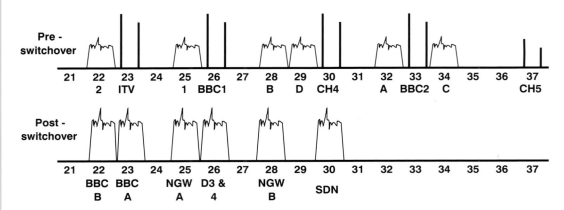

Keywords

5.2 Principles of Radio and TV aerials

A receiving aerial must intercept the electromagnetic wave radiated from a transmitter. The wavefront creates a field around the aerial, which "induces" a current in the conductors forming the aerial. If the aerial can be made to resonate at the frequency being received, the capacitative and inductive components will cancel, leaving only the resistive component. The aerial is most efficient under these conditions, which will occur when the aerial is half a wavelength long with the cable connection at its centre.

Another way of looking at the situation is to consider what would happen if the aerial were to be one whole wavelength long.

At any point in time, if one end was receiving a positive peak of the waveform, the other end would be receiving the next positive as well and there would be zero current at the centre.

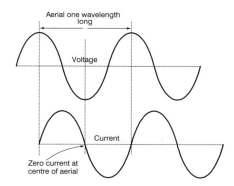

• Half Wavelength Dipole

If the aerial is only half a wavelength long, one end would be at a positive peak whilst the other end would be at a negative peak (ie. maximum voltage across the aerial) and the current at the centre would be at a maximum – this implies that the resistance is at its lowest.

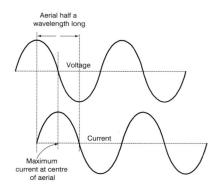

Since we have already calculated that the wavelength of 300MHz is 1 metre, then the theoretical length of an aerial half a wavelength long to receive 300MHz will be 0.5 metres. In practice, it will be only about 95% of its theoretical value, because radio waves travel more slowly through a metallic conductor than they do through a vacuum.

The practical length of an aerial half a wavelength long for the frequencies of interest is as follows:

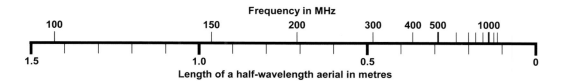

Length of a half-wavelength aerial in metres

• Wavelength
• Frequency

This type of aerial is called a **half wave** dipole and the coaxial cable linking it to the receiver is connected to the middle, one side being connected to the inner core and the other side to the outer screen of the cable.

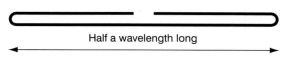

Half a wavelength long

Keywords

Polar •
Diagram

A vertically mounted dipole will pick up signals in the horizontal plane equally from all directions, but it will not pick up anything from above and below it. Its pick-up characteristics are equivalent to the shape of a ring doughnut, as shown in the perspective diagram alongside. It will pick up vertically polarised signals but not horizontally polarised ones.

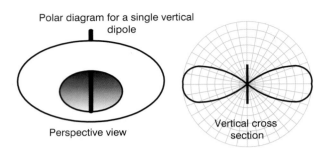

Polar diagram for a single vertical dipole

Perspective view

Vertical cross section

A vertical cross section of its pick up response is also shown in the diagram. This is called a **polar diagram** and indicates the directional properties of the aerial. The concentric circles represent the received signal level in dB, which increase in proportion with the distance from the centre of the diagram.

The same drawing shows the polar diagram (now viewed from above, instead of from the side) if the dipole is mounted horizontally. It shows maximum gain in front of and behind the dipole, and zero pick up from its ends.

A horizontal dipole can be made omnidirectional by shaping it in the form of a circle as shown alongside.

Polar diagram for a horizontally mounted omnidirectional dipole

Perspective of aerial

Horizontal cross section

It is possible to modify the reception characteristics of a dipole by placing another "parasitic" element (usually half a wavelength long) nearby. This will also receive electromagnetic energy and, since it not connected to anything, it will reradiate the energy, which can also be picked up by the dipole. This extra energy will either add to or subtract from the received signal, depending on its phase with respect to the energy received directly by the dipole. The relative phases of the two signals will depend on the distance between the two elements and the frequencies being received.

Reflector •
Plate

The effect of this for a vertically mounted dipole is shown in the polar response alongside. Instead of being "omnidirectional", it now has directional characteristics. It has more gain from the front and less gain from other directions.

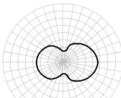

Reflector   Dipole

View of aerial from above

Horizontal polar diagram

Director •
Elements

As more elements are added, these effects become more pronounced. Most aerial designers utilise one parasitic element behind the dipole, called the **reflector,** and one or more **director** elements in front of the dipole. Reflections are typically 5% longer than the dipole and director elements are 5% shorter.

Lobe •
Troughs / Nulls •

These diagrams illustrate the effect on a horizontally polarised aerial. As more directors are added, the forward peak or "lobe" gets longer (indicating more gain in the forward direction) and the troughs or "nulls" get deeper.

Reflector

dipole

Mast

Perspective of aerial

Horizontal polar diagram

Keywords

Also, the main forward lobe gets narrower, indicating that the aerial is becoming more directional.

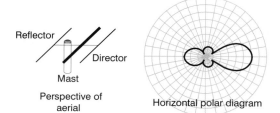

Reflector / Director / Mast
Perspective of aerial
Horizontal polar diagram

High gain aerials can minimise the effect of unwanted reflections – they can be orientated to minimise the gain in the direction that the reflection is coming from. Some manufacturers market these as "anti ghost aerials".

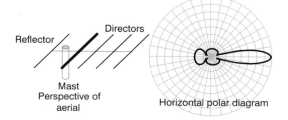

Reflector / Directors / Mast
Perspective of aerial
Horizontal polar diagram

Three of the important parameters to consider when specifying an aerial are:

- **Gain** The maximum gain in the direction of the main lobe (normally expressed in dB with reference to the gain of a single half wave dipole)

- **Beamwidth** The acceptance angle of the main forward lobe (in degrees between the points where the signal level falls by 3dB)

- **Front-to-back ratio** The ratio in dB of the gain in the forward direction to that in the opposite direction.

An aerial has both capacitance and inductance and behaves like a tuned circuit, with a "characteristic impedance". It can be designed with a high "Q" factor, which means that it has high gain over a small frequency band, or a low Q factor, with lower gain over a wider frequency band. For this reason, TV aerials which operate over a small group of channels (called grouped aerials) have more gain than "wideband" aerials designed to cover the whole of the UHF band. The term **bandwidth** refers to the range of channels (or frequencies) covered by an aerial.

Almost without exception, all the constituent items that together make up a radio, TV or satellite reception system have a characteristic impedance of 75 Ohms. This is to ensure maximum power transfer between each source of energy and its corresponding load. It is therefore important that the aerial has an impedance of 75 Ohms so that it matches correctly to the 75 Ohm cable downlead.

A half wavelength dipole has its lowest impedance at its centre point. Some aerials utilise a **folded dipole** which consists of two half wavelength dipoles connected together at their ends (ie in parallel). The spacing between these elements must be small compared with the wavelength of the frequencies being received.

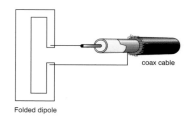

coax cable
Folded dipole

The impedance of the aerial can be modified by varying the diameter of the two elements. If the two diameters are the same, the impedance of the aerial is about 300 Ohms and this can be matched to the 75 Ohm cable by using a small transformer. This has the added advantage of matching the "balanced" (or symmetrical) aerial to the "unbalanced" (or non-symmetrical) coaxial cable.

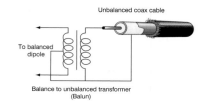

Unbalanced coax cable
To balanced dipole
Balance to unbalanced transformer (Balun)

- Aerial Parameters

- Q Factor

- Bandwidth

- Characteristic Impedance

- Folded Dipole

- Transformer

5

Keywords

Aerial Groups •
Balun •

Such a component is called a **ba**lance-to-**un**balance transformer or **"balun"**. A balun helps to reduce the ingress of interference and it is absolutely essential for all new installations to use an aerial with an integral balun for receiving digital terrestrial signals. Less expensive "contract" aerials are just not good **enough for this purpose -** whilst they may deliver enough signal, they are much less immune to the pick up of impulse noise which causes "blocky" digital pictures.

The analogue TV channels broadcast from any transmitter in the UK were carefully chosen to minimise any interference between them. They were also grouped so TV aerials would need to operate over a relatively small band of frequencies. Aerial manufacturers therefore make aerials to cover a single channel, a group of channels or the whole UHF band.

Grouped Aerials •

As already stated, the smaller the aerial bandwidth, the higher its gain so the more signal it delivers to the coaxial cable. Grouped aerials therefore deliver stronger signals than their wideband counterparts. Another advantage is that smaller bandwidth aerials reduce the reception of unwanted signals and interference outside the band of interest.

Grouped aerials were designed to cover the channels used by each transmitter and most manufacturers colour code each end of the main boom arm.

Aerial Colour •
Code

With the advent of Channel 5 services, the aerial groups were extended and the diagram alongside shows the new groups. It is possible that older grouped aerials may not cover all the channels shown in the diagram.

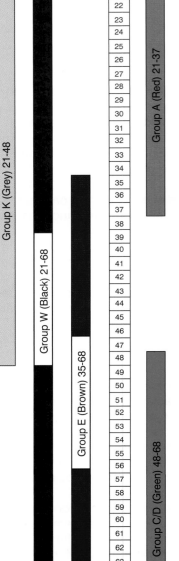

UHF TV aerial groups

Some years ago, the Independent Television Commission (ITC) was given the task of specifying UHF TV channels for the new digital terrestrial services. These had to be chosen to minimise interference to and from the existing UHF channels, in neighbouring countries. The ITC tried to ensure that the digital channels were in the same aerial groups as the analogue channels from the same transmitter. This is possible for some, but not all, transmitter sites. This is why some viewers can receive the new terrestrial digital channels with their existing grouped analogue aerials whilst others will require a new aerial.

As the analogue switch-off progresses, the UHF channels carrying some of the digital multiplexes will be rearranged to allow for more transmitters to broadcast digital signals, and for some of the UHF frequencies (channels 33 to 38 and 63 to 68) to be reallocated for other services such as the broadcast of TV programmes to mobile phones.

Keywords

• Yagi Aerials

The least expensive "contract" aerials are based on the traditional **Yagi** design that offers a good compromise between high gain and directivity. Such an aerial typically consists of the following:

• A half wavelength folded dipole, sometimes incorporating a balun
• A reflector spaced 0.15 of a wavelength behind the dipole, consisting of either a flat plate or a series of rods above and below the dipole and typically 5% longer.
• A series of directors spaced in front of the dipole at intervals of 0.10 of a wavelength and typically 5% shorter
• A central boom arm to support the above items
• A mast clamp to fix the aerial to the mast, allowing the aerial to be mounted with its elements either vertical or horizontal.

Yagi aerials are normally specified according to the total number of elements, including the dipole and reflector. 10, 14 and 18 element aerials are common throughout the industry. 10 and 14 element versions are normally end mounted but the 18 element version is usually supported by a cradle mounted in the centre of the boom.

Yagi aerials can be obtained for single channels, groups of channels or the whole UHF frequency band. The bandwidth of a Yagi can be increased by making the director elements progressively shorter towards the front of the aerial.

Whilst adding more director elements to a Yagi aerial can further increase its gain and directivity, such an aerial with more than 18 elements becomes physically very long and obtrusive. Aerial designers have therefore resorted to other means to obtain improved performance.

• X type Aerials

One such design is called the **X type** pressed element aerial, which has a number of dipoles mounted in parallel. These can be grouped or wideband, with up to 100 elements. Some use full wave dipoles to achieve better matching characteristics. They are of use in weak signal strength areas where the highest possible gain is required, or to minimise ghosting where nearby tall buildings would otherwise degrade the picture quality. The reflector element normally consists of a wire mesh or grid, to minimise wind resistance.

Another variation is called the **X type wire rod** aerial, where the dipoles are made of wired formed in the shape of a bow tie.

• Bow Tie Aerials

Yet another version is the stacked **grid** or **panel** aerial, where several directors are stacked vertically in front of a grid reflector. The interconnections between the directors are cross-connected to "phase match" the outputs. An important feature of a grid aerial is its excellent front-to-back ratio, useful for viewers who are midway between two transmitters with identical TV channels, or where there is strong interference from behind the aerial. A grid aerial is not as directional as an equivalent Yagi or X type array, nor does it have as much gain. Grid aerials are usually wideband.

• Grid Aerials

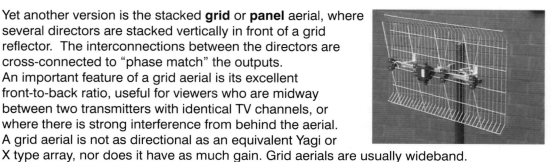

Keywords

Multi Boom •
Aerials

Log Periodic •
Aerials

Benchmark •
Standards

It is also possible to combine the features of both X type and Grid type aerials using a substantial grid reflector and dipoles on two or more booms.

Another type of wideband aerial is called the Log Periodic. This has a series of director elements that get shorter towards the front of the aerial, the longest and shortest being cut to be half a wavelength long at the lowest and highest UHF channels respectively. The directors are mounted on two boom arms to allow for cross connection of alternate elements. The result is an aerial with less overall gain, but with very little change in gain across the whole UHF band. It also has smaller side and back lobes. It is especially suitable for digital reception, except in areas of weak signal strength where a higher gain aerial will be necessary.

In some cases, the signal may be degraded by reflections, in which case the directivity of the aerial will be important.
It may therefore be necessary to use an aerial with a narrow beamwidth or with pronounced peaks and nulls in its polar response, so that the effects of these reflections can be minimised.

In other cases, the aerial may pick up interference from other TV stations elsewhere in the UHF band, in which case it would be necessary to use a grouped aerial or one with a good front-to-back ratio.

The aerial may also pick up other types of interference, for example from motor vehicles, light dimmers, nearby cellphones and radio stations. One would therefore choose an aerial with a good impedance match to the downlead cable or with a narrow beamwidth in the vertical plane.

An aerial benchmarking scheme has been introduced to identify aerials that reach a standard of performance suitable for digital reception. To obtain benchmark certification, aerial manufacturers must submit samples to an independent testing authority. Tests are then conducted to ensure that the aerial complies with or exceeds minimum electrical performance parameters, including forward gain, cross-polar protection and feeder pickup rejection.

There are four benchmark standards:

Standard 1 (the highest standard). Intended for aerials used in fringe and difficult reception areas or in systems where improved C/N is required.

Standard 2 (the intermediate standard). Intended for grouped or wideband aerials where a higher field strength is present

Standard 3 (the minimum standard). Intended for use in high field strength areas

Standard 4 Intended for log periodic aerials where a wideband aerial with better performance than standard 3 is needed

It is recommended that installers use only aerials that have been benchmarked.
An aerial must provide signals of adequate level. If the level of the signals from the aerial is not sufficient, the performance of the whole system will never be perfect. It is therefore necessary to use an aerial with sufficient gain, depending on the signal strength at the reception site.

Keywords

Most UK homes have a Yagi aerial with between 10 and 18 elements. In fringe areas, a higher gain aerial will be required. The following diagram shows typical gains (in dB with reference to a single half-wavelength dipole) for different types of aerials, across the UHF band (channels 21-68):

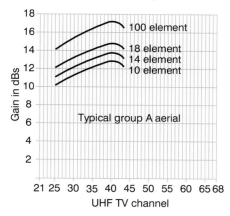

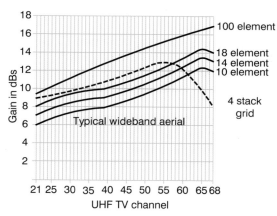

• Aerial
  Performance

The following conclusions can be drawn from this diagram:

- The gain tends to increase for higher channels
- The biggest aerial has only 4dB more gain than a 10 element Yagi aerial
- A grouped aerial has typically 4dB more gain than the equivalent wideband version.

To summarise, the important parameters to consider when specifying an aerial are:

• Aerial
  Parameters

- **Benchmarked Aerial** Only use benchmarked aerials
- **Gain** The maximum gain in the direction of the main lobe (normally expressed in dB with reference to the gain of a single half wave dipole)
- **Bandwidth** The UHF channels that an aerial has been designed to receive
- **Beamwidth** The acceptance angle of the main forward lobe (in degrees between the points where the signal level falls by 3dB)
- **Front-to-back ratio** The ratio in dB of the gain in the forward direction to that in the opposite direction.

5.3 UHF Signal Measurements

In the world of telecommunications, noise is degrading interference, not something we hear. Extraneous noise is picked up by an aerial from space, nearby objects (especially warm or hot ones), light dimmers, electrical appliances etc. Noise is also generated by all electronic components due to the random motion of electrons in matter. It can occur over the whole of the telecommunications band of frequencies, just over a specific band, or at a single frequency. The effects of noise can sometimes be minimised by using a filter to reduce the noise and interference outside the frequency band of interest, or by using a grouped aerial instead of a wideband version.

• Noise

Noise can enter a reception system via the aerial or coaxial cable, or it can be generated within the system by electronic items such as amplifiers and frequency converters. Amplifier noise figures are quoted in dB and, the lower the noise figure, the better.

Before the invention of the transistor, amplifiers with valves were used to boost signals. Valves utilised heaters to increase the emission of electrons from their cathodes, thus increasing their thermal noise at the same time. Engineers therefore used a coolant such as liquid nitrogen to reduce the temperature of the amplifier, thus reducing the thermal noise. However, modern integrated circuits have such good noise figures that such techniques are no longer feasible to improve the noise performance of amplifiers.

• Noise
  Generation

Keywords

**Analogue •
Signal Levels**

If the received analogue signal level is allowed to fall to too low a level, the received picture and/or sound quality will be degraded by the noise level. The lower the signal level, the more this is likely to happen. If the received signal level is then amplified, this will not help because the noise is boosted as well! As a general rule, you can never make a bad signal good again. The solution is not to let it get bad in the first place.

This is the mistake made by untrained TV aerial installers and Do-It-Yourself enthusiasts. Noise on an analogue TV signal results in white dots or "snow" on the picture. They fit a "Booster" behind the TV set, only to find that the picture quality has not improved at all because the noise was boosted as well as the signal.

**Amplifier •
Location**

Having received a good signal at the aerial location, it is then necessary not to let its level drop too low on the cable route to the receiver and an amplifier can help to achieve this. An amplifier is therefore used to maintain the signal beyond its output at an acceptable level, not to improve its quality at its input. The DIY enthusiast referred to above should have fitted the booster at the aerial location, before the signal had dropped to an unacceptable level due to the attenuation of the coaxial cable.

**Carrier/Noise •
Ratio**

The ratio between the level of an analogue signal and the level of noise in the same frequency band is known as the carrier to noise ratio (C/N ratio). This is quoted in dB. The lowest C/N ratio anywhere on the system limits the overall performance of the entire system.

If the signal level is too high, it can overload the electronic circuits in amplifiers and receivers, causing distortion. The signals within a channel can interact together, causing intermodulation distortion, whilst those between channels cause crossmodulation distortion. These effects will degrade the C/N ratio. Therefore, for each part of a reception system, there is a window of operation between two levels, within which the signal level must be kept. If the signal anywhere in the reception chain falls outside the window of operation, the overall performance of the system will be degraded. The window of operation for an amplifier will depend on its noise figure and maximum output capability, but the window of operation at outlet sockets is specified to give acceptable performance using normal domestic receivers.

The window of operation to achieve satisfactory results for domestic analogue systems is as follows, in dBμV:

**Analogue Level •
Windows**

	FM Radio	DAB Radio	TV
Minimum signal level anywhere between the aerial terminals and the receiver input	54	30	60
Recommended minimum level at receiver input	60	40	60
Maximum signal level at receiver input	74	70	80

It is essential to measure the analogue signal level of each TV channel using a calibrated signal level meter or spectrum analyser. If the signal level anywhere on a TV reception system falls below 60dBμV, noise (or snow) will be visible on the picture.

No test equipment is available to measure analogue picture quality on a TV screen. Instead, we assess the degradations or impairments by looking at the picture, according to the following CCIR impairment scale:

5

Keywords

• CCIR
  Impairment
  Scale

• Noise Levels

• Digital Signal
  Levels

• Cliff Effect

Quality	Grade	Impairment
Excellent	5	Imperceptible
Good	4	Perceptible but not annoying
Fair	3	Slightly annoying
Poor	2	Annoying
Bad	1	Very annoying

As a general guide, the relationship between the lowest analogue signal level (anywhere on the system) and the resultant picture quality is as follows:

Lowest signal level (dBµV)	60	54	48	42	36
Resultant CCIR picture grade	5	4	3	2	1

This does not mean that noise-free pictures will always be achieved if the signal level is more than 60dBµV. The noise level may have been increased due to the use of an amplifier with a high noise figure (see section 6.3) or because a VCR or DVD player is set to the same UHF channel as an incoming digital multiplex from the aerial, either from the transmitter being used (probably wiping out the digital picture) or from another transmitter, causing an increase in the noise level and resulting in a graining analogue picture (the inexperience installer will then fit an additional amplifier to fix the problem, just making matters worse).

Installers should target for a picture quality with a minimum grade 4 on every TV channel. Of course, the degradation may be due to factors other than low signal level, such as reflections, intermodulation or cross modulation distortion, or electrical interference – the main reason for a low grade picture should be recorded on the job sheet.

Digital signals also have a window of operation. Too high a level will overload the amplifier or receiver, and, if the signal is too low, noise will degrade the performance of the system, causing errors to occur.

Digital pictures have two states. They are either of perfect quality (CCIR grade 5) or non existent (grade 1), so CCIR grading us not used. Instead digital signal quality is always defined by the number of errors occuring in the data received. If errors occur in the signal reaching the video decoder in the TV receiver, square blocks (or horizontal "slices" comprising several such blocks) will appear randomly over the picture, usually at areas of high action or detail. As the number of errors increases, the whole picture will freeze and then disappear. These errors can be due to a number of reasons:

- The received digital signal is too low, causing errors to reach the decoder.
- The received analogue signal is too high, causing the tuner in the digital receiver to overload.
- The C/N ratio of the received signal is not good enough, causing the noise to introduce errors.
- There is high action simultaneously on several programmes in the same multiplex.

The last reason is solely under the control of the broadcaster and there is nothing that the installer can do about this. The other reasons may be due to the fact that the signal received by the aerial is just not good enough (sometimes not under the control of the installer either) or because the signal levels between the aerial and receiver are outside the satisfactory window of operation, causing the C/N ratio to be degraded.

The fact that digital pictures disappear suddenly is referred to as the "cliff effect", as previously described. The installer needs to know just how close to the edge of the cliff he is. It may be that the system is right at the edge, yet still giving perfect pictures. It is impossible to tell just by looking at the pictures and, the next time it rains (or when the

Keywords

signal level changes for whatever reason) the pictures will freeze. **He must measure the digital level and C/N ratio on each multiplex** to ensure that the signals are within their defined windows of operation.

Adjacent Channel •
Interference

Digital TV transmitters transmit at much lower power than their analogue counterparts (usually 20dB less or at one hundredth of the power) for several reasons:
- Being more "rugged", they are more immune to interference.
- Because digital channels are sometimes adjacent to an analogue channel, they would interfere with the analogue channel if they were any higher. This is called adjacent channel interference.

Co-channel •
Interference

- If they were any higher, they would interfere with analogue programmes broadcast on the same channel from other transmitters. This is called co-channel interference.

The rugged nature of digital signals means that they can be received at lower levels than their analogue counterparts. However, measuring the signal level is not as easy. Analogue meters are designed to measure signal level at a single frequency whereas digital meters must measure the equivalent digital power over the whole frequency band occupied by the multiplex – 7.61MHz.

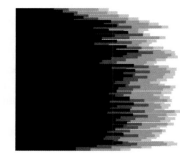

Another reason for not using an analogue meter can be seen from the illustration alongside. Where would one measure the level – at the peaks or the troughs, and where if the level slopes across the multiplex?

DTT Signal •
Levels

A terrestrial digital TV receiver will function with an input level of between 45 and 70 dBμV. At the lower level, there is a risk of interference from impulse noise from, for example, a nearby fridge or central heating thermostat switching on, causing the picture to block or freeze. The recommended minimum level is therefore 50dBμV.

To summarise, the window of operation on each Digital Terrestrial Television (DTT) multiplex to achieve satisfactory results for single domestic installations is as follows, in dBμV:

Minimum signal level anywhere between aerial terminals and receiver input	45
Recommended minimum level at receiver input	50
Maximum signal level at receiver input	70

An analogue signal of more than 75dBμV on any UHF channel may overload a digital receiver, causing the pictures to freeze. On occasions where the digital multiplex is transmitted 20dB lower than the analogue signal levels, the maximum digital level is therefore 20dB less or 55dBμV. If any of the digital multiplexes are more than 20dB lower than the analogue levels, then the maximum digital level is reduced still further.

It can be seen from the above paragraph that the window of operation for digital signal levels a relatively small, usually 50 to 55dBμV, or a range of just 5dB! The installer must be far more accurate with digital levels than he ever was for analogue TV levels. He might think of amplifying a signal that is too weak, but this may not help, because it will amplify the noise as well.

He must therefore measure the carrier to noise ratio on each multiplex, in addition to the signal level. Some makes of digital meter will measure both the signal level and C/N ratio at the same time.

5

Keywords

• Carrier/Noise
Ratio

• Masthead
Amplifiers

• Bit Error Ratio
(BER)

The agreed limits for C/N ratio on domestic DTT installations are as follows for 64QAM multiplexes:

Reliable reception	26dB or better
Marginal reception	23-25dB
Unreliable or no reception	22dB or worse

These limits can be reduced by 4dB for 16QAm multiplexes.

If the C/N ratio is too low at the aerial terminals, an amplifier will not help matters and the aerial signal must be improved by other means. If it is just acceptable, then the use of a masthead amplifier may help to keep the signal level and C/N ratio within acceptable limits at the input to the digital receiver. In such cases, the amplifier gain must be as low as possible – just enough to compensate for the losses between the aerial and the receiver(s). High gain masthead amplifiers must be avoided wherever possible.

This diagram summarises the aerial and masthead amplifier requirements for DTT signal levels measured at the aerial terminals.

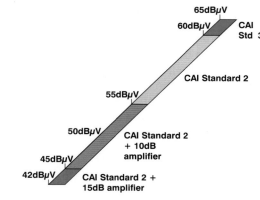

Whatever the signal level and C/N ratio, the sole factor that determines the performance of a DTT reception system is the number of errors reaching the digital receiver and whether the receiver can cope with them.

The **BIT ERROR RATIO (BER)** is the ratio of the number of bits that the detector in the demodulator is NOT able to detect to the total number of bits transmitted. <u>In effect, it is the system "goodness" factor</u>.

The lower the BER, the better.

Digital receivers will operate satisfactorily if the BER before error correction is equal to, or better than, 2E-4 (2 errors in every 10 000 bits of data).

The methods of measuring signal levels, C/N ratios and BER are given in part nine.

5.4   TV Amplifiers

The purpose of using an amplifier is to improve the C/N ratio of the signals received at the TV outlet socket(s). It is essential to position the amplifier in the system <u>before</u> the signal is degraded, because the amplifier will increase both the signal level and the noise level of the input signal. If the signal from the aerial is weak, it may be necessary to use an outdoor "masthead" amplifier mounted close to the aerial. For stronger signals, an indoor amplifier may be adequate.

The choice of which indoor or outdoor amplifier to use depends on the following:

Keywords

UHF Amplifier Parameters

- **Bandwidth** The amplifier may be required to boost FM radio, DAB and UHF TV signals, in which case the required bandwidth must be at least 87.5-860MHz. If it is to be used for UHF TV channels only, it can be either a wideband version (470-860MHz), a grouped amplifier covering one aerial group or an amplifier for just a single TV channel. Use an amplifier with the smallest possible bandwidth to reduce or eliminate the noise outside the bands of interest. Some types of amplifiers have separate inputs for FM, DAB and TV, whilst others have a single combined input – in such cases, the various inputs must be first combined together.
- **Gain** The input TV signal level may be just over the required minimum, in which case an amplifier will be useful to increase the levels so that subsequent losses due to cable, splitters, outlet plates and flyleads do not cause the signal to drop below the required minimum. Ideally, the amplifier gain should be just enough to compensate for these losses.
- **Noise** Amplifiers contain electronic components that will generate their own noise, which will add to the noise present at the input terminals. Amplifiers have different noise figures and low noise amplifiers (with the lowest noise figure) should be used wherever possible.
- **Maximum output** This is normally stated for two channel operation for a specific level of distortion. If any TV channel exceeds this level, all the analogue pictures may be distorted and the Bit Error Ratio of digital signals may be dramatically impaired Care must be taken to ensure that the maximum input level (which is the maximum output level minus the amplifier gain) is not exceeded. Do not use an attenuator to achieve this because this will degrade the C/N ratio – use an amplifier with a lower gain.

Amplifier Derating

The risk of distortion will be increased if two or more amplifiers are operated in tandem. Similarly, increasing the number of channels through an amplifier will increase the amount of distortion caused by the amplifier (digital muxes and analogue TV channels may be ignored in this regard if they are more than 15dB weaker than the strongest channels). For these reasons, all amplifiers must be derated (or their maximum output reduced) according to the following rules:

Derating Rules

1. Each time that the number of amplifiers in tandem is doubled, derate the maximum output of each by 3dB.
2. Each time that the number of TV channels is doubled, derate the amplifier's maximum output by 3dB (assume that the output level quoted is for 2 channel operation, unless stated otherwise).

Whilst the analogue channels are still available, it is the analogue channels that are counted. When the analogue channels have been discontinued, the digital power levels will be increased and it will then be the digital channels that are counted.

The table alongside summarises the above rules to give the required derating in dB for each amplifier. If the number of amplifiers or TV channels is increased but not doubled (say, from two to three), the rules still apply and one can interpolate the required derating.

No of Channels	No. of amplifiers in cascade			
	2	4	8	16
2	3dB	6dB	9dB	12dB
4	6dB	9dB	12dB	15dB
8	9dB	12dB	15dB	18dB
16	12dB	15dB	18dB	21dB

If there is any risk of fluctuations of the input signal levels, it would be advisable to de-rate the amplifier outputs by a further 3dB, to allow for this eventuality.

Keywords

• Masthead
  Amplifiers

Masthead Amplifiers

These are normally fitted as close as possible to the aerial, in order to receive the strongest possible input signal. Indeed, some are mounted inside the aerial connection box itself.

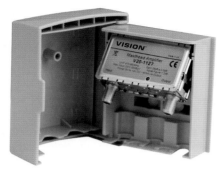

The amplifier can be mounted on the same mast as the aerial, and just below it. Ensure that the input and output coaxial cables enter from below, so that rainwater does not run down the cable and into the amplifier.

Masthead amplifiers are available with gains of between 4 and 34dB before derating. Typical noise figures are 1.8dB and 2.8dB for grouped and wideband amplifiers respectively, although the latest wideband versions have noise figures as low as 0.8dB. The original versions had saddle-and-clamp connections, but most modern versions use F connectors.

Masthead amplifiers need a source of DC power (normally 5-12V) which is supplied from a **P**ower **S**upply **U**nit **(PSU)** at one of the receiver locations. This voltage is relayed to the masthead amplifier on the same coaxial cable that is bringing the amplified signals back down to the receiver(s).

• Power Supply
  Unit

The specification for an amplifier indicates its current requirements in milliamps (mA) and one must ensure that the psu is capable of providing this amount of current. For instance, if the amplifier needs 40mA, the PSU must have a rating of 40mA or more. If two amplifiers are wired in tandem with one consuming 25mA and the other 30mA, the PSU rating must be at least 55mA.

Most masthead amplifiers are designed to receive the DC power via their output connector but not to pass this on to the aerial input connector, in case the aerial shorts it out. If two such amplifiers are wired in tandem, the first one would use the 12V but not pass it on, so the second amplifier would have no power. This can be overcome by using a cascade amplifier in the first location, the only difference being that a cascade amplifier will pass the 12V to its input terminals as well. Be careful not to fit a **cascade** amplifier closest to the aerial.

• Cascade
  Amplifier

If signals are being received from two different transmitters on separate aerials, try to balance the signal levels by amplifying the weaker signals, rather than amplifying them all. In such cases, make sure that the DC power reaches the amplifier but not the other aerial by using a signal combiner with DC pass on the appropriate leg. Some makes of masthead amplifier have a switchable power-pass facility.

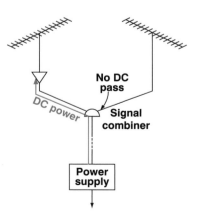

No DC pass

DC power

Signal combiner

Power supply

Keywords

Masthead amplifiers are now available with several outputs, so all the distribution to the rooms can be achieved with cables on the outside of the dwelling.

Indoor •
Amplifiers

Indoor Amplifiers

These are usually mains powered. Versions with a single output can be connected via a splitter to feed several TV outlets. Other types have up to eight separate outputs plus an additional high level output – make sure that this is properly terminated with a 75 Ohm resistor if it is not used. Some can also provide 12V to power a masthead amplifier. Most modern amplifiers use F connectors.

Typical multi-output indoor amplifiers have gains of 6-8dB and a maximum output of 85dBμV, whereas single output versions can have a much higher gain and maximum output.

Three typical uses for an indoor amplifier are as follows:

Set-Back •
Amplifier

- To allow the signal from the main lounge to be distributed to one or two TV receivers in other rooms. A "set back" amplifier has just enough gain to overcome the subsequent losses through splitter and coaxial cables. It has a typical maximum output of 85dBμV.
- At a central location, to distribute signals to up to 16 outlets throughout the house. Multi output. Again, low gain and maximum output – typically 95dBμV.
- For larger homes and multi dwelling units, to boost TV signals to higher levels to overcome subsequent network losses. Some versions have a single output of up to 120dBμV, feeding a splitter(s) and/or "spur" cables (see section 6.4).

Interstage •
Gain Control

Some amplifiers incorporate a gain control on the input. If this is turned down, the ratio of the incoming signal level to the amplifier noise level will be reduced – in other words, the carrierl to noise ratio will be reduced. This is not good practice, especially for digital terrestrial TV signals. It is much better to amplify the incoming signals first and then attenuate them. Such amplifiers are said to have **"interstage"** gain controls and are much preferred for digital work. Alternatively, one could use a masthead preamplifier to boost weak signals at the aerial location followed by a main amplifier in the loft with an attenuator on the input – you would then have, in effect, a "dual" amplifier with an interstage gain control.

Attenuators •

If the level of the incoming signals is too high and the amplifier does not have a gain control, the level can be reduced by using in-line attenuators. These have a male connector at one end and a female connector at the other end, and either F or IEC versions are available. The amount by which the signals will be attenuated is always marked in dB on the

Keywords

• Attenuator
  Types

• A/V Remote
  Control

• CE Marking

• Splitters

• Combiners

outside of the metal case. They can be daisy chained if necessary – for instance a 3dB attenuator followed by a 6dB version will attenuate the signals by a total of 9dB.

There are two important points to consider:
• Will the attenuator pass the frequencies of interest? There are normally different versions for terrestrial radio/TV and satellite applications.
• Will the attenuator pass DC current if required (for instance, to power a masthead amplifier)? Most won't, and it would be essential to use an attenuator with DC pass clearly marked on the case for such applications.

Since it now becoming popular to watch VCR/DVD and satellite programmes in other rooms, a range of amplifiers is now available to pass control signals in the reverse direction, so that the viewer can remotely control the VCR/DVD and/or satellite receiver. Such amplifiers must be able to pass such signals which can be either DC or on a sub-carrier frequency.

All electronic equipment including amplifiers for use in areas accessible to the general public must be fitted with a 13amp mains plug – it is now an offence to sell such an item without the appropriate mains plug fitted. They must also be "CE" marked to indicate that their design complies with the European legislation regarding safety and the radiation of interference. The whole subject of safety is discussed in more detail in sections 6.3 and 8.4,

5.5 Splitters, Combiners, Diplexers and Filters

Splitters and Combiners

A splitter is called a passive device because it has no gain (or amplification) and does not require any input power to perform its function. In its simplest form, a splitter will divide the incoming signal into two outputs with equal signal levels whilst maintaining a 75 ohm impedance to all three branches. The least expensive splitters use resistors to achieve this. Versions of the plastic "Y" splitter are available with IEC95 connectors as one male to two females, and vice versa. They are widely available from DIY stores and market stalls. They can also be used "backwards"

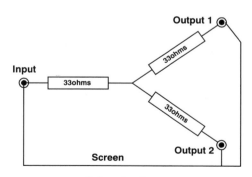

A basic 2 way resistive splitter

to combine two signals together. When used as a two-way splitter, the loss to each leg is typically 4-5dB – this is called the **insertion loss** or **"through loss"** of the splitter.

A more efficient way of splitting signals uses the principle of induction. This uses a transformer with several coils of wire wound on a small "Ferrite" core.

Another advantage of this method is that there is more mutual isolation between the outputs. This needs to be as high as possible so that an open circuit or short circuit on one output has the minimum effect on the other outputs.

Keywords

Some plastic Y splitters use the inductive principle. The more professional inductive splitters are housed in screened cases (to minimise the pick-up of interference) with integral IEC or F connectors. Various types of 2 way splitter are shown alongside.

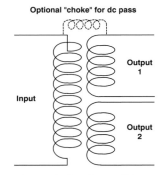

DTT •
Multiplex

Insertion •
Losses

The insertion losses of an inductive splitter depend on the efficiency of the transformer and the number of ways that the signal is split. Typical insertion losses for inductive splitters are as follows:

Number of ways	2	3	4	6	8	12	16
Through loss per leg (dB)	4.0	7.0	8.0	11.0	12.0	14.0	15.5

Asymmetrical •
Splitters

It is possible to obtain splitters with unequal losses on the output legs. For instance, one output leg could have less insertion loss at the expense of other outputs which would have a higher insertion loss. This is achieved by varying the number of coils on each winding of the transformer.

Most modern splitters with F connectors will pass frequencies between 5-2300MHz, although some have a more restricted frequency range. Check that the splitter you are using will handle all the necessary frequency bands.

As inductive splitters do not have a direct connection between the input and output, they will not pass DC power between the input (or "primary") windings and the output (or "secondary") windings. There are some instances where this would be necessary, for instance when relaying DC voltage from a power supply unit (PSU) to a masthead amplifier.

This can be achieved by connecting a high inductance "choke" between the input winding and one or more of the output windings, as shown in the diagram alongside. This will pass the voltage between the windings, whilst having a negligible effect on frequencies in the radio and TV bands. Versions are available with DC pass on one leg only, or on all legs and with power pass in both directions or in one direction only.

DC Pass •

Optional "choke" for dc pass

Input

Output 1

Output 2

2 way inductive splitter

The wire used in a choke is relatively thin and has a limited current carrying capacity. It is therefore necessary to check that the current rating of the splitter is sufficient, especially if the PSU is to supply more than one amplifier – otherwise the choke will act as a fuse, with disastrous results!

A splitter can usually be used backwards as a combiner.

Diplexers

A "diplexer" is a two way splitter or combiner that incorporates bandpass filters to make it frequency selective. It can be used to combine or separate two or more signals in different frequency bands whilst maintaining isolation between inputs. Typical examples are FM/TV combiners and TV group combiners. The respective bandwidths are defined as a range of frequencies outside which the signal levels are attenuated by more than 3dB. A two way version is called a diplexer, whilst a three way version is called a triplexer.

A diplexer has two main advantages over the equivalent splitter:
• Because it is frequency selective, it will reduce or eliminate noise and interference outside the frequency band being relayed.
• It has a significantly lower insertion loss than the equivalent splitter or combiner – 2dB or less is typical.

Some outlet plates incorporate diplexers or triplexers to separate the signals on a single coaxial cable into two or more frequency bands. Versions are available with DC isolation. Typical versions are shown alongside.

FM/TV diplexed outlet (capacitor symbol indicates DC isolation)

FM/TV/SAT triplexed outlet

Some diplexed and triplexed outlet plates incorporate dc isolation for safety reasons – this requirement is discussed fully in later sections. Such outlets usually have a capacitor symbol on the front plate. It is important to remember that isolated outlets will not pass DC power to a masthead amplifier or remote control signals between rooms, so they cannot always be used.

Since these outlet plates incorporate electronic components on the circuit board behind the front plate, it is most advisable to use versions that have a metal screen over the circuit board, in compliance with the latest European legislation. This will reduce the possibility of pick up of external interference. However, screened outlets are physically deeper than the unscreened versions, so it is advisable to check that the flush conduit box is deep enough to accommodate a screened outlet plate. Always try to use screened outlets for digital terrestrial TV reception systems.

Because some twin outlet plates are designed for use with two coaxial cable inputs (one to each outlet socket), it is necessary to check that the plate does in fact incorporate a diplexer before assuming that this is the case. A diplexed outlet will have coils and capacitors on the rear circuit board.

Filters and Levellers

"In line" filters are available to reduce the effect of unwanted signals and interference. Typical uses would be to remove out-of-band traffic interference, Citizen Band (CB) signals, and interference generated by the new **T**errestrial **T**runked **R**adio **(TETRA)** emergency communication services.

There are two basic types:
• Band pass filters, that pass the wanted frequency bands whilst attenuating all other frequencies.
• Notch filters, that eliminate (or notch out) the interfering signals. These are very sharp filters and some are tuneable over a band of frequencies.

Keywords

All such filters will have a minimum insertion loss that is usually of the order of 2dB. Filters can also be used to separate individual TV channels or groups of TV channels so that their relative levels can be adjusted. This may be necessary if one channel is lower or higher in level than the others, which would otherwise reduce further the window of operation.

Levellers •

Such filters can be purchased in groups to cover all the channels broadcast by a particular TV transmitter. A **filter/leveller** typically incorporates five such filters and adjustable attenuators, together with an output diplexer. Being passive devices, they do not require a source of external power and are normally not power passing. Some versions have a single input followed by the appropriate input diplexer. The insertion loss is typically 2-20dB depending on the setting of the adjustable attenuator.

The required channels must be specified when purchasing these units since they cannot be realigned to different channels without the use of very specialised test equipment.

Cluster Filters •

Whilst it is not possible to obtain separate filters using adjacent TV channels, the bandwidth of each filter can be increased to cover two or more channels (or a "cluster" of channels). Such a device is shown in the drawing alongside, and these **cluster filters** are widely used to adjust the relative amplitudes of clusters of TV channels, especially where the digital multiplexes are adjacent to the analogue channels. Cluster filters have the added advantage of reducing all unwanted signals to an acceptable level and removing interference outside the channels of interest.

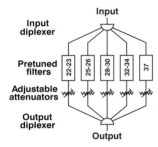

A 5 channel cluster filter for Crystal Palace

5.6   Mounting Hardware

Brackets •
Poles •

Brackets and poles are made using three types of material:
- Stainless steel – this is expensive and tends to be used for marine applications only.
- Aluminium (or "Alloy") - relatively light and creates its own protective coating.
- Mild steel – stronger than aluminium but liable to rust.

Steel brackets are sometimes spot-welded but continuous welds are much preferred. They are treated in one of three ways to prevent rust:
- **Painting.** The brackets are dipped first into a degreasing bath and then into a bath of zinc-rich paint. This is the least expensive method but the bracket will start to rust after a short time, especially if the coating is damaged by scratches. Painted brackets generally have a dull silver finish.
- **Plating.** The metal is electroplated with a thin coating of zinc and then passivated to improve its anti-corrosion performance. This gives a greeny-yellow finish and provides protection for up to ten years.
- **Galvanising.** Brackets are degreased and then dipped into a bath of molten zinc, which reacts with steel to provide a good bond between the steel and the very hard outer zinc layer and is difficult to scratch. The outer zinc layer is much thicker than that obtained by electroplating and will provide protection against rust for many years. A galvanised bracket can be identified by its shiny silver-coloured finish.

It is strongly recommended that only galvanised brackets are used for aerial installations. Poles are generally made of aluminium, although galvanised steel poles are sometimes used for large aerial arrays because they are stronger. Nuts, bolts and washers must also be protected against rust – these are normally plated.

Keywords

• V Bolts
• U Bolts

• Chimney
  Lashings

• Polykit

• PET Strapping

There are two popular sizes of V bolts or U bolts for fixing masts to brackets:

• Small, for masts of up to 1.5" diameter
• Large, for 1.5-2" masts

Bigger sizes are also available, for masts and poles of up to 4.5" diameter. The bracket holes are slotted to ensure that the mast can be mounted vertically, even if the surface of the wall is uneven.

Poles are normally fixed to the fabric of a building using either a chimney lashing bracket or a wall bracket.

Chimney Lashings

There are three main types of chimney lashing bracket:

• Standard lashing, with 6-12" spacing between the V bolts
• Cradle lashing, with 8-13" spacing between the V bolts
• Double lashing – these are always fitted in pairs and are needed for poles longer than 8ft when mounted on chimneys.

The accessories needed to mount a chimney bracket are collectively known in the trade as a **"Polykit"**. A typical such kit comprises the following items:

• Galvanised steel lashing wire – normally 7 strands, each 1.2mm diameter
• 3 steel corner plates
• 2 J bolts with nuts
• 2 V bolts with nuts (small or large as appropriate)

Other types of chimney lashing are also available utilising a stainless steel 50mm band or **P**oly**E**thylene **T**erephthalate **(PET)** strapping (rather like pallet straps) in conjunction with ratchet brackets. These do not usually require corner plates.

5

Keywords

Wall Brackets •

T & K Brackets •

Mast Diameter •

Mast Wall •
Thickness

Roof Fixings •

Wall Brackets

Three main types of wall bracket are in general use:

- **T & K.** 12-48" (subtract 2" to obtain the stand-off distance from wall). Bigger versions sometimes incorporate side bracing. They are usually purchased as a pair.
- **Composite**. 6 x 6" to 12 x 18".
- **Facia brackets.** These are used to fix a short mast to a wooden facia board.

Poles and Masts

These are made of galvanised mild steel or aluminium, 1"- 2" diameter and 1ft - 20ft. long. Larger diameter poles are available for special applications. Some poles have swaged ends so that short lengths can be joined together.

Poles can be straight or cranked. A double cranked pole is sometimes known as a "swan-necked" pole.

Mast diameter does not in itself determine its strength. This is also governed by the wall thickness of the mast material. Thickness is often quoted as a "gauge" or SWG. The conversion between SWG and wall thickness is as follows:

SWG	18	16	14	12	10	8	6
Wall Thickness (mm)	1.2	1.6	2.0	2.6	3.2	4.0	4.8

The required wall thickness of a mast depends on its length and what aerials will be fitted to it. The following table gives the maximum mast length for a typical domestic installation with up to two aerials:

Mast dia.	Alloy wall thickness	Steel wall thickness	Maximum length
25mm	1.2mm	1.2mm	6ft
32mm	1.6mm	1.2mm	8ft
38mm	1.6mm	1.2mm	10ft
50mm	2.0mm	1.6mm	20ft

"Through the Roof" Fixings

On occasions where there is no chimney or gable end to the dwelling and the walls are covered with hung tiles, it may be necessary to remove a roof tile from the pitched roof and mount the pole to one of the internal loft beams. Several types of replacement tiles are available with waterproof gaskets, to ensure that water does not penetrate inside the dwelling

The "universal" type has a sheet of lead flashing that can be easily shaped to overlap the hole left by the missing tile. More sophisticated versions are available from roofing tile

Keywords

manufacturers that exactly match the shape and colour of the missing tile (but there are many such shapes and colours).

It goes without saying that a cap must be fitted to the top of the mast to prevent water from running down the inside of the mast and into the house!

Accessories

The range of accessories available includes the following:

- Mast clamps to join two poles together at right angles –

• Mast Clamps

    1" x 1", for two 1" poles

    1" x 2", to join a 1" pole to a 2" pole

    2" x 2", (also known as an eight nut clamp), for two 2" poles.

- A universal 2" mast clamp for joining poles or fixing a pole to a railing.

- Mast couplers, to join together two masts of the same diameter.
- Aerial cradles and mast clamps.
- 2" guy wire collars (either 3 or 4 way).

• Mast Couplers

• Guy Wire Collar

- Lashing wire, normally sold by weight.
- Lashing wire strainers, to adjust the tension of guy wires.
- 2" mast bases, for use with very long masts.

• Strainers
• Tensioners

Loft Fixings

• Loft Fixings

It is not recommended to fit aerials in lofts. However, fixings available for this purpose include:

- A loft spike – a short piece of aluminium tube with a screw embedded in one end.

One can "stab" the tube into a wooden beam and screw it in with a rotating motion in just a few seconds.
- A cranked pole with a split or wing bracket. These are fixed into place using wood screws.

Lightning • Protection

Lightning Protection

It is always good practice to earth a mast to protect the installation against damage and interference from atmospheric electricity during thunderstorms.

Down • Conductor

This can be achieved by installing a "down conductor" between the mast and either the building's lightning protection system or another suitable earth. The down conductor must have a minimum cross sectional area of 16mm^2 copper, or 25mm^2 aluminium. This is normally in the form of a plastic coated flat strip of metal and requires specialised jointing materials and fixings.

Never compromise the integrity of a lightning protection system – always bond to the existing down conductor to it without disconnecting it. Strip back its outer pvc cover and use outer clamp to make the bond.

Never let copper come into direct contact with aluminium because they will react together over time and cause corrosion at the joint. It is necessary to first tin the copper using solder, before making the joint.

All these materials are readily available but it is recommended that installers either seek specialist advice before attempting such work or employ the services of a professional lighting protection company.

5.7   Installation Techniques

General Principles

The topic of Health and Safety is beyond the scope of this book. However, the following principles need to be reiterated:

- Make sure that your public liability and employers liability insurance policies are valid and sufficient.
- Be safety conscious at all times. Working at heights is a dangerous occupation, both for you and anyone underneath you. Consider if a ladder is a safe working platform. Make sure that it is properly positioned and secure. Fix it before you climb it and always have three points of contact with it – normally two feet and one hand, or two feet and a safety rope. Be aware that working during inclement weather poses greater risks.
- Wear the correct apparel. A hard hat, goggles, tool belt and steel capped boots should always be available for use when considered necessary.
- Always respect the danger of mains electricity and thunderstorms, especially in wet or damp conditions.
- Ensure that whatever you install is properly fixed and that the structure is strong enough to carry the additional load.

In addition, consider the aesthetic aspects of your work. Would the aerial be less conspicuous in another location? Can access always be obtained for maintenance purposes? Try not to position fixings over patios and doorways; the ground below could become contaminated with excrement from birds perching on the brackets.

Wall Fixings

Most installers use a battery drill with an SDS bit. The bit pushes into the chuck with a twisting motion and the pneumatic action of the drill makes drilling holes in bricks very much easier. Before starting to drill, mark the required hole depth on the drill bit with a piece of insulation tape rolled around it.

Don't ever drill into the top three courses of bricks (or six courses from the apex of a gable end); these bricks could easily become loose either during or after the installation, causing all sorts of problems. Also try to avoid fixing into soft bricks or breeze blocks – they may never provide a secure fixing.

Always drill into the brick, not the mortar. You will never know if the cement mix was correct when the structure was built. Drilling into a mortar line can cause bricks to separate from the mortar, either straight away or over time. Ensure that the hole will not be too big for the fixing you intend to use.

10mm plastic wall plugs with 8mm coach screws are normally used to fix wall brackets for domestic installations, in preference to expansion bolts (Rawlbolts or similar) which can easily crack a brick if overtightened. For larger installations, chemical anchors are available to provide an even more secure fixing. When in doubt, seek advice from a qualified structural engineer.

Ensure that there is some form of vertical support for the pole. T and K brackets are normally fitted as a pair. Two K brackets are also acceptable to spread the load over a greater area, but not two T brackets on their own. The K bracket is normally fitted at the bottom, because the wall is generally stronger lower down.

The vertical spacing between the T and K brackets should be as large as possible and certainly not less than one sixth of the pole length **(50cm for a 3m pole, 1m for a 6m pole, and so on)**.

Keywords

- Health and Safety

- Ladder Safety

5

- Aerial Location

- Wall Fixings
- SDS Drill Bits

- Types of Fixings

- T & K Brackets

Keywords

T and K brackets have slotted holes to allow for some lateral movement. Fit the top bracket first and then use a plumb-bob to determine the lateral position of the bottom bracket so that the pole will be vertical. It is always advisable to use plate washers on wall fixings and U bolts.

SDS Sockets •

Whilst it is possible to tighten a wall fixing using a spade ended, ring or ratchet spanner, this takes time and does not do much for your knuckles! It is preferable to use a socket and ratchet for this purpose. An even better solution is to acquire a ring socket (usually 13mm) fixed to an SDS shank and use your battery drill to do all the work. This saves a lot of time. Then use a ring spanner just to check that each fixing is fully tightened.

If a mast bends or breaks in a high wind, the failure invariably occurs at or just above the top U bolt because this has been tightened too much, causing the pole to deform and weaken. Great care should therefore be taken not to overtighten the top U bolt.

Chimney Fixings •

Chimney Fixings

Chimney • Stability

Always assess the structural stability of a chimney before fixing an aerial to it. Look for cracks and check if the mortar is crumbling away. Try pushing it backwards and forwards to see if it moves – you would be surprised to find that many chimneys are just not safe, and fitting an aerial will cause even more instability.

Never drill holes in chimneys. They are usually only one brick thick and the bricks could easily become loose. With disastrous results as shown in the following pictures

Don't ever use the top three courses of bricks on a chimney - always fit the chimney lashing kit lower down. With a clearance of at least 3 courses to the top of the bracket.

Try to avoid mounting aerials directly over the top of a chimney. The chemicals in the smoke could shorten the life of the aerial. Use a cranked pole to position the aerial to one side. If this is not possible, ensure that the aerial is at least 1.2M above the top of the chimney.

The vertical spacing between the U bolts on a chimney bracket must be at least one sixth of the total mast length. On this basis, the longest pole on a 13" cradle lashing is 6.5 feet. Poles longer than this need two separate lashing kits placed the appropriate distance apart.

Lashing • Splices

The lashing wire must first be spliced to one of the J bolts. This can be done at ground level and the procedure is as follows:

Keywords

1. Bend the lashing wire round the J bolt twice, with the free end of the wire 20cm long.

2. Use a pair of pliers to squeeze the two wires together so that they lie alongside each other.

3. Unwind one of the seven strands back to the J bolt and wrap it round both wires six or seven times, making sure that adjacent turns touch, but do not overlap each other. Bend the free end of the strand out of the way.

4. Unwind the next strand and wrap it round both wires six or seven times in the opposite direction to the first strand.

5. Repeat the process for the other five strands, changing direction each time. The complete splice should be at least 70mm long.

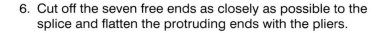

6. Cut off the seven free ends as closely as possible to the splice and flatten the protruding ends with the pliers.

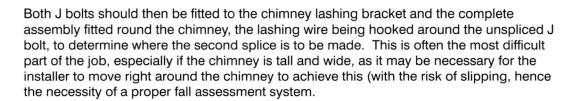

Both J bolts should then be fitted to the chimney lashing bracket and the complete assembly fitted round the chimney, the lashing wire being hooked around the unspliced J bolt, to determine where the second splice is to be made. This is often the most difficult part of the job, especially if the chimney is tall and wide, as it may be necessary for the installer to move right around the chimney to achieve this (with the risk of slipping, hence the necessity of a proper fall assessment system.

Make sure that the lashing wire is in the same horizontal plane around the chimney and that it is pulled as tight as possible, before cutting the wire to length (leaving the same 20cm tail). This is very important – too loose a wire means that the lashing can never be fully tightened.

The next step is to complete the second splice in exactly the same way as the first. This is normally done in situ although beginners may wish to dismantle the lashing and complete the second splice at ground level. All that then remains is for the installer to refit the whole assembly around the chimney (if applicable), fit the three corner plates under the lashing wire (positioning each one so that it is over a brick, not the mortar line), and tighten the nuts on the J bolts so that the whole assembly cannot move at all. This is best achieved by using a very deep 13mm socket with a ratchet handle.

Keywords

Whilst this may seem to be a long-winded process, an experienced installer can install a complete chimney lashing in five or six minutes. Lashing kits are also available with the first J bolt already crimped to the lashing wire, in order to save time on site.

Tile Fixings •

If the coaxial cable from the mast is to be run down the outside of the roof, it is necessary to secure it to every third or fourth tile. Do <u>not</u> attempt to drill the tile or you will blunt the drill bit. Take a single strand of lashing wire about 40cm long and bend it as shown alongside, then place it over the cable and slide the two free ends under the tile. Pick up all the loose offcuts of lashing wire and dispose of them properly.

Aerial Choice •

Aerial Choice, Siting and Alignment

In strong signal strength areas, look at neighbouring aerials to get an indication of direction of transmitter and amount of aerial gain required.

Aerial Siting •

In any case, it may be advisable to carry out signal measurements with an aerial on the roof to determine which transmitter to use, the relative signal strengths and whether ghosting or interference may be a problem for TV reception. If you have no experience of the area, it is suggested that you make your initial measurements with a 10 or 18 element standard wideband TV aerial or a log periodic on a short hand-held pole, preferably using a spectrum analyser with a picture display. Remember that not all transmitters cover the whole range of services, especially for DAB and DTT.

Since every job will have different requirements, it is only possible to give general guidelines when choosing which aerial to use and where to locate it. Try turning the aerial completely round through 360°, first mounted horizontally and the vertically. In each case, try these tests in several locations where it would be possible to mount the aerial – if possible, along the whole length of the roof. Check first that the signal strength is sufficient on each channel using the minimum levels given in section 5.3, and then that there is no ghosting on analogue pictures, or interference on the spectrum display. Observe the level of electrical noise and interference - does this reduce if the aerial is lowered?

You can only then decide which aerial to install, bearing in mind that the minimum levels given are at the receiver, after the coaxial cable loss. It is once again emphasised that the quality of the signals from the aerial will usually determine the overall performance of the whole system – you must have sufficient signal level at the aerial terminals. Boosting the signal will also boost the noise, which does not improve the C/N ratio!

Keywords

Changing from a wideband TV aerial to a grouped version can give up to 4dB more signal, and changing from a 10 element to a 100 element aerial can give up to 4dB more signal as well. In fringe reception areas, it is often possible to get more signal by increasing the height of the aerial – sometimes, as much as 1dB for every extra foot of height. In any case try to mount the aerial so that it looks over the roof instead of through it. Remember also that if a tree is blocking the signal path, its foliage can cause drastic variations in signal levels. It may be better to locate the aerial on the garden wall or outbuilding if this has a less obstructed view towards the transmitter.

Higher gain aerials are also more directional and can therefore reduce the effect of reflections and interference. If interference is present from the rear, consider using an aerial with a high front-to-back ratio, such as a grid or panel version. It may also help if the aerial is mounted where a wall will screen the aerial from the effects of the unwanted reflections or interference.

When finally aligning the aerial for digital reception, check that the signal levels, C/N ratio and BER are all better than the required minimums. Aim for the best overall performance on all channels - you will sometimes find that the level of one TV channel is different from that of the others depending on the orientation of the aerial - in such cases the aerial should be rotated for the maximum signal on the weakest channel.

• Aerial Alignment

Some customers will require reception from more than one transmitter. This is often the case for FM radio where transmissions of local radio stations come from a different direction to those of the main transmitter. In such cases, use an omnidirectional aerial if the signals are strong enough (an "omni" aerial has some 8dB less gain than an FM Yagi). Otherwise, use two FM Yagi aerials diplexed together.

For the simultaneous reception of signals from two different TV transmitters, use the appropriate grouped aerial for each transmitter and combine the outputs using a grouped diplexer. The aerial receiving the weakest signals should be mounted at the top of the mast, the second aerial about 1m below it and the diplexer a further 1m down the mast. Alternatively, both aerials could be mounted on a single crossbar fitted to the top of the pole with a suitable clamp. Each aerial must be orientated on the mast so that, when it is rotated to optimise the signals from the weakest transmitter, the second aerial is also receiving acceptable signals. Some transmitters use the whole of the UHF frequency band, making combining a much more difficult task.

• Diplexed Aerials

It is possible to diplex the signals from TV, FM and DAB aerials on to one coaxial cable by using suitable diplexers.

If it is necessary to increase the mast height by a significant amount in order to obtain satisfactory signals, two or more 20ft. poles can be coupled together using couplers. In all such cases, guy wires **must** be fitted to provide additional support. Each guy wire would be connected to the mast using a three or four way mast collar and fitted with a strainer to adjust its tension. The bottom end of the guy wire is normally anchored to the masonry using an "eye" bolt (a Rawlbolt with an eye instead of a hexagonal head). The eye bolt should be located so that the tension is applied sideways, not "end-on".

Multiple Aerial Arrays

• Multiple Aerial Arrays

It may be possible to improve both analogue and digital picture quality at locations where a single aerial will not produce satisfactory results.

Keywords

Every time the number of aerials is doubled, the theoretical increase in gain is 3dB. However, care must be taken to ensure that this 3dB is not lost in the signal combiner. For instance, a 2 way splitter used backwards (as a combiner) would lose the 3dB you have just gained!

Aerial •
Combiners

It is also not acceptable to parallel the cables from the two aerials. Two 75 Ohm aerials in parallel would be 37.5 Ohms - a total mismatch to the 75 Ohm coaxial cable. It is necessary to use a transformer to match the impedances and eliminate any combining losses. These are normally incorporated into two way

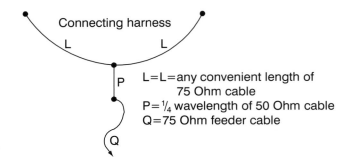

Connecting harness

L = L = any convenient length of
        75 Ohm cable
P = ¼ wavelength of 50 Ohm cable
Q = 75 Ohm feeder cable

Stacking •
Combiners

and four way **stacking combiners**, but one can be made using a quarter wavelength stub of 50 Ohm coaxial cable. The relationship between frequency and wavelength is as follows:

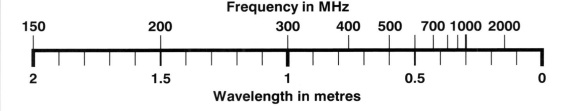

Frequency in MHz

150   200   300   400   500   700 1000 2000

Wavelength •
Frequency •

2   1.5   1   0.5   0

Wavelength in metres

Aerial Gain •

To increase gain

If a single high gain TV aerial will not receive sufficient signal, it is possible to increase the received signal level by combining the outputs of two or more aerials. However, this is not a job for the faint hearted - the signals can subtract just as easily as they can add together.

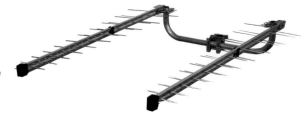

It is good practice to make cable lengths A and B the same to within 1cm. The aerials must be mounted side by side and the signals combined using a stacking combiner as described above.

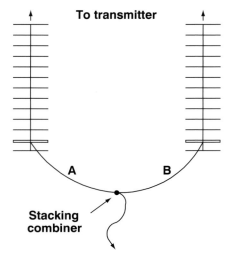

To transmitter

A   B

**Stacking
combiner**

Keywords

One aerial should be fixed in position and the other aerial moved forwards and backwards, and sideways (ie varying the spacing between the two aerials) for maximum signal on the level meter at the most important TV channel - in theory, the gain will be optimised at one frequency only.

To increase the front-to-back ratio

As shown below, one aerial should be mounted one quarter of a wavelength in front of the other, and cable length A should be a quarter of a wavelength longer than cable B:

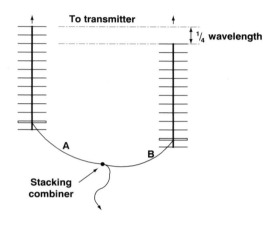

• Aerial Front-to-Back Ratio

To eliminate ghosting

• Aerial Ghosting

Instead of optimising the two aerials for maximum gain, they can be adjusted to minimise the effect of a strong reflection. They should be mounted side by side with the spacing between the two booms as shown below:

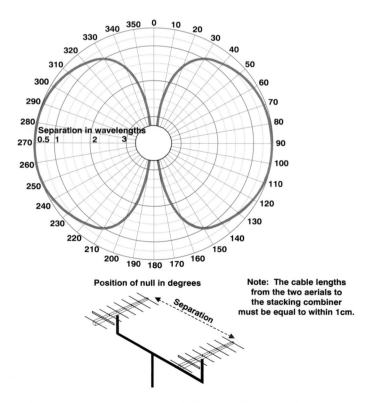

This solution is for one frequency only, not a whole band of frequencies.

Keywords

Cable Routing •

Cable Fixing •

Cable •
Management

Drip Loop •

Cable Joint •
Sealing

Cable Routing and Fixings

Coaxial cables should be fixed to masts using insulation tape or cable ties (sometimes called tie-wraps). Most installers prefer tape, which should be easy to peel off the reel and break without the use of a knife. Use at least two layers of tape for each fixing. If using cable ties, take care not to pull them too tight (or you will squash the cable) and don't forget to cut off the free ends.

Fix the cable neatly along the aerial boom at intervals of 20cm down the mast. The cable should ideally be on the north side of mast in order to shield cable from the ultra violet rays of the sun, which would otherwise make the outer sheath brittle with time. The cable should not wrap around the pole and must run outside the U or V bolts. Leave a service loop in an inconspicuous position – this should be a single turn of diameter greater than the minimum bending radius for the cable concerned.

Cables are attached to brick walls using cable clips fixed into the mortar at a minimum every 10 courses on vertical runs and at every second brick for horizontal runs. The rules regarding the handling and installation of coaxial cables are as follows:

- Don't remove the end-sealing cap until you are ready to use the cable, to minimise the risk of moisture ingress. Reseal the unused end of the cable after use.
- Roll the cable drum along the ground or use a horizontal pole through the middle to spool it off. Do not lay the cable drum flat on the ground and pull the cable off from above or it will twist and kink.
- Never install the cable with sharp bends. the minimum recommended bending radius is ten times the cable diameter (70mm for 7mm diameter cable, or about the same radius as a full reel of insulation tape).
- Always use the correct size of cable clips. A clip that is too small will squash the cable, causing an impedance irregularity. **Never** use staples to clip coaxial cable.
- When clipping horizontal cable runs, always fit the clip with the nail below the cable, so that it will still support the cable if the plastic clip breaks.
- Ensure that the connectors are the correct size to fit the cable being used, otherwise they will never fit properly.
- When running a cable through a wall, never run the cable from above, directly into the hole (because water will run down the cable and straight into the hole). Route the cable down past the hole and enter the hole from below, thus creating a **drip loop** so that rainwater will drip off.

Cable joints should be avoided wherever possible, the alternative being to replace the two cables with a single one without any joints at all. However, there are occasions where it is just not possible to replace both cables (for instance, when one disappears inside a cavity wall) and there is no alternative other than to make a joint.

In such (rare) instances, the joint can be made using TV or F connectors using the appropriate coupler. The following protection must also be applied:

- Seal the joint using self-amalgamating tape tightly wrapped (stretching the tape to half its width), the tape extending at least 30mm either side of the connectors.
- The cable should be routed downwards either side of the connectors so that water cannot run into the joint.
- The joint should be supported so that there is no strain on the connectors.
- The completed joint should be positioned so that it is sheltered from direct rainfall, or with a plastic joint box (with bottom entry) if no such shelter is available.

Again, it must be emphasised that cables should be joined only when this cannot be avoided.

It is important to keep the input and output cables of an amplifier well apart to prevent

Keywords

interference due to "crosstalk". Avoid running such cables side by side and if they cross, this should be at right angles.

It is not recommended to run cables down the middle of a cavity wall – the cable would not be supported and such an installation would be very time-consuming.

Cable between buildings must be supported on a catenary wire:

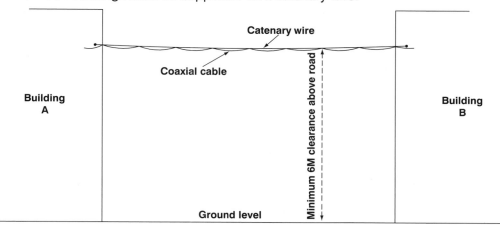

• Catenary Wire

Coaxial cable is available with an integral catenary wire, but most installers use separate chimney lashing wire or hard drawn copper wire for this purpose.

Cable and catenary wire are usually fixed together using insulation tape or cable ties. A more professional way is to thread the coaxial cable and catenary wire through the centre of a hank of soft copper wire, anchor one end and walk down the length of the cables letting the binding wire spool out behind you, thus fixing the cable and catenary wire together: The catenary wire must then be fixed at each end using eye bolts positioned so that the tension is sideways, not end on. There will always be a sag in the catenary, which should be typically 1.5% of its length in winter and 2.5% in summer.

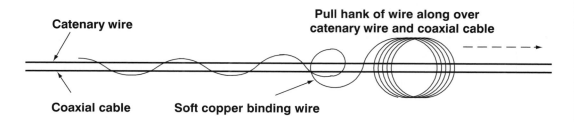

Catenaries should be at least 6m above a road, although it is advisable to check with your local council in this regard. And those for direct burial should be coloured green. Underground cables should be at least 450mm below ground level and cable ducts should also be green in colour.

Drilling Holes through Walls

• Drilling through Walls

Never try to route the cable through a double-glazed window frame – you could break the vacuum seal between the two panes of glass if you do! It is much neater if you drill through the wall so that the cable enters the room as near as possible to the TV receiver.

Before starting to drill:
• Check position of mains and other cables under plaster. Use a mains detector / metallic stud locator if available; otherwise, observe the comments given in section 3.4 (mounting flat panel displays).

Keywords

5

- Check that there is no obstruction such as a water downpipe on the outside wall and that the external end of the hole will be above ground level.
- Never drill through a damp-proof membrane. Check on the outside of the house that the hole will be above it.
- If there is a silk or fabric wall covering, cut a slit in the fabric with a sharp knife; otherwise, the drill bit may catch and tear the fabric.

Always drill from the inside out. Slope the hole gently downwards towards the outside of the building – the angle should be about 20° below horizontal.

Take the hammer action off for last 2cm, otherwise you will "blow" a brick (i.e. dislodge a flake from its surface). For minimum damage to the outside brick, drill a small pilot hole first.

After the cable has been installed, seal the hole with a suitably coloured sealant.

Mains Power • in Lofts

Installing Mains Power in Lofts

Whilst some amplifiers can be remotely powered from a downstairs room, others require a source of mains power in the loft. Most electrical circuits in the floor of a loft are lighting circuits – it is rare to find a power circuit in such locations.

Fused Spur •

It is permitted to attach one power socket to a lighting circuit if it is terminated with a **"fused spur"**. This is a plate incorporating a fuse holder (normally fitted with a 3amp fuse) and a grommet, through which a cable can be connected to electrical equipment such as TV amplifiers. Ensure that the fused spur is not connected to the light switch side of the lighting circuit – otherwise the amplifier will lose its power whenever the light is switched off!

The provision of such power is best left to a qualified electrician. However, the TV installer should be aware of the regulations in this regard, if he undertakes the work:

- Strictly speaking, all alterations or additions to fixed wiring installations must be tested and certificated to be in accordance with BS7671 (wiring regulations, 17th edition).
- A minor electrical installation works certificate is required for any modification to an existing circuit. The electrical tests are –
    - Earth (circuit protective conductor or CPC) continuity
    - Insulation resistance
    - Polarity
    - Earth loop impedance
    - RCD (where appropriate).

The test results are recorded in the appropriate boxes on the certificate and the declaration signed by the installer to confirm compliance with the regulations.

The absolute minimum requirements for a fused spur in a loft are:
- An earth continuity test using a multimeter between the new unit and the main earthing terminal, to confirm the presence of earth (CPC) continuity, even though this conductor may not be necessary for the amplifier.
- Polarity must be confirmed with the appropriate device.
- The fuse rating must be appropriate to the load.

Keywords

• Outlet Plates

• SOB

• FOB

• Pattress Box

• Diplexed Outlets

• Modular Outlets

• Flyleads

Outlet Plates and Flyleads

It is not essential to have an outlet plate – the coaxial cable could be connected directly to the receiver. However, many customers prefer to have an outlet plate fitted as this makes the installation look neater.

Outlets are available incorporating either IEC or F connectors, in two formats:

- **S**urface **O**utlet **B**ox **(SOB)** – for fitting on the window sill or skirting board.
- **F**lush **O**utlet **B**ox **(FOB)** - for fitting to a standard UK 3"x3" flush mounted conduit box.

A FOB can be surface fitted using a surface adaptor which is known in the trade as a pattress or pattra box.

FM/TV diplexed outlets are available in both the FOB and SOB formats. By convention, the IEC outlet socket is usually male for TV and female for FM/DAB.

Several manufacturers of domestic electrical fittings offer flush plates in a variety of finishes including brass, with either isolated or non-isolated sockets. Isolated versions are preferred for safety reasons because they will not pass mains voltages from the aerial socket of a faulty TV receiver to the rest of the system (TV receivers generally do not incorporate an earth wire in their mains leads). However, isolated sockets will not pass DC volts to a masthead amplifier, so they cannot always be used. Isolated sockets usually have a capacitor symbol on the front plate. Not all versions meet IEC standards and some only stop low voltages, not mains voltages.

Flush outlet plates are available in a variety of formats (some incorporating diplexers), including the following:
- TV (non isolated)
- TV (isolated)
- FM/DAB + TV (non isolated)
- FM/DAB + TV (isolated)
- TV + TV (with one or two cable inputs)
- Satellite (with one or two F connectors)
- FM/DAB/TV (non isolated) + Satellite
- FM/DAB/TV (isolated) + Satellite
- FM/DAB + TV (non isolated) + satellite
- FM/DAB + TV (isolated) + satellite (with one or two F connectors)

Versions are also available incorporating additional connectors for a reverse TV feed (to watch the selected satellite programme in other rooms) and for one or more telephone connections.

It is always preferable to use screened outlet sockets, if the flush conduit box is deep enough.

The "flylead" between the wall socket and TV receiver (or VCR) could be a either male-to-female or male-to-male versions depending on the type of wall sockets. The interlinking leads between the VCR / DVD and TV receiver need to be female-to-male.

Always use double screened flyleads. Inexpensive flyleads consisting of a very thin (3mm diameter) single screened coaxial cable with moulded IEC connectors are often encountered in people's homes. These must <u>not</u> be used and should always be replaced. Their screening properties are very poor and they have been known to have an insertion loss of 7dB!

Keywords

Remote Control Facilities

It is relatively straightforward to be able to watch the output of a satellite receiver or VCR located in the lounge on the other TV receivers in the house, and also to control these devices from another room. The signal distribution requirements are discussed in the next section and the remote control facility can be achieved in two ways:

- Using a low power radio transmitter at the remote viewing point and a radio receiver at the device to be controlled, to relay the infra-red handset signals to a "remote eye" located in front of the device.
- Using the coaxial cables carrying the signal to the other rooms to relay the infra-red control signals in the reverse direction. There needs to be a dc path between the rooms in question and any in-line TV amplifiers would have to be fitted with a dc bypass facility.

There are several makes of equipment on the market to provide such facilities.

5.8 Typical Domestic Systems

Chinmey • Installation

The picture below is an illustration of a typical domestic TV installation using a chimney lashing kit.

Dont use top 3 courses of brickwork

Mast holds aerial away from top of chimney

Cable exits sloping downwards

Cable taped on north side of pole

Bracket on transmitter side of chimney

Service loop in cable

No sharp bends in cable

Corner brackets over bricks, not mortar

Cable clipped at every 4th course

Ensure that the chimney is strong enough, before fixing anything to it.

Notice how the cable is positioned well away from the top of the chimney. When this is not possible, the aerial should be at least 1.25m above the top of the chimney, to smoke or chemical contamination.

The cable should be taped to the pole every 20cm with a service loop at the bottom, to allow for removal of the mast for maintenance.

The cable from the chimney should be fixed to every fourth roof tile and routed behind the rain gutter if possible. It should be run vertically down the wall with cable clips at least every ten courses. The radius of bends should be at least ten times the cable diameter and horizontal runs should be clipped to every second brick. The cable should enter the house from below (so as to leave a drip loop) and the hole must be sealed after the cable has been installed. Where possible the colour of the cable, clips and sealant should match the colour of the wall finish, although black cable has the best ultra-violet protection.

This picture shows a wall-mounted domestic TV installation in a weak signal strength area:

• Wall Mounted Installation

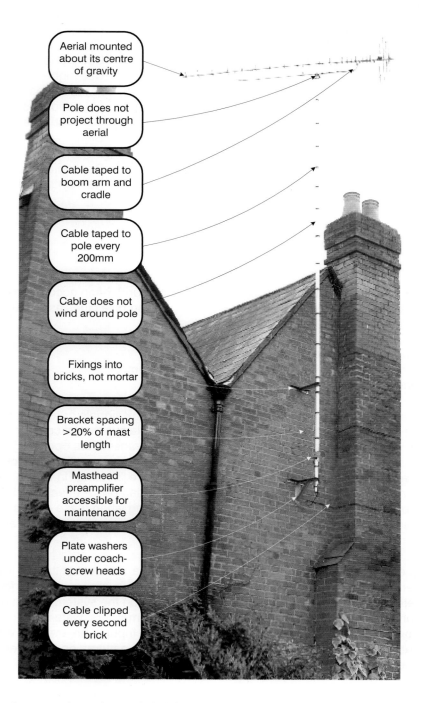

Aerial mounted about its centre of gravity

Pole does not project through aerial

Cable taped to boom arm and cradle

Cable taped to pole every 200mm

Cable does not wind around pole

Fixings into bricks, not mortar

Bracket spacing >20% of mast length

Masthead preamplifier accessible for maintenance

Plate washers under coach-screw heads

Cable clipped every second brick

The top bracket must be at least six brick courses below the apex of the gable-end. In this instance, the masthead amplifier has been mounted at the bottom of the pole so that it is accessible for maintenance. In <u>very</u> weak signal strength areas, it may be preferable to mount it higher up (say, 1m below the aerial) to eliminate the cable loss of 1dB or so, before the signal is amplified.

Keywords

FM Radio •
Troubleshooting

5

5.9 Troubleshooting

FM Radio

Some of the problems encountered and their possible solutions are outlined below.

Problem	Possible cause	Possible solution
Some stations not received	Aerial too directional	Change aerial
Poor sound or loss of stereo	Weak signal	Increase signal levels
Signal "flutters" intermittently	Aircraft overhead	Tip aerial downwards
Signal fades	Atmospheric conditions	Use higher gain aerial
Station changes intermittently	Atmospheric conditions	Use higher gain aerial
Signal blanks out or distorts	Out of band interference	FM bandpass filter
Intermittent whistle	Out of band interference	FM bandpass filter
Intermittent clicks	Electrical interference	Mains suppression filter
Intermittent interference	Airborne interference	Better system screening
Hiss	Low signal	Increase signal levels
Distortion of "S" and "Z" sounds	Multipath reception	Reorientate aerial
Background twittering (birdies)	Adjacent channel (normally affects stereo)	Reorientate aerial

Analogue TV •
Troubleshooting

Analogue TV

Degradations can result in the distortion of picture and sound, often accompanied by loss of Teletext and NICAM stereo sound. These distortions can give clues as to the reason for the degradations, which fall into three main groups:

- Poor or inadequate signals picked up by the aerial.
- Distortion or interference caused by the reception system.
- Interference from outside sources.

It may be possible to reduce or eliminate the effects of weak signals or reflections by realigning or replacing the aerial. A more difficult problem is that of co-channel interference, when signals are also received from distant transmitters operating on the same TV channels. This is often due to abnormal atmospheric conditions, which can last for several days. One can sometimes see a second picture "floating" in the background, an increase in the background noise level or a fine "Venetian blind" effect with horizontal and vertical bars. Broadcasters sometimes issue a warning when these effects occur. Adjacent channel interference can cause the same effects, plus diagonal lines across the screen.

Distortion due to the reception system is usually due to the incorrect setting of levels, which inherently affect the carrier to noise ratio as well. The overall system performance is usually determined by the lowest signal level anywhere on the system, which must be within the correct window of operation. Check for faulty amplifiers, waterlogged cables and faulty connectors. In addition, too much signal at the input of an amplifier will result in "intermodulation" distortion, causing such degradations as patterns on the screen, other pictures in the background, "squiggly" verticals and loss of synchronisation.

External •
Interference

External interference can arise from many sources, examples of which are as follows:

- DECT and TETRA relay equipment
- Microwave transmitters.
- Overhead power cables.
- Motor vehicles

Keywords

- Nearby "out of band" transmitters such as walkie-talkies, amateur and CB radio enthusiasts and cellphones, which overload amplifier circuits and produce "in-band" distortion.
- Unsuppressed domestic fittings and appliances such as electric motors, thermostats and light dimmers.
- Mains borne interference.

The effects caused by such interference include dots of interference all over the picture, horizontal bands of interference (sometimes only for a fraction of a second), wavy lines across the picture and (in the case of narrow band signals) "Moire" patterns (ripples that move around) over the screen.

There are several ways to reduce or eliminate such interference:

- Eliminate the source of interference – this is sometimes beyond your control.
- Fit suitable filters – most interference is below the UHF frequency band so a high pass filter may help; microwave and cellphone frequencies are higher so use a low pass filter with a sharp cut-off above 860MHz.
- Improve the screening of the system – check that all cables (including flyleads) are double screened and connectors are correctly fitted.

In extreme cases, it may help to fit a ferrite choke in line with the screen of the coaxial cable.

Interference may also come from an adjacent satellite receiver or computer, resulting in wavy lines on the picture. Try moving these units further away or turning them round. Check also that SCART leads are fully screened.

The following illustrations of analogue TV interference are reproduced by courtesy of the Radiocommunications Agency:

- Analogue TV Interference

1) Weak signal or just a grainy picture. Overall grey picture with possible bursts of colour.

2) Motor interference. Note the overall random nature of the interference.

3) Interference from a thermostat. Note the precise parallel banding of the interference.

Keywords

5

4) Interference from a computer.

5) Co-channel interference. Note the weak picture in the background and the sync. bars running through the picture.

6) Ghosting. Note the repetition of the car headlight, vertical bridge support and cycle paniers.

7) A narrow band (12kHz) FM signal interfering with the vision carrier.

8) A narrow band (12kHz) FM signal interfering with the colour sub-carrier.

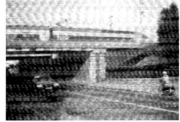

9) An AM signal (80% modulation) interfering with the TV vision carrier.

10) An AM signal (80% modulation) interfering with the TV colour sub-carrier.

Keywords

• Digital TV
  Troubleshooting

Digital TV

All the above comments apply equally for digital reception except that such degradations have a more dramatic effect – complete loss of picture and sound.

A quick way to see how close you are to the "digital cliff" is to temporarily insert a 6dB attenuator in line with the receiver input, to simulate a reduction in signal level. However, if there is no picture (or sound), there is no alternative but to measure the signal parameters with a digital meter, at the receiver input. If these are not satisfactory, they must be repeated from the aerial downwards until the cause of the problem is found. The flow charts on the following pages should help to explain the troubleshooting sequence on DTT systems.

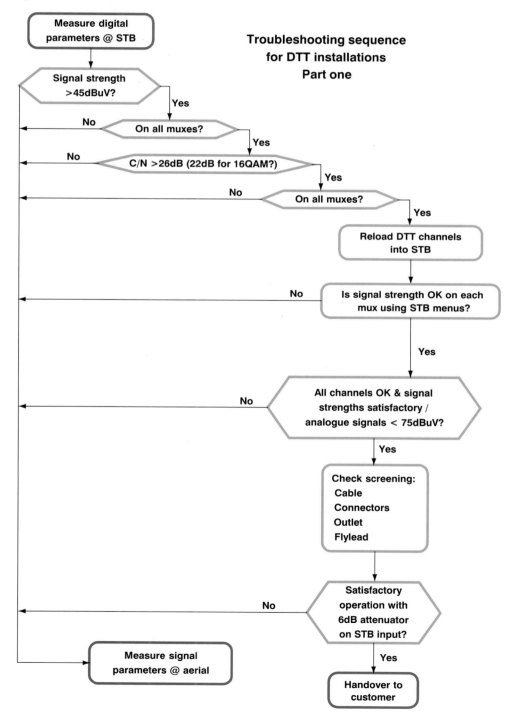

**Troubleshooting sequence
for DTT installations
Part one**

- Measure digital parameters @ STB
- Signal strength >45dBuV?
- On all muxes?
- C/N >26dB (22dB for 16QAM?)
- On all muxes?
- Reload DTT channels into STB
- Is signal strength OK on each mux using STB menus?
- All channels OK & signal strengths satisfactory / analogue signals < 75dBuV?
- Check screening:
  Cable
  Connectors
  Outlet
  Flylead
- Satisfactory operation with 6dB attenuator on STB input?
- Measure signal parameters @ aerial
- Handover to customer

Keywords

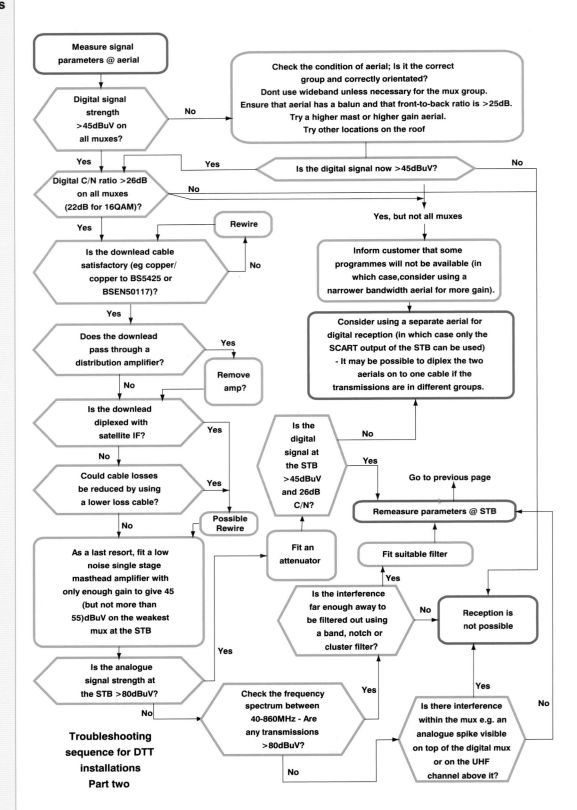

Measure signal parameters @ aerial

Digital signal strength >45dBuV on all muxes? — No → Check the condition of aerial; Is it the correct group and correctly orientated? Dont use wideband unless necessary for the mux group. Ensure that aerial has a balun and that front-to-back ratio is >25dB. Try a higher mast or higher gain aerial. Try other locations on the roof

Yes

Is the digital signal now >45dBuV? — No

Yes

Digital C/N ratio >26dB on all muxes (22dB for 16QAM)? — No

Yes, but not all muxes

Yes

Is the downlead cable satisfactory (eg copper/copper to BS5425 or BSEN50117)? — No → Rewire

Inform customer that some programmes will not be available (in which case, consider using a narrower bandwidth aerial for more gain).

Yes

Does the downlead pass through a distribution amplifier? — Yes → Remove amp?

Consider using a separate aerial for digital reception (in which case only the SCART output of the STB can be used) - It may be possible to diplex the two aerials on to one cable if the transmissions are in different groups.

No

Is the downlead diplexed with satellite IF? — Yes

Is the digital signal at the STB >45dBuV and 26dB C/N? — No

No

Could cable losses be reduced by using a lower loss cable? — Yes → Possible Rewire

Yes → Go to previous page

No

Remeasure parameters @ STB

As a last resort, fit a low noise single stage masthead amplifier with only enough gain to give 45 (but not more than 55)dBuV on the weakest mux at the STB

Fit an attenuator

Fit suitable filter

Yes

Is the interference far enough away to be filtered out using a band, notch or cluster filter? — No → Reception is not possible

Is the analogue signal strength at the STB >80dBuV? — Yes

No

Check the frequency spectrum between 40-860MHz - Are any transmissions >80dBuV? — Yes

Is there interference within the mux e.g. an analogue spike visible on top of the digital mux or on the UHF channel above it? — No

Yes

No

Troubleshooting sequence for DTT installations Part two

Keywords

• Impulse Noise

If the electrical parameters are within their limits, the problem may be due to **impulse noise** – interference of short duration that can cause the receiver to lock up and freeze. Such electrical noise can be generated by a variety of sources such as unsuppressed electric motors, microwave interference, mobile radios and ignition interference. The display alongside shows a typical example where the C/N ratio is degraded whenever a portable electric drill is used nearby.

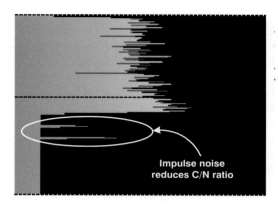

Impulse noise reduces C/N ratio

There is no magic cure for this. One must simply apply good engineering practice to minimise the pick-up of this interference by examining each part of the reception system in turn:

- **Signal levels** High digital signal levels will make the system more immune to the effects of impulse noise.
- **Aerial** Consider the use of a filter or a grouped aerial instead of a wideband version to minimise the pick-up of unwanted frequencies. If the aerial is looking over a busy road, try tilting the aerial upwards by, say, 10 degrees – the polar diagram (or footprint) is then above any potential source of interference, thus reducing it or losing it completely! The vertical forward acceptance angle of a good aerial is perhaps ±15 degrees, and varies little over a ±10 degree range.
- **Masthead amplifiers, splitters and outlet plates** Recent European legislation requires that all electrical products that are to be connected to an electrical power supply must be CE marked. This ensures that they meet a standard concerning the ingress and egress of electrical interference. Such products are invariably screened to minimise the pick-up of electrical interference such as impulse noise.
- **Coaxial cable downlead** It is absolutely essential that only double screened tape-and-braid coaxial cable is used for all digital installation work. Existing analogue systems that were wired with sub-standard cable and now have to be upgraded for digital signals will always be prone to the pick-up of impulse noise. It is strongly recommended that only benchmarked cables are used for all UHF systems.
- **Connectors** Crimped or compression versions provide superior screening to the twist-on versions.
  All F connectors should be spanner-tightened to preserve the integrity of the screening.
- **Flylead** Thin interconnecting flyleads fitted with moulded IEC connectors have extremely poor screening properties and should always be replaced with double-screened versions (if necessary, made up on site with an offcut of good quality cable and two appropriate connectors).
- **Electricity supply** Impulse noise sometimes enters the system via the mains wiring. It may be advantageous to fit a mains filter of the type sold for use with computer products.

One common way for impulse noise to enter the reception system is via the screen of the coaxial cable. Interference picked up on the screen is relayed through the aerial dipole and down the inner conductor of the cable to the aerial socket of the digital receiver.

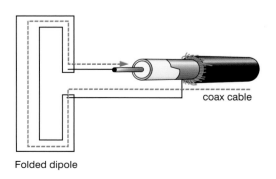

coax cable

Folded dipole

Keywords

This interference can be reduced by using a transformer between the aerial and the coaxial downlead. The dipole is a "balanced" device – completely symmetrical and can be used either way up – whereas the cable is "unbalanced" with the screen connected to earth.

Aerial Balun •

By using a Balanced-to-unbalanced transformer (known as a Balun) with the unbalanced earth connected to the centre of the balanced winding, any interference is significantly reduced –

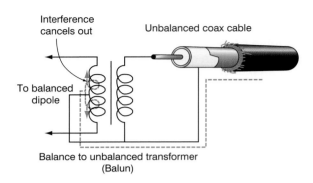

Interference cancels out

Unbalanced coax cable

To balanced dipole

Balance to unbalanced transformer (Balun)

practical tests have proved that an aerial with an integral balun will provide up to 14dB more immunity to the pick up of impulse noise.

TETRA •

Terrestrial Trunked Radio (TETRA)

This is a new secure communications system introduced for the emergency services in the UK. Most big cities now have TETRA relay sites transmitting several hundred watts of power, mainly in the 390-400 MHz frequency band, the second harmonic of which falls in the UHF channel 60, causing interference (which looks like tyre tracks) across an analogue picture and freezing of digital pictures. Such transmissions can overload a nearby masthead amplifier (especially an unscreened one), causing all sorts of intermodulation distortion.

Tetra filters can reduce or eliminate these effects if fitted before amplification and some masthead amplifiers now incorporate such filters on their inputs.

5

Part Six - UHF Signal Distribution

6.1 Coaxial Cable and Connectors

Types of Cables

The purpose of cables is to relay the received signal from the aerial(s) to the receiver(s) whilst maintaining an acceptable signal quality. For TV and satellite reception, this is achieved using coaxial cables with an impedance of 75 ohms.

A coaxial cable has a central metallic inner core surrounded by one or two outer metallic screens and an overall outer sheath. The material providing the insulation between the inner core and outer screen is called the **dielectric**. All coaxial cables recommended for radio, TV and satellite reception must be manufactured to the European standard BS EN 50117.

Double screened coaxial cable as recommended for DTTV aerial installations

PVC Outer Jacket
Braid / Outer Screen
Foil / Inner Screen
Cellular / Air spaced Inner Insulation
Solid Copper Centre

The inner core is a solid (not stranded) annealed copper wire that sometimes has a coating to prevent interaction with the chemicals used to stick the dielectric material to the inner core during the manufacturing process. The best material for the outer screen(s) is copper although aluminium is sometimes used because it is less expensive.

The most efficient dielectric material is air. This cannot be used on its own because some means of supporting the inner core must be provided. This support can be given by using a semi air spaced dielectric with a honeycomb or cellular structure, supporting discs at regular intervals or a thin plastic "rod" wound around the inner conductor in a spiral fashion. A solid or foam dielectric material is more rigid (making the cable less prone to kinking) and helps to stop moisture from penetrating into the cable, but it is not as efficient as air.

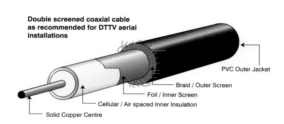

Types of dielectric

Solid   Foam   Semi air spaced   "Bamboo"

The best overall outer sheath material for outside and underground use is polyethylene, because it is waterproof. Versions are available with thicker sheaths for use either in an underground duct, or for burial direct in the ground. However, polyethylene must **never** be used indoors because it supports combustion (it burns). Indoor cables normally incorporate a polyvinyl chloride (PVC) sheath. The normal outer sheath colours are black, brown and white but black is preferred because the colour is achieved by adding a material called carbon black - this stabilises the sheath against the effects of the sun (which contains ultra violet rays that can make the sheath brittle over time, causing it to crack). Special cable sheaths are also available for high fire risk areas. These are called "Low Smoke/Zero Halogen" (abbreviated to LSOH or LSNH).

The ducts used for underground services are colour coded and underground TV cable ducts are always green in colour.

Keywords

- Coaxial Cable

- Cable Screens

- Cable Dielectric

- Cable Sheaths

- Polyethylene

- PVC

- LSOH
- LSNH
- Cable Ducts

Keywords

Coaxial • Composite Cables

Special types of cable used in our industry include those where up to five coaxial cables are joined together in a "ribbon" format or contained in a single circular pvc sheath, and coaxial cables incorporating a steel "catenary" wire (used for unsupported spans between buildings). Some cable manufacturers mark the outer sheath of the cable at regular intervals to show how much cable is left on the drum.

Cables must be handled and fitted correctly as described in section 5.7.

Characteristic • Impedence

The characteristic impedance of a cable is determined by the sizes of its inner and outer conductors, which in turn determine the inductance and capacitance of the cable. Nearly all the cables used in our industry must be 75 Ohms, the only normal exceptions being the inputs to some FM radio receivers and DAB (Digital Audio Broadcasting) receivers, which can be 300 Ohms and 50 Ohms respectively. Matching transformers may be required for these special instances.

Cable Screens •

Cable Screens
Two types of cable are commonly used in our industry:

Single screened
This consists of copper strands woven into a screening braid around the outside of the dielectric. The better types use more copper strands and therefore provide increased screening against outside interference.

Double screened
This consists of two touching concentric screens. The inner one is normally a metallic tape (usually copper although aluminium is used in the less expensive versions). The outer screen is almost invariably a closely woven copper braid. This should be tinned if the inner tape is made of aluminium since copper and aluminium must not be allowed to touch each other.

The cable screen has an impact on the electrical performance of the cable in a number of ways:
- Its diameter affects the impedance of the cable.
- Its resistance affects the signal loss on the cable.
- The number, material and thickness of the screen(s) determine its effectiveness to prevent the ingress of unwanted interference. This is important for both low signal strength areas (where the interference would degrade the analogue TV picture quality or cause loss of digital pictures) and high signal strength areas (where the strong TV signals would be picked up on the cable, causing a reflection to the left of the main analogue TV picture or possible corruption of the digital signals).

Cable • Benchmarking

It is absolutely necessary to use double screened tape and braid coaxial cable for the relay of both terrestrial and satellite digital signals. The benchmarking scheme guarantees the performance of such cables. It is strongly recommended that only benchmarked cables are used for all TV coaxial relay systems.

Keywords

Cable Losses

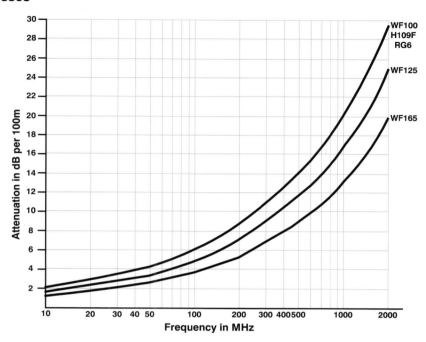

The chart on the previous page shows that the electrical losses on a coaxial cable depend on two main factors:

- The quality and construction of the cable
- The frequencies being relayed

The next table shows the attenuation in dB per 100m over the range of frequencies used in the world of radio, TV and satellite reception:

Freq (MHz)	RG6	H109F	WF100	WF125	WF165
5	1.8	1.4	1.3	1.1	0.8
50	4.4	4.3	4.3	3.4	2.6
100	6.1	6.1	6.1	4.9	3.7
200	8.9	8.8	8.6	7.1	5.4
450	13.5	13.3	13.2	11.0	8.6
600	15.6	15.4	15.4	12.7	9.9
860	18.9	18.9	18.7	15.5	12.0
1000	20.5	20.5	20.0	16.8	13.3
1200		22.6	22.0	18.5	14.8
1500		25.7	24.7	20.8	16.9
1750		27.9	26.9	22.6	18.6
2050		30.6	29.4	24.9	20.4
3000		38.7	36.2	31.0	25.8

The cables with the lowest loss are physically much larger and are used for main feeder routes or on long cable runs where it is vital that the loss is kept to an absolute minimum. They are more expensive and require special connectors because of their larger overall diameter. The cables shown with the higher losses are more commonly used in the domestic environment to link aerials and satellite dishes to their respective receivers.

- Cable Losses

9

Keywords

Standing Wave •

Cable •
Terminators

TV Connectors •

IEC95 Connector •

TV Plug •
Assembly

The loss along a cable is also affected by what is connected to it at each end. The "source" and "load" impedance must match the impedance of the cable, all of which should be 75 Ohms. For receiving systems, this is especially important for the load impedance. Otherwise, the mismatch will cause some of the energy to be reflected back along the cable, causing a reflection or **standing wave**. Looking back along the cable, the "in phase" reflections will cause an increase, whilst the "out of phase" reflections will cause a decrease in the signal levels. This could also cause a ghost to the right of the main image on analogue terrestrial TV receivers or degradation of the digital signal. It is therefore most important that all unused cable drops and unused outputs of signal splitters are fitted with a 75 Ohm termination. Connectors are available that incorporate such a termination, or a 75 Ohm resistor can be fitted between the centre conductor and the outer screen of the cable.

TV Connectors

The push-on male connector that fits the aerial socket of a European TV receiver is variously known as a TV plug, Belling plug or IEC95 male connector. It is available in screw-on or crimp versions. The components of the screw-on version are shown alongside.

The following procedure should be followed to fit such a connector to a standard 7mm diameter coaxial cable:

- Fit the cap over the cable with the threaded end towards the end of the cable.

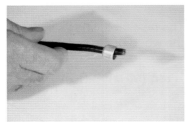

- Strip off the last 22mm of the outer insulation of the cable.

- Fit the metal claw over the metallic cable screen(s) with the points of the claw away from the end of the cable.

Keywords

- Fold back the outer (braided) screen over the claw and trim with a pair of side cutters so that the individual wires of the braid do not overlap beyond the pointed ends of the claw.

- Fan out the wires of the braid so that they are evenly spaced around the circumference of the claw.

- Trim off and remove all the visible part of the cable inner screen (by nicking one edge and tearing the rest off).

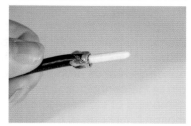

- Trim off the dielectric material, leaving 2-3mm of insulation showing.

- Bend a slight kink in the metallic inner core of the cable half way along the length that is showing (see note below).

- Slide the inner core of the connector over the inner core of the cable with the pin away from the cable, and push on until it butts up to the dielectric of the cable, trimming off any part of the inner core of the cable that protrudes beyond the end of the pin.

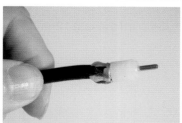

- Slide the outer sleeve of the connector over the inner core, with the threaded end towards the cable (the metallic cable screen should now be trapped between two concentric pieces of metal).

Keywords

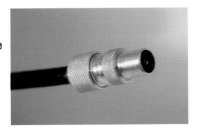

- Screw the cap of the connector on to the outer sleeve tightly, forcing the points of the claw to bite into the cable – it should now be impossible to pull the connector off the cable without using very considerable physical force.

Note: Some types of connector incorporate a screw clamp to ensure good contact between the centre core of the cable and the centre pin of the connector. For all other types of connector, **it is strongly recommended that the centre core of the cable is soldered to the centre pin of the connector.**

Whilst the screw-on version is widely used, it is now considered preferable to use the **crimp** version.

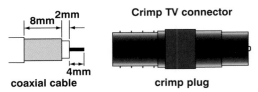

The cable should be prepared as shown in the diagram alongside. It is important that the distances are correct so that the centre core of the cable makes proper contact with the centre pin of the connector. Push the cable into the crimp end of the connector using a twisting motion until none of the screen can be seen and crimp the connector using a crimp tool of the correct size.

Suitable cable strippers are available that prepare the cable for insertion into the crimp connector without having to cut the cable with a knife. Simply insert the end of the cable into the tool and rotate the tool twice using a circular motion, then pull the tool off the end of the cable.

Female versions of the TV connector are available, or a male connector can be converted into a female using a female-to-female "coupler" or joiner.

F Connectors

The screw-on male F connector has been widely used in the USA for many years and is the type of connector used by most Sky installers. The fitting procedure is as follows:

- Strip off the last 12mm of the outer insulation

- Fold back the outer braid

Keywords

- Trim off and remove the visible part of the cable inner screen (the copper tape)

- Trim off the dielectric material leaving 2-3cm of insulation showing

- Screw the F connector on to the end of the coaxial cable until the centre conductor (known as the **"stinger"**) protrudes at least 2mm beyond the end of the connector

The **crimp** version of the F connector is favoured in preference to the screw-on type, since it incorporates a concentric tube that slides under the braided screen, thereby giving superior screening qualities.

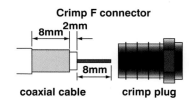

The cable preparation is normally performed using a two or three blade cable stripper to trim the cable end, as shown alongside. If the same cable stripping tool is used for TV connectors and F connectors, is should be readjusted to allow for the longer cable centre core when used with F connectors.

Crimp F connector

8mm · 2mm

8mm

coaxial cable · crimp plug

The connector in then pushed on to the prepared end of the cable until the stinger protrudes at least 2mm beyond the end of the connector, and secured using the crimping tool.

Another type of F connector is the **compression** type, which also originates from the USA.

Keywords

The cable preparation is the same as for a crimp connector, and a special compression tool is used to secure the connector.

An F type T bar tool can be used to provide additional pressure when fitting any of the above types of F connector on to a coaxial cable.

The procedures described in this section relate to standard 7mm diameter coaxial cables. Special F connectors and tools are required when using larger diameter coaxial cables.

Female-to-female F joiners are widely used to connect two F connectors together. F-TV adaptors are also available.

Home •
Distribution

6.2   Distribution within the Home

For viewing in a single location, the UHF aerial feed can be looped via a VCR (and also a DVD player if applicable) to the aerial input socket of the TV receiver:

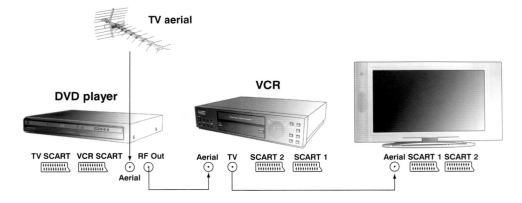

Each of the ancillary units adds a UHF channel and the receiver can be tuned to watch any of the channels.

UHF •
Modulator

If the DVD player does not have an integral UHF modulator (or if the receiver does not have a SCART input), it will be necessary to use stand-alone external modulator:

Keywords

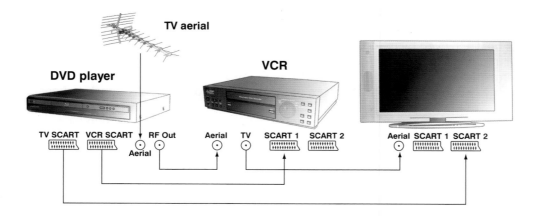

Each of these units generates its own UHF channel which is then combined with the incoming channels. The actual UHF channels used should be carefully chosen so as not to conflict with one another, using the rules detailed in part 6.5.

Superior performance can be achieved by using SCART connections, either instead of, or in addition to, the UHF connections:

• SCART
  Connections

9

Many homes now have two or more TV receivers that are connected to a single radio or TV aerial. The house builders provide a single coaxial cable from the loft to the main living room, and sometimes to the kitchen and bedroom(s) as well. These cables are sometimes linked together "in tandem". The occupier will then employ an installer to supply all the materials and provide a working system, possibly with FM radio, DAB and analogue/digital terrestrial TV services in each room.

Some customers would also like to be able to watch the selected Sky channel or a DVD programme in all rooms. To achieve this, the outputs of the aerials should be diplexed together and connected via the Sky receiver or DVD player before they are distributed to the other rooms as shown below:

117

Keywords

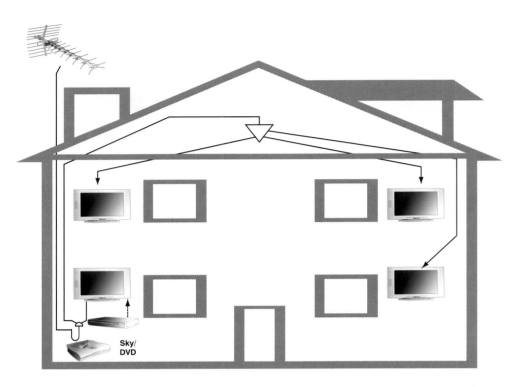

Sky/
DVD

Whilst it is essential to keep all the signal levels within their respective windows of operation, it is also necessary to ensure that the levels of the off-air TV signals and the additional channels added by the Sky receiver or DVD player are substantially the same. This is best achieved by measuring the TV signal levels at the output of the equipment in the living room and before they are relayed to the distribution amplifier in the roof space. The terrestrial signal levels can be adjusted at the Sky receiver input with an attenuator or amplifier as appropriate so that they are the same as that of the locally generated channels.

New •
Buildings

For new buildings, the builder should generally be advised to make provision for radio and TV services as follows:

- Use only high quality double screened (tape and braid) coaxial cable (preferably benchmarked).
- A separate such cable between the loft and each room (not in tandem).
- One additional coaxial cable between the loft and the main TV viewing room (for a reverse feed back to the loft)
- Additional coaxial cables to the main viewing room for the provision of satellite services.

Keywords

• Multi-Dwelling Units

• MATV

• Loop Wired Networks

• Tree-and-branch Networks

• Tree-and-bush Networks

6.3   Multi-Dwelling Units

Many accommodation blocks provide for radio and TV distribution using a **M**aster **A**ntenna **TV (MATV)** system. Such systems are designed to relay some or all of the following services:

- FM radio
- DAB broadcasts
- UHF analogue TV channels (and sometimes VHF channels as well)
- UHF "Freeview" digital multiplexes

These various services are relayed in various frequency bands on a single coaxial cable network:
- FM   87.5 – 108MHz
- DAB   215 – 230MHz
- UHF   470 – 862MHz

Loop wired networks

This relatively inexpensive solution uses a single coaxial cable to link viewing households to one another in a continuous chain or loop. Special outlet plates are required for such systems. If there is a fault at any point in the chain, all households are affected. This can become a major maintenance headache because access may be required to all dwellings to remedy the fault. Loop wired systems are no longer recommended at all.

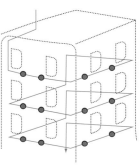

Tree-and-branch networks

Spur cables run down or along the building and are connected via a separate "drop-in" cable to each dwelling using a "Tee" insert that provides isolation from the main network. This is the type of system that has been installed in most apartment blocks during the last fifty years. Whilst perfectly adequate for terrestrial TV relay, it cannot easily be upgraded for satellite TV if there are common cables serving more than one dwelling.

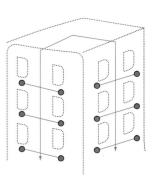

Tree-and-bush networks

A separate coaxial cable links each dwelling to a "node". If there is more than one such node, the nodes must be linked together with at least five coaxial cables (called a "backbone"). This type of network can be used to relay terrestrial TV and satellite TV signals simultaneously. A switching unit (called a "multiswitch") is fitted at each node, usually line powered from a central location.

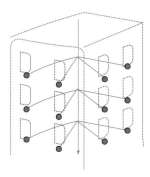

Keywords

Star Wired •
Networks

Star wired networks

A separate coaxial cable links each dwelling to a multiswitch at a central node. This method is preferred for all new systems in small buildings.

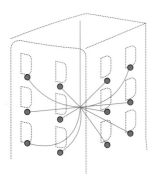

Tree-and-bush and star wired networks can be configured as Integrated Reception Systems (IRS) as described in section eight.

The remainder of this section deals with the upgrading of Tree and Branch systems for the relay of analogue and digital terrestrial radio and TV services.

Upgrading Tree-and-Branch Systems

There are many tree-and-branch distribution systems in apartment blocks throughout the UK, relaying analogue terrestrial TV services (and sometimes FM radio as well). Most were installed long ago when the building was constructed with the coaxial drop-in cables in conduits buried under the plaster. The spur cables linking the floors are normally inside risers that are sometimes accessible.

Systems in these buildings cannot easily be upgraded to relay satellite TV signals, but it may be possible to carry out modifications to make them suitable for relaying digital terrestrial TV programmes and DAB broadcasts **if the existing coaxial cables are of a high enough quality.**

An initial inspection will determine if double-screened cables have been used; If so, and channelised amplifiers and filters have <u>not</u> been fitted, it may be possible to measure digital signal levels at the outlet locations to check the performance of the existing system.

The system itself will almost certainly need to be upgraded to provide reliable DTT reception and to minimise the effects of impulse noise. The following parameters should be checked:

Aerial site:
- Structural rigidity
- DTT/DAB signal levels and C/N ratio
- Benchmarked TV aerial.
- Screened masthead amplifier (if used)
- Mast earthed to lightning protection system (if applicable) and head end equipment

Head end equipment
- Sufficient amplifier output levels for each channel to achieve the required "window-of-operation" at each outlet socket
- Amplifiers derated for number of channels and number of amplifiers in tandem
- All connectors crimp type and spanner tightened
- All incoming and outgoing cables earthed to the **M**ain **E**arth **T**erminal **(MET)**

Outlet plates:
- Screened type
- Levels, C/N ratio and BER

Spur Cables •

Main Earthing •

Keywords

In most cases, the outlet signal levels will need to be increased to achieve all the required signal parameters.

Many analogue tree-and –branch systems utilise high output amplifiers followed by network splitters to feed each spur cable. One way to increase the launch levels would be to use a separate launch amplifier for each spur cable – this would eliminate the losses introduced by the splitters.

MATV System Concepts

Each system must be designed to deliver signal levels within the operating windows shown on the drawing alongside.

To improve the performance of a system, it is important that all the wanted incoming analogue UHF signals are of the same strength and that the UHF digital muxes are of a suitable level to maximise the window of operation. (An exception to this would be where pre-emphasis is applied to the higher channels to compensate for the greater cable losses at the higher frequencies).

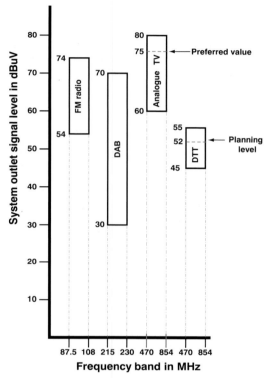

Operating windows

• MATV System Concepts

• Main Operating Windows

Some of the methods of achieving this are as follows:

- **Filter leveller** (equaliser): This will eliminate unwanted channels and allow for independent adjustment of the amplitude of the wanted channels. It is normally used for analogue signals only.

- **Cluster filter:** This uses the same principle except that some of the filters are tuned to pass more than one (adjacent) channel. It is useful where analogue and digital signals are transmitted on adjacent channels and allows for the individual filtering and levelling of each cluster of channels.

• Filter Leveller

• Cluster Filter

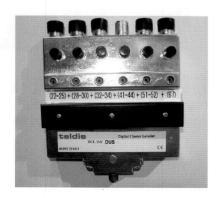

Programmable •
Cluster Filter

- **Programmable cluster filter-amplifier:**
  This provides the same facilities as a
  cluster filter, with the following additional
  advantages:
  > Programmable on site
  > Better filtering
  > 10 clusters (typical)
  > Inbuilt amplification
  > High launch levels

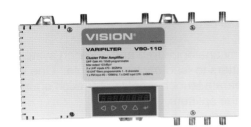

Programmable •
Filter / Amplifier

- **Frequency-agile filter / amplifier:**
  Recent improvements in filter design
  have resulted in the introduction of
  filter/amplifier combinations, either
  for single UHF channels (with up to
  14 such channels in one unit) or for
  clusters of channels. The filtering
  is sufficient to allow for adjacent
  channel operation, and such units
  can have an output launch level
  of up to 120dBμV. A typical unit is
  shown alongside.

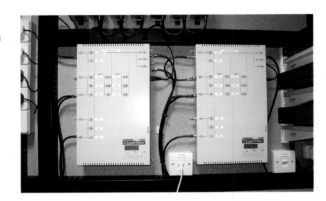

6

UHF Channel •
Amplifiers

- **DTT channel amplifiers.** Amplifiers are now available for single UHF digital or analogue
  channels, even when they are on adjacent channels, so that the amplitude of digital
  multiplexes can be increased with respect to the analogue channels. Using this
  technique, the digital multiplexes can be raised to acceptable levels without the analogue
  channels overloading the set-top box. Such amplifiers are normally adjusted so that the
  digital multiplexes are 15dB below the amplitude of the analogue channels. A typical 11
  channel assembly is shown below:

All the above techniques give the added advantage of filtering the input signals and
therefore reducing the effects of interference in other frequency bands, such as the TETRA
communication system now widely used by local authorities in the UK.

Keywords

• Satellite
  Remodulator

• DTT
  Demodulator

• UHF Signal
  Levels

• UHF Window
  of Operation

Programme Sources

Other TV programmes may be required in addition to the locally available terrestrial channels.

The picture alongside illustrates the type of equipment available to provide six satellite programmes. Each of the video/audio outputs can be modulated on to a UHF carrier, for distribution together with the terrestrial TV services.

This picture shows the equivalent six-channel DTT demodulator, also requiring six modulators to provide additional UHF TV channels.

Signal Levels

The overall gain of the system can affect the window of operation, as shown in the following diagrams, which illustrate the relationship between signal or noise levels and the overall system gain ie. the amplifier gain (if fitted) less the cable and splitter losses.

The first diagram shows the required analogue signal level at the aerial the achieve 80dBµV at the STB and the corresponding noise level, the difference between the two lines being the analogue carrier to noise ratio:

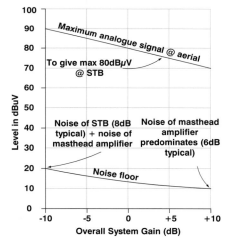

The second diagram shows the corresponding digital signal and noise levels to give 26dB C/N.

It is necessary for the digital signals to be within the window of operation for the system to work satisfactorily. If there is no amplifier and a 10dB cable loss (-10dB overall gain), analogue signals of between 66 and 90 dBµV at the aerial will keep the digital muxes within the window. If there is an 18dB masthead preamplifier and an 8dB cable loss (+10dB overall gain), analogue signal levels of between 60 and 70 dBµV at the aerial should work satisfactorily.
Note that the window of operation is smaller

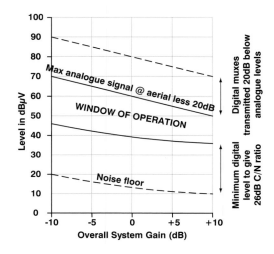

123

Keywords

if an amplifier is used. It is reduced even further when the minimum signal level at the outlet is specified as 45dBμV!

The next step is to check the C/N ratio and BER of the digital signals to ensure that they are within acceptable limits. The signal quality indication on each STB should also be checked to ensure that the BER is satisfactory. However, this indication is only effective for a signal level greater than 2dB above the "foldover" point (ie. minimum signal level) for the receiver. Below this level, it would be possible to have a good BER indication but to lose the digital picture completely if the signal level were to drop by more than 2dB! It is for this reason that the minimum digital signal level is specified as 45dBμV, to allow for a margin above the foldover level. For the same reason, the minimum digital planning level is increased to 52dBμV for distribution systems to allow for higher levels of interference.

The BER indication can also be degraded if the flatness of the spectrum across the multiplex is worse than 7-8dB or if a serious ghost exists and it is necessary to determine which of these is the cause.

Impulse Noise •

It is difficult to measure the effects of impulse noise because it has to occur whilst you are watching, although some spectrum analysers can be set to count the number of data errors occurring over a pre-determined time. Interference visible on the spectrum display should ideally be at least 20dB lower than the signal levels.

Amplifier •
Specifications

Amplifier Specifications

An amplifier cannot itself improve the carrier to noise ratio of a signal. It can however improve the performance of a system by compensating for the loss in the relay cables between the output of the amplifier and the outlet points. Provided that the noise contribution of the amplifier to the digital receiver's intrinsic noise is small, the receiver will see a better C/N ratio than without the amplifier. If the gain of the amplifier is much higher than the loss it is to correct for, then its noise contribution will not be small.

UHF Amplifier •
Types

UHF amplifiers can have a bandwidth of a single channel, a group of channels or the whole UHF band.

UHF Single •
Channel Amplifiers

Single Channel UHF Amplifiers
As the name implies, a single channel UHF amplifier will provide amplification and filtering of a single UHF TV channel. Its most important parameters are maximum gain and maximum output, and some such units incorporate automatic gain control (AGC). The filter alignment is sometimes different for analogue and digital signals, in which case a digital channel amplifier can be used for analogue, but not vice versa. The filtering in most units is sufficient to allow for adjacent channel operation, and channel amplifiers can have an output launch level of up to 129dBμV.

Optimum performance of AGC amplifiers will only be achieved if the input signals are correct. For instance, if the unit has an AGC range of 20dB, a nominal gain of 40dB and a maximum output of 120dBμV, its input signal must be in the range 70-90dBμV for the AGC to operate correctly. Its design input level should therefore be in the middle of this range i.e. 80dBμV.

UHF Wideband •
Amplifiers

Wideband Amplifiers

In this context, a wideband amplifier can operate over a frequency range of at least 470-854MHz (UHF channels 21-68).

Keywords

Applications of wideband amplifiers in MATV systems include the following:
- To pre-amplify the terrestrial "off-air" signal input
- As a launch amplifier into a cable network
- As a repeater amplifier, further down the network.

The most important signal parameters are gain and maximum output, the latter being derated in accordance with the number of channels being relayed and the number of amplifiers in tandem. For amplifiers with variable gain and slope adjustment, these controls should preferably be mid-stage, as outlined in section two.

• Amplifier
Derating

Some wideband amplifiers also cover the VHF band, with either a single input or separate inputs for FM, DAB, UHF etc. These amplifiers can consist of either a single amplifier or two separate "split-band" amplifiers with input/output filters. Amplifiers with a higher output capability are generally of the split-band type.

• Split Band
Amplifiers

Cable TV companies use wideband amplifiers on CATV systems. These are more expensive than those made for MATV applications, but their gain flatness, matching and signal handling capabilities are excellent.

Amplifier Noise

• Amplifier Noise

As previously stated, the performance of any TV relay system depends on its overall C/N ratio.

Noise comes from two sources:
- External noise, picked up by the aerial and cable network
- Internal noise generated by the amplifier(s).

• Noise Sources

The noise figure of an amplifier is the amount in dB by which the noise at the output of an amplifier is greater than it would be if the amplifier input was a perfect 75 Ohm resistor at a temperature of 290K. The noise in such a perfect resistor is called the "reference noise" and is as follows:

• Reference
Noise

2dBμV for analogue
4dBμV for digital.

As an example, if an amplifier with a noise figure of 8dB is operated with a digital signal input level of 52dBμV, its output C/N ratio can be calculated as follows:

C/N	=	input level	-	reference noise	-	noise figure		
(dB)		(dBμV)		(dBμV)		(dB)		
C/N	=	52	-	4	-	8	=	40dB

When amplifiers are operated in tandem, you can't just add all the noise figures together when calculating overall system performance. The calculation is complicated, but, as a general guide, if the amplifiers are all operating in tandem at the same input level, the output C/N ratio will decrease by 3dB every time that the number of amplifiers is doubled (1 to 2 to 4 to 8 etc).

• Noise
Accumulation

It is therefore obvious from the formula above that an increase of 6dB in the input signal level will give a 6dB increase in the output C/N ratio. Magic? Well, yes, but there are other considerations – what about signal distortion?

Keywords

Inter-modulation • Distortion

Cross modulation • Distortion

6

Electrical • Safety

Amplifier Distortion

The maximum output of an amplifier is limited by the distortion that it introduces. Above a certain level, the amplifier becomes "non-linear" and introduces "sum-and-difference" frequencies – this is called (second order) "inter-modulation" distortion.

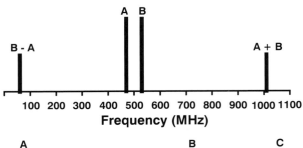

If more than two carriers are present, they can all interfere with each other, causing (third order) "cross-modulation" distortion. The interfering frequencies should be at least 60dB less than the wanted carriers and the maximum outputs of amplifiers are often quoted on this basis.

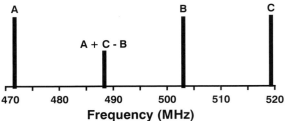

Cross modulation increases by 3dB each time that the number of interfering analogue TV channels is doubled. Digital multiplexes, because they are at relatively low levels (at least 15dB below the analogue signal levels), do not therefore contribute to the channel loading of an amplifier. This subject is covered in more detail in part 6.5.

Requirements for Electrical safety

The "Consumer Protection" act of 1987 imposes a General Safety Requirement regarding the supply of goods to the general public. The relevant requirements of the IEE wiring regulations, BS EN 7671 (latest edition) must also be complied with.

As an employee or installer, **you must not supply goods to consumers** if they are not reasonably safe, having regard to all the circumstances, including marketing, instructions, warnings, description of goods, safety standards and means by which the goods could have been made safer.

These regulations are enforced by Inspectors from the Health and Safety Executive and the Local Authorities. Non compliance can imply criminal negligence, resulting in police investigation and possible imprisonment.

The last person on site is always responsible for leaving the system in a safe condition, even if the unsafe condition was caused by others. If he believes that the system is not safe, either electrically or mechanically, he is duty bound to eliminate the cause of the unsafe condition (e.g. by switching off or removing the equipment in question) and to inform the user and his superior in writing of the action that he has taken.

The purpose of these requirements is to prevent serious injury either to a system user or to maintenance personnel due to the presence of hazardous voltages on the system. These could be generated by a faulty TV receiver or other mains operated equipment connected to the system. For instance, many TV receivers have a "live" chassis (the metalwork behind the rear cover) which could, under fault conditions, cause a dangerous voltage to be present on the aerial input socket and therefore on the whole cable relay network.

All new MATV distribution systems must be electrically bonded to the building's main earth terminal, as detailed in part 8.4 of this publication.

Keywords

• MATV Network
Planning

• Line Powering

• Network
Isolation

• Head End
Equipment
• Feeder Cables

• Spur Cables
• Drop-in Cables

• Spur Inserts

• Outlet Plates

• Repeater
Amplifiers

• Terminating
Resistors

• Subscriber Taps

• Subscriber
Insert

• Through Loss
• Side Loss

6.4   MATV Network Planning

Signal Levels

This section illustrates the design principles for tree-and-branch systems for the relay of FM radio, DAB and analogue/digital terrestrial TV signals.

The signal levels at each outlet must be within correct operating windows as previously specified. Repeater amplifiers are sometimes needed to achieve this. Such amplifiers may have to be line-powered via the coaxial cable if local mains power is not available. Systems can be planned using analogue or digital signal levels, depending on which services are to be relayed. One would normally plan for a minimum signal level on highest UHF TV channel (channel 68) of 52dBμV into digital receiver, at furthest outlet. This would need 54dBμV at end of cable, allowing for a 2dB loss through the outlet plate and flylead. It is also important to ensure that isolation is achieved between outlets so that a fault at any outlet does not affect the rest of the system – this is why TV splitters cannot be used on MATV systems.

Component Parts

The relevant cable TV terminology includes the following:

- **Head end equipment** - all the equipment necessary to amplify and process the signals received from the aerial(s), for distribution on the coaxial cable network.
- **Feeder cables** - the main coaxial cables originating at the head end equipment to distribute the signals to other parts of the building or neighbourhood.
- **Spur cables** – the coaxial cables that "spur off" down a corridor or street.
- **Drop-in cables** (subscriber feeds) – the cables that connect each outlet to the distribution network.
- **Spur inserts** – used for the interconnection of feeder and spur cables.
- **Subscriber taps,** sometimes called "Tee inserts" (see below) – these connect together the spur and drop-in cables. Different values are available to balance signal levels. They will pass DC power on spur cables but not drop-ins, and provide isolation between each outlet and the rest of the system. 1, 2, 3 or 4 way versions are available.
- **Outlet plates** – available in either flush mounted or surface mounted formats. They incorporate either single or diplexed sockets, for the connection of FM radio, DAB or TV receivers.
- **Repeater amplifiers** – used along the cable network to increase the signal levels. They can be powered either from a local mains supply, or from the head end equipment via the feeder and spur cables.
- **75 Ohm terminating resistors** – used to terminate the ongoing spur of the last tee insert on each spur cable. It is essential that these are fitted so that the whole system is matched to 75 Ohms, otherwise standing waves will introduce major degradations to the signal quality.

Subscriber Taps

Indoor and outdoor versions are available, either with saddle-and-clamp connectors or in sealed metal cases with F connectors.

A subscriber tap or tee insert is defined by two parameters:

- **Through loss**, sometimes called insertion loss
- **Side loss**, sometimes called tap loss.

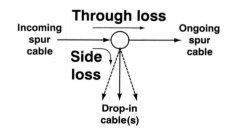

Keywords

Insert Values •

MATV Cable •
Losses

MATV Network •
Example

It is necessary to use correct value of insert. For instance, close to the end of a cable network where the signal level is relatively weak, you would need a subscriber tap with a low side loss. Since much of the energy is transferred to the drop in cable, there would be less available to pass to subsequent outlets i.e. the insert would have a high through loss. Nearer to the head end equipment, the signal level on the spur cable would be higher and you would not need to transfer as much to the drop in cable. In this case you would use a subscriber tap with a higher side loss and a correspondingly lower through loss. Typical losses for one, two, three and four way taps are as follows:

Side loss in dBs	Through loss in dBs			
	1 way	2 way	3 way	4 way
12	1.5	2.5	5.6	6.5
15	1.0	2.0	3.0	6.5
20	1.0	1.75	2.3	3.0
25	0.7	1.25	1.5	2.0
30	0.6	1.0	1.2	1.75
35	0.5	0.75	0.8	1.25

Using this information together with the cable losses, it is possible to calculate which value of subscriber taps to use in order to obtain the correct signal levels at each outlet. Typical cable losses for the relevant frequencies are as follows, in dB per 10m:

Service	Freq (MHz)	H109F	WF100	WF125	WF165
FM Radio	100	0.6	0.6	0.5	0.4
DAB	230	1.0	1.0	0.8	0.6
Terrestrial TV	470	1.4	1.4	1.2	0.9
	860	1.9	1.9	1.6	1.2

Worked example

The following example illustrates the planning procedure for a DTT tree-and-branch cable network with a minimum signal level of 52dBμV into each digital receiver. The project is to provide such a service for an existing small two-storey hotel with nine guest rooms, as shown alongside.

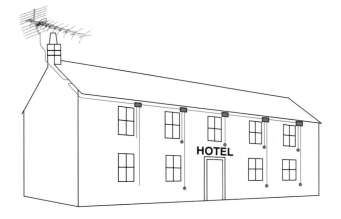

Start by deciding on the cable layout. In this case, it is probably better to cable on outside of building with the spur cable and subscriber taps under the eaves where they will be sheltered from the weather. The vertical drop-in cables terminate in surface mounted outlet plates in each room. The aerial could be mounted on the chimney with the head end equipment in the loft.

Keywords

• MATV Network
  Schematic

• MATV Network
  Losses

Prepare a network schematic showing cable lengths in metres and decide which grade of cable to use for spur and drop-in cables:

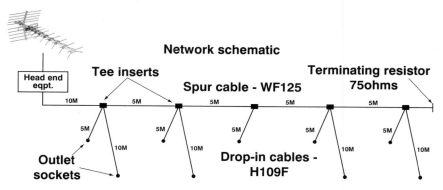

Mark the cable losses in dB at the highest frequency to be relayed (usually 860MHz). Identify the furthest point (the location where the signal level will be weakest) and mark minimum digital signal level as 54dBμV – this allows for a 2dB loss through the outlet plate and flylead.

The procedure is then to work back towards the head end equipment, calculating the signal levels required to achieve 54dBμV at the furthest point on the system. For instance, if the loss on the drop-in cable is 1.9dB, the signal level at the top of the drop-in cable will need to be 1.9dB higher, or 55.9dBμV:

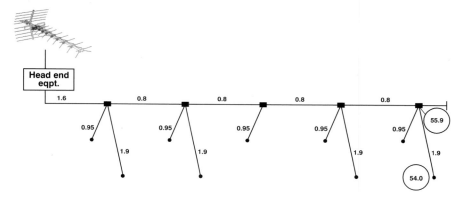

Next, choose the value of the subscriber tap to be used. Since it will feed the furthest point, its side loss should be the minimum possible, or 12dB. Its through loss does not matter since the through leg will only be connected to the terminating resistor. A 2/12 tap is needed because it feeds two outlet locations.

Mark the required input level to this insert on the schematic. In this case, it will be 12dB higher, or 67.9dBμV:

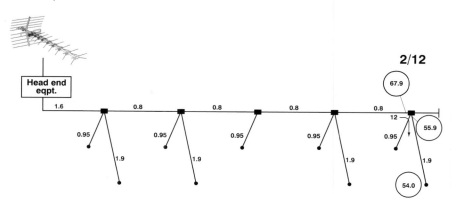

Keywords

Since the loss on the spur cable is 0.8dB, the signal level at the output of the next tap will need to be 0.8dB higher, or 68.7dBµV.

The next job is to choose the most suitable subscriber tap to feed the next two outlets, ensuring that the signal levels are at least 54dBµV. In this case must be 2/12 because all the other values have a higher side loss that would result in too low a level at the outlets. Mark the insert through and side losses on the schematic and calculate the resulting signal levels.

The next tap feeds only one outlet. A 1/12 would do the job but a 1/15 is a better choice since it has a lower through loss feeding the subsequent outlets. Always use the subscriber tap with the lowest through loss to give at least the minimum level at the outlets that it feeds:

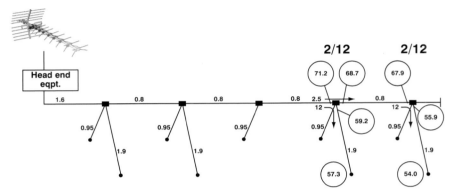

Specify the remaining taps using the same criteria. Always use the subscriber tap with the lowest through loss to give at least the minimum level at the outlets that it is connected to:

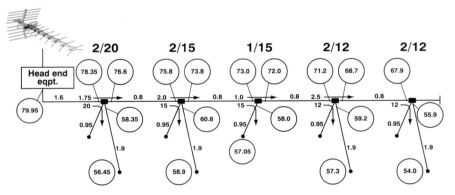

It is now apparent that a launch level of 79.95dBµV is required to achieve a signal level of at least 54.0dBµV at each outlet.

A site test will determine the signal level available from the TV aerial. Amplifiers must be used with sufficient gain to raise this level to 79.95dBµV.

It is also necessary to recalculate the losses at 470MHz to determine the launch levels at the lower frequencies. The levels will be higher because the cable losses are less. It may be advantageous to fit an equaliser to pre-emphasise the higher frequencies, thus compensating for the greater cable losses. An ideal situation would be to have positive slope at the amplifier, negative slope at the furthest point, and zero slope half way along the network.

Pre-emphasis •

A check must also be made to ensure that the maximum rated output of the amplifier is sufficient, after the derating rules have been applied, taking into account the analogue signal levels which will be up to 20dB higher than the digital levels.

Keywords

If FM radio and DAB services are also to be relayed, it will be necessary to repeat the network planning procedures at each of the relevant frequencies starting with the minimum value at the furthest point, to determine the required launch levels for each of these services.

All the above procedures started with the minimum signal level at the furthest point and worked backwards towards the head end equipment, to determine the lowest possible signal launch levels. It is possible to work in the opposite direction, starting with an assumed launch level from the head end equipment and working in the other direction, specifying subscriber tap values to achieve the minimum signal levels at each outlet location. This method is more relevant for larger systems where repeater amplifiers may be required along the network to extend the system reach.

It is most important to ensure that the necessary safety procedures are adhered to, either by using screened isolated outlets throughout the network, or by earthing the whole system, as detailed elsewhere this document.

Larger Capacity Systems

It is possible to add additional TV channels to a MATV distribution system. Systems of this type are used in schools, hotels and apartment blocks. Typical applications could include:
- Programmes originating from a VCR
- CCTV security or access control pictures
- Computer-generated data or images
- FM or DAB radio channels, accompanied by a suitable caption
- Local or foreign satellite programmes.

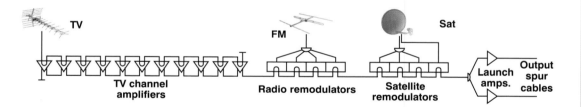

They are called **S**atellite **M**aster **A**ntenna Tele**V**ision **(SMATV)** systems because, historically, the additional locally modulated channels tended to be satellite. The principles outlined previously also apply to these systems, although more care must be taken during the planning and commissioning stages, especially when both analogue and digital TV channels are to be relayed.

- SMATV

Modulators incorporated in domestic equipment are not suitable for use on large MATV systems. Most produce spurious signals within the UHF band that cause interference with other UHF channels. Use a stand-alone modulator with video/audio inputs, which incorporates filters in its output stages.

- Modulators

Inexpensive modulators are usually of the "**D**ouble **S**ide**B**and" **(DSB)** type, producing sidebands on either side of the carrier, thus doubling the bandwidth requirement. However, since each sideband contains all the video information, it is possible to suppress one sideband completely. Better quality modulators use a compromise technique known as **V**estigial **S**ide**B**and **(VSB)** transmission, whereby part of the lower sideband is removed leaving just 1.25MHz of DSB information adjacent to the vision carrier frequency.

- DSB Modulators

- VSB Modulators

Some large capacity systems utilise a separate amplifier for each UHF channel, which serves two purposes:

Keywords

Equalisation •
Slope

- It is then possible to adjust the amplitude of each channel independently.
- All the unwanted signals are filtered off.

This can be followed by wideband UHF amplifiers to increase the launch level into each spur, and for reamplification at remote locations. The output level of each wideband amplifier must be derated according to the number of channels being relayed.

For large systems, the cable slope across the UHF band makes it more difficult to keep all the channel amplitudes within their correct windows of operation at each outlet location. The window can be widened by increasing the levels of the digital signals with respect to the analogue levels by using DTT signal processors or specialised UHF digital channel amplifiers.

Some MATV amplifiers incorporate the facility for launching the higher frequencies at higher output levels, to compensate for the greater cable losses at higher frequencies. This technique is called **equalisation** or pre-emphasis and the difference between the gain at the low and high ends of the frequency band is referred to as the **slope** adjustment. For instance, a UHF TV amplifier with a 4dB positive slope would have 4dB more gain at 860MHz than at 470MHz. Some makes have provision for plug-in equalisers whilst other versions incorporate an adjustable slope control.

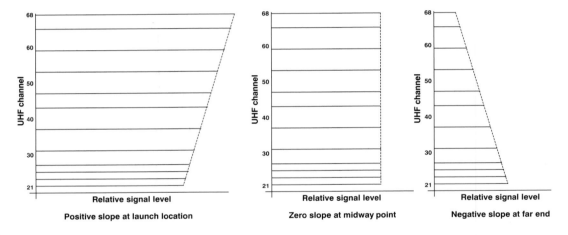

Positive slope at launch location   Zero slope at midway point   Negative slope at far end

MATV amplifiers with high output levels sometimes incorporate more expensive electronics such as a push/pull output stage and split band amplifiers, resulting in greater cost. These are often followed by splitters that will reduce the signals to more normal levels. It may therefore be more economical to use a lower output amplifier on each spur cable than a one high output amplifier.

Ensure that all the equipment automatically resets to the appropriate parameters after a mains power failure.

Keywords

• Choice of UHF Channels

6.5   Choice of SMATV Relay Channels

When adding locally generated analogue programmes, care must be taken to ensure that they do not interfere with one another, resulting in picture degradation of analogue pictures and complete loss of digital pictures.

There are several rules to follow in this regard:

1 Don't use strong analogue or digital channels not being relayed on the system.
If reception is possible from two or more terrestrial TV transmitters and only one is to be relayed on the system, it would be unwise to use the other transmitter channels. Otherwise, if these are picked up on the coaxial cables, you could end up with two different analogue programmes on the same TV channel resulting in co-channel interference on the locally generated analogue channel.

2 Don't use adjacent analogue channels.
Since the UHF output channel from most domestic equipment is what is known as "double sideband", its frequencies also extend to the channel below. Also, the UHF tuners in some older TV receivers are not sharp enough to eliminate adjacent channels. For these reasons, do not use adjacent channels. The broadcasters can use digital multiplexes adjacent to analogue TV channels only by restricting the digital power levels so they do not cause interference.

3 Leave a gap in the channel allocations to allow for the connection of a VCR in any room.
It could be that each viewing location has its own VCR that generates an additional UHF TV channel. Provision should be made for this eventuality by leaving space for such a channel in the UHF TV spectrum. Whilst the VCR output channel can be set anywhere in the UHF band on newer VCRs, older versions often have a limited tuning range, often between channels 30-39. Because of rule 2 (above), the gap will need to be at least 3 channels.

4 Don't use analogue channels five apart.
A TV receiver can radiate interference five channels higher than the channel it is tuned to, which could degrade the picture quality on nearby TV receivers.

5 Don't superimpose an analogue channel on a digital multiplex.
Even if digital reception is not required, using a digital channel for an analogue programme will increase the noise level on the analogue signal, thereby degrading the picture quality.

6 Avoid channels with local sources of interference.
Since interference from such things as local radar and aircraft beacons (especially on channel 36) can cause interference, avoid using such channels.

Method of Channel Selection

This is best done in steps as illustrated in the following example:

• UHF Channel Selection

• Prepare a chart like the one alongside, listing the UHF channels 21-68.

21	22	23	24	25	26	27	28	29	30
31	32	33	34	35	36	37	38	39	40
41	42	43	44	45	46	47	48	49	50
51	52	53	54	55	56	57	58	59	60
61	62	63	64	65	66	67	68		

133

Keywords

- Mark each of the off-air analogue and digital terrestrial TV channels that you intend to relay on the system (this example shows the analogue Crystal Palace channels shaded yellow and the digital muxes shaded blue).

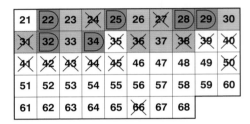

- Cross off all the strong analogue and digital TV channels from nearby transmitters that are not being relayed on the system, if applicable (the Hannington channels in this case, shaded grey).

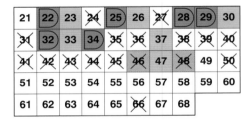

- Cross off any remaining channels adjacent to the analogue channels being relayed.

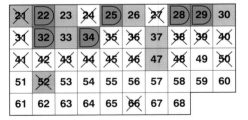

- Decide which channel to leave vacant for remote VCRs, and circle the number (channel 47 in this example) – this must not be next to, or five channels away from, any channel shaded yellow. Also cross off the two adjacent channels.

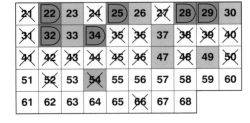

- Cross off any remaining channels which are adjacent to, or five away from (in both directions), any channel shaded yellow.

- You can then choose one of the remaining UHF channels (usually the lowest) to relay the first of the locally generated programmes – channel 49 in this example. Cross off any that are adjacent or five away in both directions.

- Repeat this process for the other locally generated channels – in our example, there is enough space for a total of ten locally generated channels (the ones shaded yellow) without breaking any of the rules.

If more than ten local channels are required, it is possible to relay additional channels in the VHF band 120-470MHz, and there are TV sets available that have VHF tuners fitted as standard.

Intermodulation Distortion

In the above example, if all of the terrestrial analogue channels are even numbers, the "taboo" channels occur with odd number relationships. It would therefore seem that the best arrangement would be one in which all the spacings are an even number of channels and indeed from this point of view that is the case. We could use UHF channel converters to change the odd-numbered channels to even numbered ones. A plan using for example channels 22, 24, 26, 28 and 30 would not suffer from any of the effects discussed above, and would avoid the digital multiplexes. Alternatively, we could use just odd-numbered channels, in which case all the "taboo" channels would be on even numbers. However, other considerations also apply, as outlined below.

When several frequencies are passed through an amplifier, their sum and difference frequencies can be generated, resulting in "intermodulation" distortion, as discussed in part 6.3. Two such frequencies create 2nd order distortion, and three frequencies can cause 3rd order distortion. This is best explained by way of the following example:

Assume that we have a system in which we are distributing, among others, TV signals on the following carrier frequencies:

471.25 MHz	(channel 21)	"n"
487.25 MHz	(channel 23)	(n+2)
503.25 MHz	(channel 25)	(n+4)
519.25 MHz	(channel 27)	(n+6)
535.25 MHz	(channel 29)	(n+8)

then by intermodulation, there will be, for example, unwanted outputs at:

2nd order

$$471.25 + 535.25 = 1006.5 \text{ MHz}$$
$$535.25 - 471.25 = 64 \text{ MHz}$$
$$2(519.25) - 503.25 = 535.25 \text{ MHz}$$
$$2(487.25) - 503.25 = 471.25 \text{ MHz}$$

3rd order

$$471.25 + 519.25 - 503.25 = 487.25 \text{ MHz}$$
$$503.25 + 535.25 - 519.25 = 519.25 \text{ MHz}$$
$$535.25 + 471.25 - 487.25 = 503.25 \text{ MHz}$$

It can be seen that the 3rd order products in this example fall at the carrier frequencies of the input channels and these are not the only ones so to do. If we were to work out all of them we would find that the centre channel (in this case channel 25) would be inundated with unwanted signals from this effect and the other channels would be less affected the further away we get from the centre.

Keywords

Carrier Offsets •

All the carrier frequencies are not absolutely precise. Small differences in the carrier frequencies will occur due to deliberate "offsets" in the broadcast transmitters and inaccuracies in any frequency conversion oscillators. Thus, the products they generate will not fall exactly on the carrier frequencies but they will be grouped in clusters closely spaced on either side of them.

Composite •
Triple Beat (CTB)

This special form of 3rd order intermodulation is known as composite triple beat or CTB (beat is just another word for intermodulation product) and, if it is generated at sufficiently high level, it manifests itself as a very specific form of interference on analogue TV pictures. The result is a picture that appears to have been taken looking through a waterfall or as a blurring of the picture that varies in intensity down the picture and which at the same time moves vertically through the picture.

Although this has not been considered particularly relevant to SMATV but much more of a problem for the designers of large Cable TV systems, the inter-modulation products generated could corrupt digital signals. It therefore makes a difference to our system planning if we have several channels that are spaced in frequency by equal amounts. Where such a frequency plan is adopted, it would be wise to set the limits for 3rd order inter-modulation somewhat higher than the recognised limit for single product interference. That limit is set in the British Standard (EN) at a carrier to interference ratio of 57 dB. It should be raised to 60 dB to account for any composite triple beat resulting from small numbers of channels that are spaced by nominally equal amounts.

It must also be remembered that, for any amplifier operating at more than its derated maximum output, a further increase of 1dB in its output level will result in a 2dB increase in intermodulation distortion!

Gap Fillers •

6.6 Gap Fillers

It is technically possible to use low-power gap-fillers to provide additional coverage in areas where terrestrial reception is poor.

Such schemes can be relatively expensive since the infrastructure costs (housing, mains power, transmitting tower etc.) can be considerable.

Ofcom •

It is also necessary to obtain approval to rebroadcast TV transmissions from The Office of Communications (Ofcom). These transmissions may have to be on different UHF channels to those being received in the vicinity, so aerials in different frequency groups may be required.

For these reasons, it is necessary to consider the other options, before embarking on such a scheme. These options may include:

- Improving existing individual TV reception by using high gain grouped aerials on tall masts.
- The use of a community cable TV system to relay signals to each dwelling from a site where good reception is possible.

Keywords

• Relay Sites

• Coverage Area

• Propagation
  Charts

• Freznel Zones

• Planning
  Permission

• Lightning
  Protection

Relay Site
There are several aspects to be considered when choosing a suitable relay site:

Reliability of TV Reception
It is imperative that a site test is carried out to ensure that signals of adequate quality are available over a period of time. Some spectrum analysers can log digital errors over a pre-determined time interval. Otherwise, it may be necessary to connect a pen recorder to a field strength meter and leave it running overnight. The photograph alongside shows such a monitoring system.

Coverage Area
A line-of-sight path is required to all dwellings requiring the service. It may not be possible to see the coverage area from the top of a tall transmitting tower until the tower is actually in place, in which case it will be necessary to predict the coverage. An ordinance survey map of the area will show the height contours, from which path profiles can be plotted on to earth-profile propagation charts that allow for the curvature of the earth:

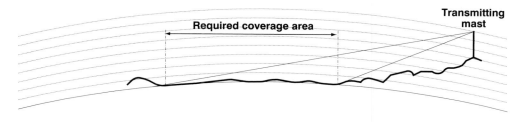

This will give a precise indication of the required height of the transmitting mast or tower. It is essential to plan for first Freznel zone clearance over any intervening obstructions. Freznel zones are described in part 4.

It is usually easier to locate the relay site outside the coverage area (instead of in the middle of it). The transmitting aerial can then be directional, giving some gain with a consequent increase in the radiated power towards the target reception areas.

Planning Permission
It is essential to check with the local authority, especially if the transmitting tower will be taller than 6M. Special requirements such as aircraft warning lights may be required.

Accessibility
This is most important, both for initial installation and subsequent maintenance.

Availability of Mains Power
Whilst solar panels and wind-driven generators could be used, mains power is the obvious choice if possible.

Lightning Protection
If the transmitting tower is the highest object in the area, it is essential to protect the installation against the effects of a lightning strike. All metal parts of the structure should be bonded together and connected to a good earth – this may be a ground spike or an earth mat, depending on the soil conditions.

Keywords

Receiving Aerial(s)

In order to ensure that the best possible signals are received, it may be necessary to use a phased aerial array, as described in part 5.7.

Retransmitting Aerial(s)

Domestic aerials should not be used since their impedance is not good enough to match that of the transmitting feeder cable, resulting in standing waves with a resultant loss of transmitting power. Some transmitters have an output impedance of 50 Ohms, in which case it would be necessary to use a 50 Ohm feeder cable, 50 Ohm connectors and a transmitting aerial with 50 Ohms impedance.

Impedence •

Polar Diagram •

The polar diagram of the transmitting aerial should be tailored to provide coverage of the target area whilst not wasting power by covering other areas that are uninhabited or where normal TV reception is satisfactory.

Relay Equipment

Channel •
Transposition

Current technology for small self-help schemes uses channel transposition in the UHF band, without demodulation:

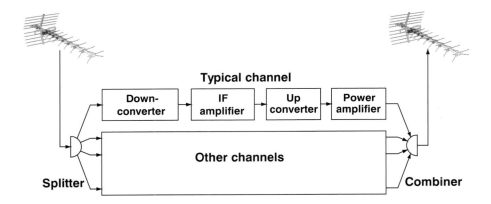

The components of such a system are as follows:
- An input splitter. This usually incorporates stop-filters tuned to the output channels.
- A downconverter to convert the channel to the IF band. Automatic gain control is applied at this stage.
- An IF filter and amplifier.
- An upconverter to convert the signal to its UHF output channel.
- A power amplifier.
- An output combiner which also provides isolation between its inputs.

There are several hundred analogue transposer systems in use throughout the UK and digital versions are being developed. It will be necessary to ensure that any degradation of the digital signal quality is kept to an absolute minimum so as to maintain a reasonable window of operation at the domestic receiving sites.

Part Seven - Satellite TV Reception

Keywords

- Arthur C Clarke

- DTH Satellites

- Clarke Belt
- Geostationary Orbit

- Boresight

- Uplink
- Downlink

- Latitude
- Longitude

- WARC

- BSB

- Astra

7.1   Satellite Locations

In 1945, a scientist called Arthur C Clarke published an article in the UK journal "Wireless World", predicting that a satellite at a precise location over the equator would appear to be stationary and provide inexpensive communications over one third of the earth's surface.

All the "Direct to Home" (DTH) satellites are located over the equator at an altitude of some 36000km. in what is now known as the "Clarke Belt". They are in **"Geostationary Orbit"** which means that they orbit the earth at the same speed that it rotates (ie. once every 24 hours) so they appear to be stationary when viewed from the earth's surface.

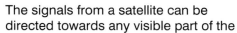

The signals from a satellite can be directed towards any visible part of the earth's surface, the centre of the beam being called the **boresight.** The beam can be concentrated on a specific area or spread out to cover many countries (obviously at lower power). Transmissions are **uplinked** to a satellite from one or more countries simultaneously in one frequency band, and **downlinked** to receivers in another frequency band. Some applications requiring two way communication can uplink and downlink simultaneously from the same site.

Orbital Positions

Because all the DTH satellites are over the equator, they are at 0° **latitude**. Their positions around the equator are defined in degrees of **longitude** east or west of the Greenwich meridian.

The longitudinal positions of the geostationary satellites around the equator are allocated by an international organisation known as the WARC. The official British location is located at 31°W over the Atlantic Ocean. This was the position of the original British Satellite Broadcasting (BSB) satellite, whose broadcasts terminated in 1990.

Some countries have more than one satellite at a single orbital location. The satellites are so far away from us that they all appear to be in the same position and a fixed dish antenna can receive them all. They are all located within a 130Km cube in space. Eventually, the propulsion fuel used to keep them in position will be exhausted and they will drift away into space and fall back to earth.

The majority of satellite dishes in the UK are aligned to receive digital transmissions from the **Astra** satellites that are located at 28.2°E over eastern Africa. This is one of the orbital positions assigned to Luxembourg. They can also receive transmissions from Eurobird at 28.5°E There is another group of Astra satellites located at 19.2°E.

Keywords

Eutelsat •

Satellite •
Footprints

Astra 28.2°E •

A further group of satellites are owned by a European operator called **Eutelsat**. These occupy a number of orbital "slots" including 48°E, 36°E, 28.5°E, 21.5°E, 16°E, 13°E, 10°E, 7°E, 8°W and 12.5°W.

7.2   Satellite Footprints and Frequency Bands

A map showing the terrestrial coverage area of a satellite is known as a **footprint.**
This shows the predicted power receivable, normally in dB with reference to 1 watt (dBW). The lines on the footprint indicate locations of equal received power. A footprint clearly illustrates that the received power reduces as the distance from the boresight increases. Some versions indicate the dish size required for satisfactory domestic reception, instead of the power.

The coverage of downlink antennas on board a satellite are often tailored to cover specific countries or land masses, to increase the signal strength in these areas at the expense of large areas of ocean where reception would not normally be required.

Some satellites have footprints which cover wide areas whilst others have narrower beams just to cover specific countries. It is even possible to have beams so narrow that the same frequencies can be used from one satellite to broadcast simultaneously to two different countries without any interference between them.

Various publications give the footprints of the geostationary satellites. It is also possible to obtain this information from websites on the internet, such as "satcodx".

Astra 28.2°E Footprint

At the time of publication, there are several satellites located at 28.2°E, called Astra 2A, 2B, 2C and 2D, relaying the Sky channels to Britain and northern Europe. Dishes aimed at this orbital location will receive signals from all four satellites.

This footprint is for the Astra 2A/2B southern beam and the contours show the dish size required to receive these Ku band transmissions in Europe.

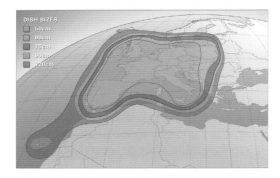

The next footprint shows the footprint of the <u>northern</u> beam in the Ku band from the same satellites:

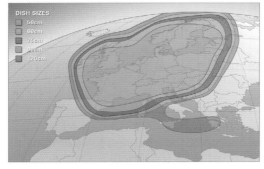

Keywords

This shows the southern beam from the Astra 2C satellite:

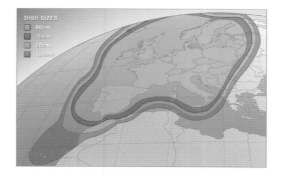

This is the northern beam from the Astra 2C satellite:

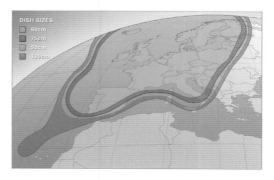

The Astra 2D satellite has more of a "spot" beam with the boresight centred on the United Kingdom:

Eutelsat also has a satellite at 28.5°E, which is receivable by the same Sky dishes – its footprint is shown alongside.

• Eutelsat 28.5°E

The contours of Eutelsat's footprints show lines of equal power in steps of 2dB. The relationship between satellite power and minimum dish size for normal domestic analogue TV reception is as follows:

• Power
• Dish Size

Power dBw	53	52	50	49	46	44
Dish Size (cm)	50	55	68	75	100	130

• FEC

This relationship also applies to digital multiplexes with a FEC of 3/4 (see part 2.7); smaller dishes can be used if more error correction is applied (for example, if the FEC is 2/3), as long as the dish is big enough to discriminate between satellites in adjacent orbital locations.

Keywords

Eutelsat 13°E •

Eutelsat 13°E Footprints

These footprints show the power in dBW from the "Hotbird" satellites.

Hotbird 6

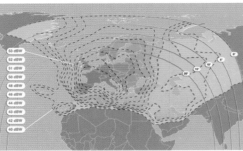

Hotbird 8

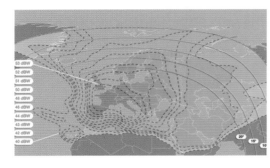

Hotbird 9

Satellite •
Frequency Bands

The Frequency Spectrum

The frequency bands used for DBS (Direct Broadcasting by Satellite) downlinks are as follows:

L Band •
S Band •
C Band •

- 1700 MHz   L band - the weather satellites use this band
- 2500 MHz   S band
- 3600-4300 MHz   C band – still used for some services

FSS Band •
DBS Band •
BSS Band •
Ka Band •

- 10700-11700 MHz   FSS (Fixed Satellite Service) band
- 11700-12500 MHz   DBS (Direct Broadcasting by Satellite) band
- 12500-12750 MHz   BSS (Business Satellite Services) or "Telecom" band
- 18800-30000 MHz   Ka band. For internet-style data transmissions – subject to degradation in abnormal weather conditions.

Ku Band •

The FSS, DBS and BSS bands (10700-12750 MHz) are collectively known as the "Ku" band. Since most UK and European installers are concerned with the reception of transmissions in this band, this publication is primarily concerned with Ku band reception, unless otherwise mentioned.

7.3   Dish Antennas

The satellites of most interest to European viewers transmit in the Ku band between 10.7 and 12.75 GHz so the wavelength is about 2.5cm. A half wave dipole would therefore be only 1.25cm long.

No one has ever produced a Yagi aerial of such dimensions for commercial use and it is much more practical to use a dish antenna to catch the signal and concentrate it at the **"focal point"** where a pick-up device receives the signal. Obviously, the bigger the dish antenna, the more signal it will catch, or the more gain it will have.

A satellite dish is **parabolic** in shape in order to focus the signals at one point. The surface contour must be accurate to within 3mm at Ku band frequencies, or it will not function correctly. A twisted or warped dish is useless and must be thrown away. Some dishes incorporate reinforcing webs to make them more rigid in high winds and most dishes have a reinforced outer rim.

A **feedhorn** at the focal point collects the received signals. This must be accurately positioned and have the right dimensions for the frequency band being received.

Dish Materials

Dishes can be manufactured from a variety of materials but must have a metallic surface to reflect the electromagnetic signals.

Metal dishes are either pressed or spun and can be manufactured in aluminium or steel. Non metallic dishes can be made using plastics or fibreglass and these incorporate a metallic coating (aluminium fret or similar) just below the surface.

Metal dishes can be solid or perforated (to improve their "aesthetic" impact on the environment) as long as the diameter of the perforations is small compared to the wavelength of the signal being received. Their electrical performance is similar although, in theory anyway, the feedhorn will look through the holes of a perforated dish into a relatively warm environment (compared with the very low temperatures of outer space) which could increase the thermal noise level, thereby degrading the overall system performance. Also, during rainstorms, the perforations can cause water droplets to adhere to the dish surface (instead of running off), causing a reduction in the received signal level.

A dish can be painted to minimise its visibility, as long as a non-metallic paint is used – avoid metal based paints such as "Hammerite". A light colour with a matt finish is recommended because the sun is located directly behind the satellite for part of the day during the time around the Spring and Autumn equinoxes – its heat could melt the feed horn at the focal point of the dish! Thermal interference from the sun also causes the electrical noise levels to increase at these times causing a degradation in the C/N ratio.

Dish Design

Dishes can be deep or shallow. The focal point is further away for a shallow dish so the acceptance angle of the "feedhorn" at the focal point is much less, thus simplifying the feedhorn design and making the positioning of the feedhorn during installation less critical. On the other hand, a deep dish will provide more protection against the pick up of extraneous terrestrial interference.

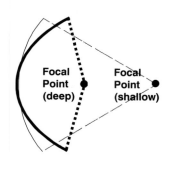

Focal Point (deep)   Focal Point (shallow)

Keywords

• Dish Antennas

• Focal Point

• Parabolic

• Feedhorn

• Dish Materials

• Dish Painting

• Dish Design

The distance of the focal point from the centre of the dish can be calculated using the formula

$$f = \frac{D^2}{16d}$$

Where D = overall dish diameter

d = depth of dish between rim and centre

Dish Types •

Types of Dish

Prime Focus •
Type

In concept, the simplest type of satellite dish antenna is the **prime focus type.**

The dish contour is a portion of a parabola and the dish points directly at the satellite being received.

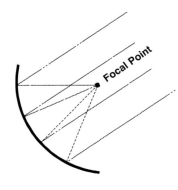

Many motorised systems utilise this type of dish. One drawback is that, if the dish is large (5 metres or more in diameter), the electronics at the focal point become relatively inaccessible.

Cassegrain •

This drawback can be overcome by using a modified prime focus design, called a **cassegrain** dish. A second (smaller) reflector is fitted to redirect the signal through a hole in the main dish to the focal point behind it, where the electronics are more accessible.
Most very large dishes (especially those used for uplinks) are of the cassegrain type. This design was also used for DTH applications by one European manufacturer (their 44cm dish was called a "Sweety") but this version is no longer offered in Britain. The drawback of small cassegrain dishes is that the second reflector is relatively large and, being in front of the main dish, it gets in the way and prevents the centre of the main dish from receiving signals.

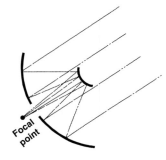

This same drawback applies to all types of prime focus dish. The physical size of anything placed in front of the reflector reduces its efficiency. This has lead to the introduction of other dish types that do not have this drawback. These utilise only a portion of the parabola (usually the top part) so that there is nothing in the way to block the incoming signal.

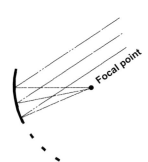

Keywords

• Offset

• Gregorian

• Torodial

• Dish Size

• Dish Location

This version is called an **offset** dish. If the dish size is increased so that its surface area is the same as it was before, its theoretical gain will be the same, but its actual gain will be greater because there is no blockage.

This is now the most popular dish type used for DTH applications throughout the world.

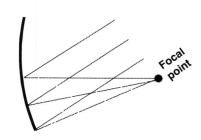

It is important to remember that an offset dish is not installed pointing towards the satellite (a mistake made by most unskilled installers). Those installed in Britain appear to be looking almost horizontally whereas they are actually receiving signals from a relatively steep vertical angle.

The drawback of an offset dish is that the boom arm (which supports the feedhorn at the focal point) is relatively long, especially for large dishes, which can make them top heavy. This can be overcome by using a version of the offset dish, called a **gregorian** dish, with a secondary reflector.

A gregorian dish retains all the advantages of the offset version and is a popular design for small motorised dishes in Britain and Europe. It is normally too expensive to be used for general DTH applications. a similar version known as a Toroidal dish, is sometimes used for multi-LNB applications, as described in section 7.8.

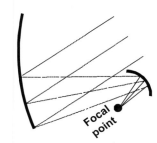

Dish Size

The dish must be big enough to provide sufficient signal. The size necessary depends on the power radiated from the satellite towards the receiving location. Most satellite programme providers specify the minimum dish size for various locations. This information is also available from computer programmes and from web sites on the internet. You can also calculate the dish size by performing a "link budget" calculation if you know the satellite power towards your location.

The dish must also be directional so that it does not receive signals from adjacent satellites in the same frequency band. The bigger the dish, the narrower its beamwidth becomes (and the more accurately it must be aligned). Ku band satellites are typically located 3° apart so a Ku band dish is designed to have a maximum beamwidth of +/- 1.5°. As a general guide, doubling the surface area of the dish (or increasing its diameter by about 40%) should increase its gain by about 2dB. A bigger dish can therefore be utilised for installations further away from the boresite to compensate for the reduction in transmitted power from the satellite as indicated on the footprint.

Dish Location

The dish must be positioned so that there is absolutely no blockage in the direction of the satellite. The signal just will not penetrate even the branches of a tree.

When deciding on the dish location, consider also the aesthetic aspects. It may be preferable to install the dish on the rear of the property looking over the roof than on the front wall. The dish need not necessarily be at roof height - there is no point in getting 5 metres closer to a satellite that is 36 000km away! On the other hand, it may need to be mounted high up to reduce the risk of vandalism or theft. Discuss the options with the customer to arrive at a mutually acceptable location for the dish.

Keywords

In Britain, the further away from due south, the lower the satellites appear to be in the sky and it is possible to receive transmissions from satellites over an arc 60°W to 60°E as long as there is no structure or obstacle in the way.

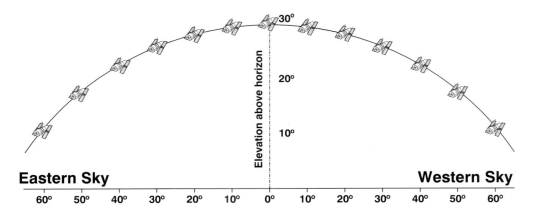

Elevation •
Azimuth •

It is necessary to know the **elevation** and **azimuth** of the required satellite(s) from the receiving site. This information can be obtained from the satellite operator, computer programmes or various web sites.

The elevation is its vertical angle above the horizon. On the equator, this could be 90° if the satellite is directly overhead. As the latitude of the reception site north of the equator increases, the elevation angle decreases, until a point is reached when the satellite is below the horizon, and satellite reception is not possible.

The azimuth is the bearing of the satellite from true south. This too depends on the location of the receiving site.

Inclinometer •
Plumb-bob •

This information can then be used to determine the position of the satellite in the sky, to ensure that there is no blockage. The elevation can be determined with an "inclinometer, or with a square of cardboard marked with the appropriate angles and fitted with "plumb-bob":

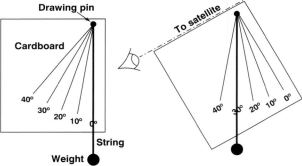

Compass •

The azimuth is measured using a compass, some versions of which have an integrated inclinometer as well. Alternatively, a "theodolite" can be used for both measurements. In all cases remember to

Magnetic •
Deviation

allow for the **magnetic deviation** between true north and magnetic north. Magnetic north is a few degrees west of true north and this deviation changes from year to year. Its value can be determined from an Ordnance Survey map of the local area.

Keywords

When using a compass, stand well away from any nearby metallic objects that could otherwise affect the compass reading.

7.4   Feedhorns and LNBs

Signals received from a satellite dish and collected by the feedhorn have the following characteristics:

- They are at a very high frequency
- They are very weak
- They are usually transmitted simultaneously in more than one mode of polarisation.

• Feedhorn

The frequencies involved (10,7 to 12,75GHz for Ku band signals) are so high that they cannot be relayed on coaxial cables at their incoming frequencies – the cable losses would be enormous. Instead, they are routed to the electronics using a waveguide. This is a circular metal tube through which the signal travels, bouncing off the inside walls. A feedhorn consists of a flared waveguide, the size of the flare being designed to receive signals from the whole of the metallic reflecting surface of the dish. These signals are then filtered, amplified and "block-converted" to a lower frequency band prior to being relayed via the coaxial cable to the satellite receiver.

• Waveguide

• Block-
conversion

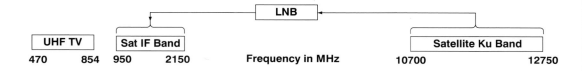

This lower band is called the satellite **intermediate frequency** (or "**IF**") band. Some means must also be provided to select the required polarity before the signal is converted to the IF band.

• Intermediate
Frequency (IF)

Some or all of these functions are carried out by a device known throughout the industry as a "**L**ow **N**oise **B**lock down converter, abbreviated "**LNB**".

• LNB

Types of Feed Horn

Whilst prime focus and cassegrain dishes are circular, the offset variants are not – being "a portion of a parabola", they are elliptical in shape. Feedhorns must therefore be designed with their waveguides shaped to receive signals from the appropriately shaped dish, and a prime focus feedhorn will not work efficiently on an offset dish. It is the combined performance of the dish and LNB (known as the G/T) that determines the overall performance of a satellite TV reception system.

The feedhorn should be positioned to receive signals from the whole of the dish face but not to look "outside" the dish. It is impossible to achieve an instantaneous cut off and dishes are designed for 100% reception over the 80% central dish area, with an "aperture edge taper" over the remaining 20%.

• Feedhorn
Design

Feedhorn acceptance angles can vary and it is important to use a dish and feedhorn/LNB as a "matched pair". It is <u>not</u> possible to move the feedhorn back and forth along the focal axis to "illuminate" the whole of the dish because the feedhorn would then no longer be at the focal point of the dish.

Keywords

LNB Location •

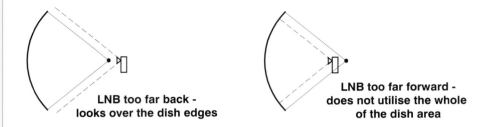

**LNB too far back -
looks over the dish edges**

**LNB too far forward -
does not utilise the whole
of the dish area**

Nearly all satellites transmit domestic programs using both horizontal and vertical polarisation.

Circular •
Polarisation

Dielectric •
Plate

A circular waveguide can relay both vertically and horizontally polarised signals simultaneously. Its diameter must be at least half the wavelength of the lowest frequency being received. It will also relay circularly polarised signals, which can be converted to linear (vertical and horizontal) polarisation using a "dielectric plate". The electromagnetic energy is extracted from the waveguide using a "probe". This is a finely tuned device of precisely the correct dimensions to deliver the electrical signal to the subsequent electronic circuits.

Voltage •
Switching LNB

The Voltage Switching LNB

This is an LNB with an integral feedhorn and two probes mounted at right angles, one for vertical and the other for horizontal reception. A switch inside the LNB selects the required polarisation.

Polarisation •
Selection

LNB •
Voltages

This switch is normally operated by changing the dc voltage supplied by the satellite receiver to the LNB via the coaxial cable. If the LNB is correctly orientated, 18V will select horizontal polarisation and 12V vertical polarisation. These voltages do not have to be exact and 15V is the changeover voltage – a higher or lower voltage will select horizontal or vertical polarisation respectively. The switching is normally carried out by devices known as pin diodes.

There will be a voltage drop on the coaxial cable due to its resistance. On occasions when this is excessive due to a long length of cable or, (more likely), poor connections, the receiver will be unable to select horizontally polarised channels because the 18V at the receiver will be less than 15V at the LNB.

Signals of the selected polarity are then amplified, filtered and converted to the lower IF band.

Block Down •
Conversion

Principles of Block Down Conversion

When two frequencies A and B are mixed together, it is possible to obtain not only A and B but also their sum and difference frequencies A+B and A-B. These are spread across the frequency spectrum and the lower frequency A-B can be separated from the others using a low pass filter.

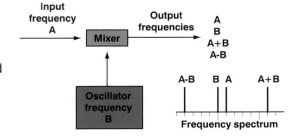

Keywords

- Local Oscillator Frequencies

- Frequencies Shifter

In practice, A is the incoming band of frequencies from the selected probe (either vertical or horizontal) and B is a single frequency generated inside the LNB by a local oscillator (usually a dielectric resonator). The output is therefore the whole of the incoming frequency band that has been dropped in frequency by the value of the local oscillator.

Local Oscillator Frequencies

The earliest Ku band LNBs used a local oscillator frequency of 10000MHz to convert part of the Ku band 10950-11700MHz to the IF band 950-1700MHz. This is why the original Ku band satellite receivers were designed with an input frequency band of 950-1700MHz.

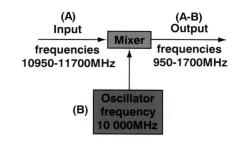

Another way of illustrating the process of block down conversion is shown in the drawing alongside. A signal level meter or spectrum analyser must be tuned to the incoming frequency less 10000MHz to measure the level of any incoming channel.

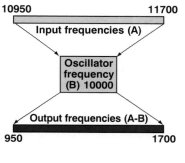

When transmissions commenced in the frequency band 10700-10950MHz, these LNBs converted the frequencies to the band 700-950MHz, but viewers were unable to access these channels because they were outside the tuning range of their satellite receivers.

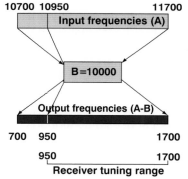

This problem was overcome by fitting a "frequency shifter" adjacent to the satellite receiver to move all the channels upwards by 500MHz. This works on the same principle, with a "B" frequency of 500MHz followed by a high pass filter to select the "A+B" frequency band. One problem with this is that all the incoming frequencies are shifted upwards, so the top frequencies are no longer within the receiver tuning range. This meant that the frequency shifter must be switched in or out of circuit, depending on which channels are required.

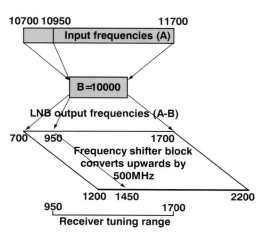

Keywords

Enhanced LNB •

Universal LNB •

22kHz Tone •
Switching

For new installations, an "enhanced" LNB was introduced, with a local oscillator frequency of 9750MHz and the receiver tuning range was extended upwards to cover the band 950-1950MHz. This eliminates the need for an external frequency shifter. If an original 10000MHz LNB is exchanged for an enhanced 9750MHz version, each programme on the satellite receiver must be retuned upwards by 250MHz.

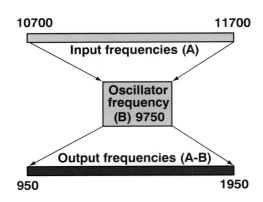

LNBs are now available with different oscillator frequencies, to convert the required satellite frequencies to the IF band covered by any satellite receiver.

The Universal LNB

A further extension of the Ku band to 10700-12750MHz led to the development of a universal LNB that incorporates two local oscillators, one for the lower frequencies and the other for the higher ones. At the same time, the satellite receiver tuning range was extended to 950-2150MHz. Such systems are now used almost exclusively to receive any analogue or digital broadcasts in the whole of the Ku band without the need for external frequency shifters.

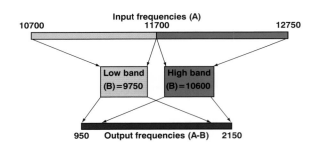

The local oscillators of a universal LNB are 9750MHz for the bottom part of the band (low band) and 10600MHz for the top part (high band). The LNB will operate on low band unless it senses a continuous frequency of 22000Hz (called a 22kHz tone) on its output connector, in which case it will switch to the high band oscillator. The 22kHz tone can be generated either internally from the satellite receiver (or spectrum analyser), or by an external 22kHz tone generator.

The diagram below illustrates how all the functions mentioned in this section are integrated into a universal LNB:

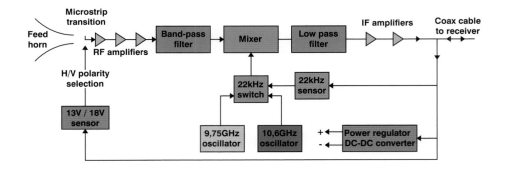

When using a spectrum analyser or level meter to measure the level of a specific channel or multiplex, the measurement frequency will be the incoming frequency less either 9750MHz or 10600MHz, depending on whether or not the 22kHz tone is present.

Keywords

LNB Gain and Noise Figure

An LNB incorporates amplifying stages both before and after the downconversion process, with a total gain of some 50-60dB. This is usually enough to compensate for the subsequent cable losses for up to 70m of coaxial cable, before further amplification is required.

The noise figure of an LNB gives an indication of the amount by which a signal will be degraded as the signal passes through it. The lower the noise figure, the better. The noise level is usually quoted as a noise figure in dB for Ku band LNBs and as a noise temperature in K for C band LNBs. The relationship between these two parameters is as follows:

Noise temp (K)	30	40	50	60	70	80	90	100
Noise figure (dB)	0.428	0.561	0.691	0.819	0.939	1.054	1.174	1.287

LNB noise figures have decreased dramatically over recent years and a modern universal LNB has a typical noise figure of 0.4-0.6dB. This can vary over the frequency band and will increase as the ambient temperature rises.

Skew Adjustment

When an LNB is orientated to its normal operating position, the application of 18V will produce horizontally polarised signals. Turning the LNB through 90° will change to vertical polarisation. At any point in between, a mixture of both polarisations will be produced – this can cause severe degradation of analogue pictures and total loss of digital signals.

It is therefore of vital importance that the LNB is rotated in its mounting clamp to maximise the "cross polar discrimination" – the ratio in dBs of the wanted polarisation to the unwanted one. This is best achieved using a spectrum analyser and rotating the LNB until the dip between adjacent carriers or multiplexes is as large as possible, or until signals on the unwanted polarity disappear completely.

System Performance

The overall performance of a satellite **TV** "**R**eceive-**O**nly" **(TVRO)** system is almost totally dependant on C/N ratio at the IF output of the LNB. This in turn depends on the quality of the dish, feedhorn and LNB, and how well they work together. Their combined overall performance is referred to as the G/T ratio or figure-of-merit, which should be as high as possible.

The diagram alongside shows the dramatic effect of C/N on the reliability of a digital TVRO system, where an improvement of just 2dB changes the number of errors from one per hour (quite acceptable) to one per minute (definitely not acceptable)!

The C/N ratio can be improved by either increasing the signal level or reducing the noise level, as discussed in the following sections.

Keywords

- LNB Noise Figure

- Noise Temperature

- Skew Adjustment

- Cross-Polar Discrimination

- TVRO

- G/T Ratio

Increasing Signal Levels

The most obvious way of improving the C/N ratio is to use a bigger dish. Doubling the dish size (say from 60cm to 1.2m) will increase the gain by more than 4dB, thus increasing the C/N ratio by the same amount. This is why bigger dishes are needed to receive signals from those satellites with beams directed towards other countries, the higher dish gain compensating for the reduced power levels from the satellite towards the receiving site.

It is also possible to increase the signal levels by using a dish with a higher efficiency. The more accurately the dish is shaped, the more signal it will collect. Professional dishes have reinforcing webs to ensure that their surface remains truly parabolic, even in the highest winds.

For a given dish size, it is worth checking the following points to ensure that it is working to its optimum efficiency:

- That there is no blockage in the direction of the satellite.
- That the dish is not warped in any way.
- That the dish is properly aligned towards the satellite. The beamwidth decreases as the dish size increases so this is even more important for bigger dishes. A 0.5° pointing error can reduce the system gain by 1dB.
- That the feedhorn matches the dish. Changing the make of feedhorn/LNB may improve the overall system performance.
- That the position of the feedhorn/LNB is correct. Try adjusting its position if the support assembly allows for this.

Decreasing Interference and Noise Levels

The overall noise performance of a reception system is determined by adding together the noise temperature of each of its components, the most important of which are as follows:

- Antenna noise temperature. Unlike terrestrial signals, satellite systems receive extremely low signals not far above the power of both galactic noise and microwave radiation from the warm earth that can be introduced via the dish side lobes. The lower the dish points towards the horizon, the more noise it will receive, so an offset dish can introduce more terrestrial noise than the equivalent prime focus version.

- Waveguide noise temperature. Any component in the system with a resistive loss will add to the thermal noise.
- LNB noise temperature. This is a key determinant of picture quality.

Typical noise figures are as follows:

Antenna noise temperature	=48K	
Waveguide noise temperature (0.5dB)	=35K	
LNB noise temperature (1.0dB)	=75K	
Total system noise	=158K	=22.0dBK

A 60cm dish that is 65% efficient has a typical gain of 35.8dB, so its G/T ratio is 35.8 − 22.0 = 13.8dBK.

The antenna noise temperature can be increased by strong interfering signals outside the satellite frequency band which cause overloading of the LNB input. Examples of such interference include:

- Microwave repeaters.
- Wideband repeaters.
- Telephone relay stations, including cellphone sites.

Keywords

- Transmissions in the video band.
- Vehicle interference.

In order to determine its point of entry into the system, the following need to be considered:

- Does it disappear when the dish is moved to another satellite?
- Can it be seen on the IF spectrum display?
- Is it on all channels?
- Is it on both polarities?

Possible solutions include the following:

- Use of a better IF cable, to provide more screening.
- Earthing the IF cable.
- Moving the dish to another location lower down, or shielded by buildings.
- Screening the dish and/or LNB.
- Use of an in-line filter (notch or bandpass) in the IF lead.
- Reducing the bandwidth of the receiver.
- Checking the LNB position.
- Using a better dish (greater surface accuracy results in smaller side lobes).
- Using a bigger dish (with a narrower main lobe).
- Using a deeper dish that gives more immunity to interference.
- Using an LNB with a different local oscillator frequency.
- Fitting an IF amplifier in the downlead, especially if the cable run is long.

The antenna noise temperature can also be degraded by interference from satellites. Always adjust the skew of an LNB to maximise its cross-polar discrimination. If there are transmissions on the same frequencies from neighbouring satellites, it may help to adjust the dish azimuth slightly for the lowest BER rather than maximum signal level.

Typical C/N Ratios

- Satellite C/N Ratios

For the reliable reception of satellite programmes under clear sky conditions, the minimum C/N ratio at the LNB output with the meter or spectrum analyser bandwidth set to 27MHz should be:

For analogue channels	15dB
For digital multiplexes	13dB for an FEC of 7/8
	12dB for an FEC of 3/4
	10dB for an FEC of 2/3
	7.5dB for an FEC of 1/2

In practice, the higher the C/N ratio, the more reliable the system will be.

Since it is not possible to switch off the satellite transmissions whilst the noise measurements are made, the noise is usually measured adjacent to the carrier or multiplex. These techniques are fully discussed in Part Nine of this publication. **Measurements must be made on several channels or multiplexes.**

Rain Degradation

- Rain Degradation

Rain will reduce the C/N ratio due to the following:

- An increase in attenuation due to scattering and absorption.
- An increase in noise power, the raindrops being considerably warmer than the background temperature of space.

- Depolarisation causing co-channel interference from the opposite polarity.

Using typical climatic statistics for Southern England, rain will degrade the C/N ratio as follows:

% of time	Hrs/year	Rain attn. (dB)	Decrease in G/T (dB)	Total rain degradation (dB)
1.0	87.6	1.0	1.4	2.5
0.6	52.6	1.2	1.5	2.7
0.3	52.6	1.4	1.7	3.1
0.28	22.8	1.5	1.8	3.3
0.23	20.2	1.7	1.9	3.6
0.15	13.1	2.0	2.1	4.1
0.11	11.4	2.1	2.2	4.4
0.09	7.9	2.4	2.4	4.8
0.07	6.1	2.8	2.6	5.4
0.06	5.3	3.4	2.9	6.3
0.02	1.8	4.6	3.3	7.9

7.5 Signal Measurements

It is important that the signal level at the receiver input is high enough to ensure that the noise introduced by the receiver does not significantly affect the overall C/N ratio, but low enough to ensure that the receiver is not overloaded. A poor C/N ratio results in black and white horizontal flecks called "sparklies" on analogue pictures accompanied by clicks on the sound and data errors in the teletext, and intermittent blocking or complete loss of picture on digital receivers.

The LNB has a gain of 50-60dB, which is usually high enough to compensate for losses of up to 70m of downlead cable plus an outlet plate and flylead. For longer lengths of cable, an in-line IF amplifier may be required. This is normally powered by the LNB voltage which is supplied by the satellite receiver.

The required satellite signal levels and C/N ratio at the receiver input under clear sky conditions are as follows:

	Analogue	Digital
Minimum signal level (dBμV)	52*	52*
Recommended signal level (dBμV)	60	60
Maximum signal level (dBμV)	77	77
C/N ratio for 27MHz bandwidth (dB)	15	12**

* In practice, the signal level can fall to 47dBμV as long as the minimum C/N ratio is achieved.
** For an FEC of 3/4 (see below); 2dB less for an FEC of 2/3.

Satellite Bit Error Ratio (BER)

As with terrestrial TV, the overall performance of a satellite TVRO system is determined by the number of errors reaching the digital receiver and whether the receiver can cope with them. This is dependant on two main factors:

Keywords

• FEC

• Error Correction

• Satellite
  Receivers

• QPSK

• CAM

- The C/N ratio at the receiver input.
- The amount of error correction contained in the received signal ie. the FEC parameters.

Broadcasters use different amounts of error correction. For instance, BSkyB have chosen an FEC of 2/3 (two thirds of the signal is data and one third error correction) to enable smaller dishes to be used with a consequent reduction in C/N ratio. Eutelsat tend to use an FEC of 3/4 so there is more room for data in each multiplex (ie. more programmes) although bigger dishes are required.

Most digital satellite receivers have a display of signal quality that gives an indication of the BER after Viterbi. As a general guide, satellite receivers can operate satisfactorily if the BER before error correction is equal to, or better than, 2E-4 (2 errors in every 10000 bits of data) for a 27MHz bandwidth and an FEC of 3/4. The locations for BER measurements are described more fully in section 9.3.

7.6   Satellite Receivers

A digital satellite receiver performs the following basic functions:
- Channel decoding ie. demodulation of the **QPSK** signal and error correction.
- Demultiplexing
- The selection of programmes under the control of the **C**onditional **A**ccess **M**odule **(CAM)**.
- Removal of the MPEG2 compression to produce an analogue video signal.
- Remodulation on to a UHF carrier frequency.
- Interfacing with the return path via a modem, PC or telephone line.

All these functions are under the control of a microprocessor which is linked to the various components using data and address buses. The following schematic illustrates how the various items are interlinked in a typical digital receiver:

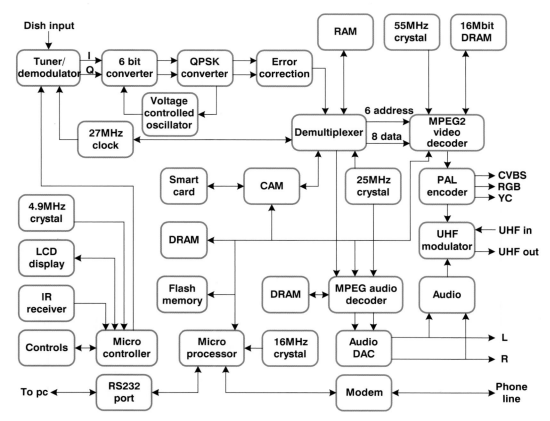

Keywords

Conditional •
Access
Multicrypt •

Simulcrypt •

BSkyB •
Installations
Freesat •
Installations

Sky Plus •
PVR •

Sky Dish •
Sizes

The receiver operating software can be upgraded by the broadcaster as new techniques are developed. For this reason, it is advisable to leave a digital satellite receiver connected to the dish and mains power at all times.

Conditional Access

For digital signals, the DVB Project Group has defined a common scrambling system, called **multicrypt**, for use via a common interface with various types of conditional access **(CA)** system. The **C**onditional **A**ccess **M**odule **(CAM)** is normally of the plug-in type, designed to accept a standard 68 way PC card. The specification allows for CAM modules to be "daisy chained" if required, so that a single digital receiver can handle more than one bouquet of programmes.

In the alternative **simulcrypt** system, some of the functionality necessary to de-encrypt services is built into the receiver itself, either as hardware or software or a mixture of both. In this case, if a viewer wishes to receive additional services from another broadcaster, it may be necessary to purchase another receiver.

7.7   BSkyB and "Freesat" Installations

BSkyB and Freesat broadcast from the Astra/Eurobird satellites located at 28.2°E and 28.5°E longitude over The Democratic Republic of Congo in Central Africa. They both use the same satellite transmissions and each service has its own programme guide. Most Freesat receivers do not have a card slot, since viewing cards are not required. BSkyB receivers have an "interactive" slot for a viewing card – Sky use the **Videoguard** encryption system and it is necessary to subscribe in order to view many of the programmes. Sky also offer many interactive services, for which a telephone connection is required.

The various makes of BSkyB receiver all use the same handset and operating software. It is advisable to leave a Sky receiver connected to the mains power at all times, since the software operating system is regularly updated (usually during the night).

The **"Sky Plus"** receiver has an integral **P**ersonal **V**ideo **R**ecorder **(PVR)** and two tuners, so that two programmes can be recorded simultaneously if two independent dish feeds are available. Freesat receivers are also available with integral PVRs. High definition receivers are also available for both the Sky and Freesat services.

Dish Size and Location

The smallest dish size in common use in England is 45cm. This is used to receive programmes from the Astra/ Eurobird satellites and is known as a "Zone 1" dish. It is actually eliptical in shape (38cm high and 53cm wide) to give a narrower beamwidth in the horizontal plane. Larger "Zone 2" 65cm dishes (58 x 72cm) are used to receive the same signals in the north of Scotland and on the west coast of Ireland where the signal is weaker.

Keywords

• Aesthetic Consideration

• Dish Camouflage

Consider the impact on the appearance of the building by sitting the dish so that it is as unobtrusive as possible.

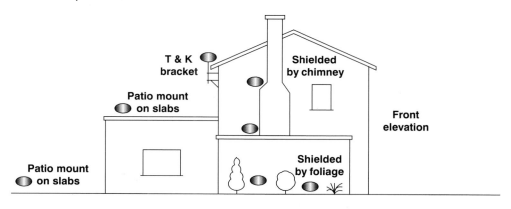

This dish is so well camouflaged that it is difficult to spot!

On the other hand you might want to paint your dish so that it will be noticed!!!

Keywords

The dish **must** be located so that there is no blockage in the direction of the satellites. Check with a compass and inclinometer, using the following angles:

Sky Azimuth •
Elevation

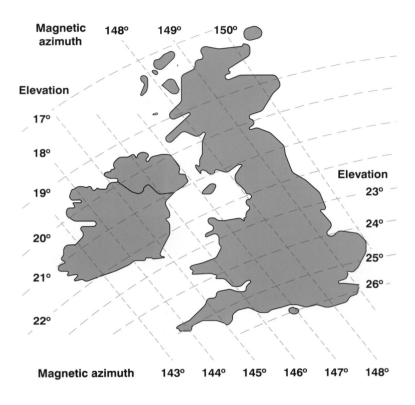

Installation Procedure

The following initial checks should be carried out before the work is started:

- Check that the customer has a BSkyB viewing card (if required).
- Agree the location of the dish antenna with the customer.
- Conduct a risk assessment for each aspect of the installation.
- Check the phone line (dial 17070 to initiate a call-back).
- Ask the customer to demonstrate that the TV receiver and VCR are fully operational, and to remove ornaments on or near to the TV.
- Agree the method of connection to the VCR and TV receiver, and the channel numbers on each for the satellite programme.

Phone Line •
Check

Sky Installation •
Sequence

The normal sequence for the installation of the dish antenna is as follows:

1. Assemble the dish and wall bracket, checking that the dish face is not twisted or warped. Ensure that the boom arm is fully engaged at the dish end, otherwise the LNB position will not be correct.
2. Mark the position of the four wall bracket fixing holes on the bricks using a spirit level and indelible marker pen. Try to choose a position where the wall surface is flat (ie. where one brick does not protrude from the wall, otherwise the bracket will not sit flat on the wall), and the holes will not be near the edge of a brick.
3. Drill the four holes using a 10mm SDS masonry bit with piece of insulation tape wound around the shank of the bit to indicate the required hole depth.
4. Insert the wall plugs so they are flush with the face of the bricks and fit the wall bracket using a ratchet spanner or 13mm socket, checking the tightness of each coach screw with a ring spanner. Do **not** hammer the coach screws into the wall plugs.
5. Mount the dish assembly on to the wall bracket and tighten the nuts on the dish bracket with a 10mm ratchet spanner just enough so that the dish can be moved easily

Keywords

in both the horizontal and vertical directions but does not move when released. Set the initial elevation using the scale on the side of the dish bracket according to the location as shown in the diagram on the previous page.

6. Connect the meter to the LNB using a push-on F connector and align the dish for optimum azimuth, elevation and skew, as described in the next section.
7. Fully tighten the 10mm nuts then check again that the dish is still at its optimum settings.
8. Fix the coaxial cable to the boom arm, fit an F connector and connect to the LNB, leaving a drip loop so that water will run away from the connector.
9. Tighten the F connector with a spanner and seal using self-amalgamating tape stretched to half its width. F connectors should preferably be of the crimp type.
10. Fix the coaxial cable to the arm of the wall bracket using cable ties, leaving a small service loop, and complete the cable run to the receiver.

Dish Alignment

The dish <u>must</u> be accurately aligned in both the horizontal plane (azimuth) and vertical plane (elevation). Do not point an offset dish directly towards the satellites - its elevation in the UK is just above horizontal.

• Sky Dish Alignment

Most UK installers use a basic satellite level meter for this purpose, in which case the procedure is as follows:

- Tighten the azimuth and elevation dish fixings just enough so that the dish can be easily moved left-right and up-down, but tight enough so that it stays in position.
- Rotate the dish so that the spirit level bubble is in the centre of its display and fully tighten the rotational adjustment fixings (but see the note below).
- Point the dish in the horizontal plane towards the satellite (using a compass to find the approximate bearing) and pointing slightly upwards.
- Connect the meter to the LNB using a push-on F connector.
- Switch the meter on and obtain the display "searching 28.2°" or "searching Astra 28".
- Move the dish gently in the horizontal plane (and then in the vertical plane if necessary) until the display changes to "satellite found".
- Continue to move the dish in both planes to maximise the signal and quality bars on the display. If the meter also displays the BER, these adjustments should be made to minimise the number of received errors.
- Fully tighten all the dish fixings, checking that the meter reading has not diminished.

• Sky Skew Adjustment

• Sky Meter Display

Note: The Astra satellites broadcast with 7.5° of clockwise skew when viewed from London. This is why LNBs are orientated slightly clockwise with respect to the vertical plane (to match the orientation of the satellites). When viewed from locations that are significantly to the east or west of London, the satellite will no longer be perpendicular to the satellites' transmissions, and the LNB must therefore be rotated or "skewed" to compensate for this.

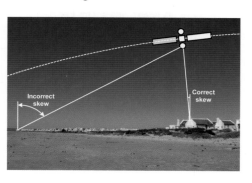

Keywords

Sky Skew • Adjustment

The LNBs on Sky dishes can be rotated and have 5 "click" positions – they are supplied preset to position 3 which is correct for most locations in England. For installations at the extreme east or west of the UK, the LNB must be rotated to positions 2 or 4, as shown on the accompanying diagram.

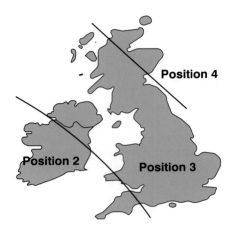

Position 4

Position 2

Position 3

The absolute reading of the vertical and horizontal quality display on the signal level meter will depend on both the accuracy of dish alignment and the prevailing weather conditions, being lower when the sky is overcast or during rainfall.

More experienced installers prefer to use a spectrum analyser for dish alignment. If the analyser can display the bit error ratio, final adjustments to the dish using the BER display will ensure that the optimum alignment is achieved. These techniques are more fully explained elsewhere in this publication.

Sky Receiver • Installation

Receiver Installation

The receiver should be connected via the VCR to the TV receiver using the UHF connectors:

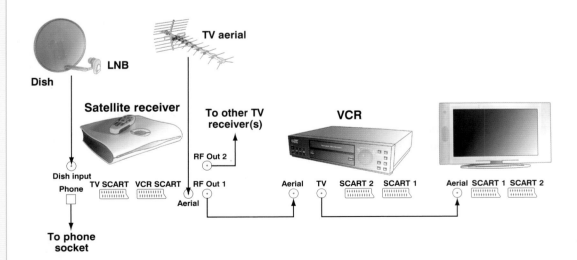

Keywords

If either the VCR or TV receiver has unused SCART sockets, the use of SCART leads in addition to the UHF connections will provide better picture quality:

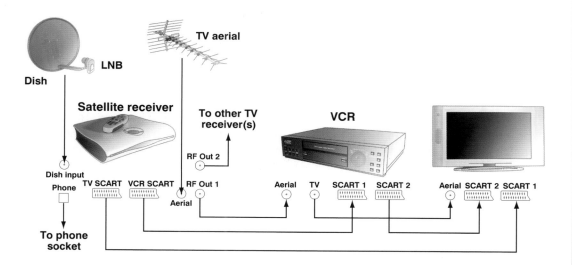

• Sky SCART Connections

For High Definition installations, HDMI leads must always be used to link the receiver to the HD display.

• Sky HD

The default UHF channel on a Sky receiver is channel 68. It is necessary to change this only if there is interference on the UHF satellite picture on any other UHF channel or on a digital picture when the satellite receiver is connected. Select a suitable unused UHF channel and set the sky receiver output channel accordingly. This should not be one channel above a used channel because the sky modulator cause interference one channel below its UHF output channel. Then tune both the VCR and TV receiver until satisfactory pictures are obtained. Use the receiver menus to set the picture, sound and phone settings to their appropriate parameters.

• Sky UHF Output

The next step is to ensure that the Sky receiver has the latest software operating system by carrying out a forced software download. Remove the mains power lead from the wall socket and reconnect it whilst holding in the "back up" button on the front of the digibox – <u>do not release the back up button for at least 30 seconds</u> or until the software download caption appears on the screen (SCART connection only) or the Standby/Message/Online indicators are illuminated. The downloading process will then take up to ten minutes to complete, after which the caption will disappear and the indicators will be extinguished.

• Software Download

The receiver must be connected to a telephone line using the connections detailed in part 11.2. A BSkyB receiver only makes outgoing calls (it does not receive incoming calls), it is only essential to connect the blue pair of wires. However, in is good practice to connect the orange pair as well, in case the customer ever connects a conventional phone handset into the new socket to make and receive telephone calls. Ensure that the connection of a sky receiver does not overload the telephone line - this is described in detail in section 11.2. The viewing card must then be activated if the customer wishes to view the encrypted channels. This is normally an automatic process with no human intervention. The BSkyB telephone recognises the subscriber's calling number and sends an activation signal via the satellite to programme the card.

• Sky Telephone Connection

• Sky Card Activation

It is then necessary to programme the handset to operate the TV receiver whenever the "TV" button is pressed. This information is stored in the handset but will be lost if the handset batteries are removed for more than ten minutes. The programming process is as follows:

• Sky Handset Programming

Keywords

1. Press TV on the Sky handset.
2. Hold down the select and red buttons together for about two seconds, until the red light on the Sky handset blinks twice.
3. Press TV on the Sky handset again.
4. Key in the four digit code for the brand of TV receiver (obtainable from the receiver handbook). The red light on the handset should blink twice (If it blinks once, recheck the code for the brand of TV and start again at step 1).
5. Press the power switch on the Sky handset.
6. If the TV switches off, press select. The red light on the handset blinks twice indicating that the IR code has been stored.
7. If the TV did not switch off, press TV then the power switch on the handset. Repeat this (press TV then the power switch) until the TV turns off (indicating that the correct code has been identified) then press select (to store the IR code). This process enables the handset to step through all the codes stored for a particular brand of TV receiver.
8. If at this point the red light blinks three times, all possible codes for that brand of receiver have been checked.
9. The first code activated to control the TV may not be correct ie. no text available on terrestrial TV. In this case, repeat the above steps bypassing the first code until the correct code is selected.
10. Turn the TV on again and press TV guide. If the TV guide appears on the screen, the set up process is complete.

It is also possible to make the TV switch to the appropriate UHF channel for satellite programmes whenever any of the Sky guide buttons on the handset are pressed:

1. Press TV on the Sky handset.
2. Hold down the select and green buttons together for about two seconds, until the red light on the Sky handset blinks twice.
3. Key in the number of the channel on the TV that will be used for watching satellite TV.
4. Press select on the Sky handset. The red light on the handset blinks twice, indicating that the set up process is complete.

Sky Interactive •
Services

Interactive Services

These include the following:

Home Shopping	Viewers can order products (including food) and pay for them by credit or debit card.
Home Banking	It is possible (by prior arrangement) to view bank statements, pay bills and set up direct debits or money transfers.
Games	These vary from simple games for children to trivia quizzes and knowledge tests for all ages, some with amazing graphics.
Information	Viewers can check such things as the weather forecast, ski conditions, resort and hotel enquiries and films showing at their local cinema.
E Mail	These can be sent to, or received from, any internet address without subscription, although call charges are levied.

On-line Gaming

Sky Telephone •
Charges

These services utilise the telephone connection – phone charges are only incurred when the telephone icon is visible on the bottom of the screen. The icon flashes when the digibox is attempting to connect and steady when the connection is established. If left idle, the digibox will disconnect from the phone line after approximately five minutes.

A black icon indicates a free call

A green icon indicates a local rate call

A red icon indicates a premium rate call.

Keywords

• Sky Handing Over

• TV/Satellite Diplexers

• Satellite Troubleshooting

Handing over to the Customer

Whilst the day-to-day operation of a digibox is straightforward, a demonstration of the following features will enable the viewer to get the most out of their system:
• Switching on and off but not disconnecting the mains power.
• The various ways of selecting programmes.
• Choosing and selecting favourite channels.
• Setting viewing restrictions.
• Changing the system set up parameters.
• The availability of the help guide and channel 998.
• How to upgrade their subscription.
• Where to find useful telephone numbers.
• What to do in the event of a problem.

TV/Satellite Diplexers

It is possible to use the existing TV aerial downlead for the satellite feed as well if the coaxial cable is of a high enough quality as long the outlet plate is not isolated and there are no splitters in circuit. This would be advantageous in situations when it would be difficult to install an additional coaxial cable.

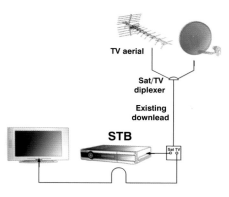

It is important that proper TV/satellite diplexers are used to combine the signals at the sending end and split them apart at the receiving end, otherwise the noise introduced by the satellite signal could degrade the terrestrial TV picture quality.

Trouble Shooting

Some of the problems and their possible solutions are listed in the attached table. The most common problems are:

• Box locking up
• Blockage from trees
• F connectors loose
• Faulty LNBs
• Telephone line disconnected.

The coaxial cable can also cause problems – check the following:

• It is not of inferior quality
• It is not damaged or terminated with improperly fitted connectors, allowing water ingress
• It is not crushed or twisted
• The bends are not too tight, causing kinking
• Cable length too great (in which case, fit an use a lower loss cable or fit an IF line amplifier).

Keywords

Problem	Possible Cause	Action to be taken
No response to handset commands	Box locked up	Remove/replace mains plug
	Handset batteries flat	Replace batteries
Constant "searching for listings" display	Software corrupted	Forced software download
	Poor signal reception	Check signal input to receiver
Receiver stays in "standby" (won't switch on)	Software corrupted	Forced software download
	Faulty receiver	Replace receiver
Intermittent blocky or frozen pictures	Poor signal reception	Check for signal blockage
	Faulty LNB	Change LNB
	Loose connectors	Tighten connectors
	Cable problem	Check cable
	Faulty receiver	Replace receiver
"No satellite signal is being received"	Loss of signal from dish	Check signal input to receiver
	LNB power switched off	Switch on LNB power using installer's menu (LNB set-up)
	Faulty receiver	Replace receiver
Constant frozen pictures	Loss of signal from dish	Check signal I/P to receiver
	Faulty receiver	Replace receiver
Some channels missing	Loss of horizontal channels	Excessive cable loss
	22KHz tone has no effect	Change LNB
		Change LNB and/or receiver
Interference on terrestrial TV channels	Incorrect receiver UHF channel	Change receiver UHF channel
	Faulty receiver	Replace receiver
Can't select terrestrial TV channels whilst recording satellite programme	SCART control switched on	Switch SCART control to "off" on picture settings menu
Distorted satellite picture or wrong colours	TV receiver does not have RGB input	Switch video output to "PAL" on picture settings menu
No interactive services	No phone connection	Check phone line using system test menu

7.8   Multi-Satellite Reception

Coverage

It is possible to receive signals from satellites over an arc of about 120° from 5° above east horizon to 5° above west horizon, assuming that there are no obstructions in the way to block the signal, and that the transmitted power towards the reception site is strong enough.

The following table lists some of the Ku band satellites receivable in the United Kingdom, together with the programme languages and typical dish sizes for digital reception in southern and northern Britain:

LONGITUDE	SATELLITE	SOUTH (cm)	NORTH (cm)	ARABIC	ARMENIAN	AUSTRIAN/SWISS	BENGALI	BULGARIAN	CROAT/KURDISH	CZECH	DANISH/SWEDISH	DUTCH	ENGLISH	FARSI	FINLAND	FRENCH	GERMAN	GREEK	HINDI/PUNJABI	HUNGARIAN	ITALIAN	JAPANESE	KOREAN	LEBANESE	MACEDONIAN	MANDARIN	MANDARIN/CHINESE	MOROCCAN/TUNISIAN	NORWEGIAN	POLISH	PORTUGESE	ROMANIAN	RUSSIAN	SERBIAN	SLOVAKIAN	SLOVENIAN	SPANISH	TAMIL	THAI	TURKISH
48E	EUTELSAT 2F1	150	150																		C																				
42E	TURKSAT 1C	80	120																																						O
36E	SEASAT	70	90							C											C											C									
28.5E	EUTELSAT 2F4	80	100							X	C						C																								
28.5E	KOPERNIKUS F2	90	120							X																															
28.2E	ASTRA2A/2B/1D	45	60				O					C,O					O																								
26E	ARABSAT2A/3A	100	120	C																																					
23.5E	KOPERNIKUS 3	120	150													I,I,I																	I,I								I
19.2E	ASTRA1E/1F/1G	60	80	C	C				X		I,M,X		C,V,I,C,X			M,V,I,V	X,C							O,C					C,C,X	M,V							M,C			I
16E	EUTELSAT W2	70	70						C		C,Y					M					C,P							O,C,C,C											
13E	HOTBIRD 1-5	70	70	P,C,V	C,V	V,M		V,P		P,X,V,P,V,I,C,M		V,I,I,X,C,P,Y,X,C,P,K,M,X,V,M			X,V,C,C,P,Y,V,C,C,C,I,M,Y	C,I	V			M,V,C,M,C,V,C,P,X,C,P,N					O,C,C,P,M					V,C,V,C,P,M								
10E	EUTELSAT W1	70	70								C					P								V					C									C,P,O
7E	EUTELSAT W3	70	70								C					C,C					C								C,C									O
5E	SIRIUS 2-3	120	120							V,K	V,P,X						K	P						V					V,C,C							V			
1W	THOR/INTELSAT	120	150				K		K	K	K,K																K			K										
5W	TELECOM 2B	60	70							C			M,X																										
7W	NILESAT101/102	150	300	C,I					C	C,C	I				I	C																							
8W	TELECOM 2D	60	80			C				C																												C
12.5W	EUTELSAT 2F2	100	150																									C										
15W	TELSTAR 12	90	90							C,P							C																					
18W	INTELSAT 705	120	250							P																							V					
27.5W	INTELSAT 605	150	150						P	P																											
30W	HISPASAT1A-1B	100	180							N																								N			
37.5W	TELSTAR 2	80	100							P																											
43W	PAS 3R	90	100							C																								C			

C = Clear	**I** = Irdeto	**M** = Mediaguard	**O** = Other	**V** = Viaccess
X = Cryptoworks	**K** = Conax	**N** = Nagravision	**P** = Powervu	**Y** = Videoguard

Some of the transmissions marked "C" are free-to-air and can be viewed without payment. Others require a "**C**onditional **A**ccess **M**odule" **(CAM)** and a viewing card, for which a monthly subscription is payable. Receivers can be free-to-air only, with embedded CAMs for a single service, or with one or more slots into which a CAM is inserted (the card is then inserted into the appropriate CAM).

Keywords

- Multi-Satellite Reception

- Programme Languages

- Encryption Types

- CAM

Keywords

Reception Equipment

Ku band analogue dishes are suitable for digital reception as well. Most smaller fixed dishes are of the offset type using a universal LNB with an integral feedhorn. The difference between the elevation of the satellite and the elevation of the dish face above horizontal is called the offset angle. Offset angles for typical dishes used in the UK are as follows:

Offset Angles •

Channelmaster		22.6°
Lenson Heath	1M steel	26.0°
Most others		22.5°
Televes		26.5°
Triax		26.0°

Prime Focus •
Dishes

Dishes bigger than 1.8M tend to be of the prime focus type for several reasons:

- Because they are directed towards the sky, they tend to pick up less ground noise.
- Being relatively large, the signal blockage introduced by the feedhorn is less significant.
- The centre of gravity is closer to the mounting pole, making them more stable.
- An offset dish of the same size would need very long feedhorn arms, thus increasing the design complexity.

C120 Flange •

Prime focus dishes are usually supplied with a matching feedhorn that incorporates "scalar rings" (to optimise the combined dish/feedhorn performance) and a circular waveguide with a standard "C120" flange. It would not be advisable to use a standard domestic universal LNB because its feedhorn would not "illuminate" the dish properly. Versions of the universal LNB are now available with a matching C120 flange in place of the feedhorn, and these are ideal if the receiver can provide voltage switching to select the required polarity.

WR75 Waveguide •

Some types of LNB use voltage switching (instead of a 22KHz tone) to select the local oscillator, the polarity being selected by other means. These LNBs have a rectangular waveguide to "WR75" standards that supports only one polarity, across its narrowest dimension. The circular C120 and rectangular WR75 waveguides must be matched using one of the following interfaces:

- A C120-WR75 adaptor (in which case only one polarity can be received).
- A C120-WR75 dual orthomode transducer (OMT) – in effect a two way waveguide splitter feeding two separate LNBs – giving both polarities on separate coaxial cables simultaneously (this can give much better cross-polar discrimination than a single universal LNB).
- A C120-WR75 "polarotor" to select either polarity – this is explained in part 7.9.

Polarotor •

Circular Polarisation

Circular •
Polarisation

It is also possible to receive circularly polarised signals. Instead of being just horizontal or vertical, the signal follows a helical or screw-like path, rotating in either a clockwise or anticlockwise direction, called right handed or left handed circular polarisation (RHCP or LHCP). The principle advantage of circular polarisation is that there is no need for a skew adjustment.

RHCP •
LHCP •

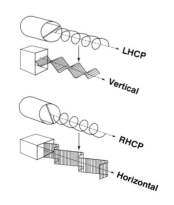

Dielectric Plate •

Circularly polarised signals can be converted to linear polarisation by fitting a "dielectric plate" in the throat of the feedhorn – this introduces a loss of up to 3dB and 1dB for

Keywords

the circular and linear signals respectively, and can severely degrade the discrimination between horizontal and vertical signals.

Reception of Other Satellite Bands

Other countries, particularly Russia and the USA, use the C band for some satellite transmissions. It is possible to receive some of these signals in Europe although the older satellites are now in "inclined orbit" and are no longer geostationary – they have to be tracked with a motorised dish moving in both the horizontal and vertical planes.

• C Band

The wavelength of a Ku band signal is approximately 2.5cm. The dimensions of a waveguide must be at least half a wavelength and are 1.905 x 0.953cm for a WR75 rectangular flange, passing the polarity across its narrowest dimension and rejecting the opposite polarity. Signals in C band are only one third of the Ku band frequencies (3.6-4.3GHz) so the wavelength is three times as long and the waveguide must therefore be three times as large. C band feedhorns are therefore  much bigger than their Ku band counterparts, as can be seen from the photograph alongside. A rectangular C band waveguide has dimensions of 5.817 x 2.908cm.

C band dishes do not need as accurate a profile so most are built to less exacting standards and do not normally perform well in the Ku band. However, a Ku band dish is perfectly adequate for C band reception as long as the bigger feedhorn does not cause too much blockage.

Of course, different feedhorns and LNBs are required for C band reception. C band LNBs have their local oscillator above the incoming frequency (as opposed to Ku band LNBs where the oscillator is below), with the result that the analogue video output of the receiver is inverted. The same receiver can be used for both bands if it has a switchable "video inversion" option on the set-up menu.

• Video Inversion

It is possible to obtain a single feedhorn with separate Ku and C band feedhorns mounted concentrically and each connected to its own LNB. This is known as a "corotor". The whole assembly is relatively large and can only be used on bigger dishes of the prime focus type.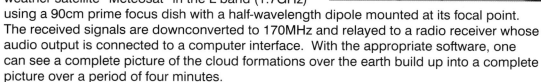

• Corotor

It is also possible to receive transmissions from the weather satellite "Meteosat" in the L band (1.7GHz) using a 90cm prime focus dish with a half-wavelength dipole mounted at its focal point. The received signals are downconverted to 170MHz and relayed to a radio receiver whose audio output is connected to a computer interface. With the appropriate software, one can see a complete picture of the cloud formations over the earth build up into a complete picture over a period of four minutes.

• Meteosat

Storing Digital Satellite Channels

Most digital satellite receivers are sold without the programmes preloaded.

A digital receiver will automatically search for TV and radio channels if the dish is aimed at a satellite whose data is included in the receiver's memory. The search procedure will take a few minutes and the names of all the programmes found will appear on the screen.

Keywords

Satellite Search •
Parameters

It is possible to instruct the receiver to search for other multiplexes, in which case the following parameters must be entered:

- Transponder frequency
- Polarization
- Symbol rate
- FEC

All the channels will then be loaded separately for each multiplex found, as long as the number of received errors is acceptable.

A more advanced search for an individual programme can sometimes be successful when the above procedure fails to download the required multiplex. It is necessary to enter some or all of the following additional data:

PID •
SCPC •
PID PCR •

- PID (Package Identification Data) video and audio codes - these are 4 character hexadecimal numbers to distinguish between SCPC signals that are close together
- PID PCR (Programme Clock Reference) sometimes called PID 4.

The Internet is a useful source for all this information!

The BSkyB digibox can be loaded with multiplexes from satellites at other orbital locations when the appropriate dish and LNB are connected (usually via a changeover switch). Limiting factors are as follows:

- There are only two symbol rate options, 22000 and 27500MHz.
- A maximum of 50 additional programmes may be loaded.
- These additional channels may not be accessed via the EPG.

Receiver Connections

Satellite •
Receiver
Connections

If two receivers are to be connected to a single LNB (eg. one analogue and one digital), possible options include:

- Using an A/B mechanical selector switch.
- Using a "priority switch". One receiver would normally control the LNB; If power to this receiver is removed, the switch would revert to the second receiver.

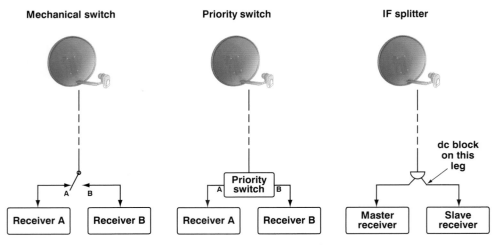

- Using a two way IF splitter. Both receivers can be used simultaneously. One leg of the splitter is normally DC blocked and the receiver connected to this leg would not be able to control the LNB.

Multiple LNB Installations

Local planning regulations in the UK prohibit the use of more than one satellite dish on a single domestic dwelling unless planning permission is obtained. However, it is possible to receive signals from satellites at two different orbital positions at the same time using one dish, by mounting two LNBs side by side.

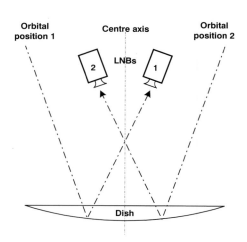

A standard dish is designed for the LNB to be located at its focal point, and its overall performance will be reduced if the LNB is moved sideways. The more that the LNB is mounted away from its centre axis, the more pronounced the loss will be. This loss will typically be 1dB if the LNB is moved 6° off its centre axis.

A typical application would be to receive digital transmissions from Astra at 28°E and Hotbird at 13°E. Some of the Eutelsat transmissions are weaker in Britain, therefore Eutelsat LNB is usually mounted on the centre axis at the focal point with the Astra LNB offset to one side on an adjustable supporting arm. It is not possible to use this technique on small domestic dishes for satellites in adjacent orbital locations (eg. 13°E and 16°E) because the LNBs are physically too large.

The LNB receiving signals from the satellite at the lower elevation must be higher than the other LNB. This effect becomes more pronounced as the orbital spacing between the satellites increases and the picture alongside shows the relatively large difference in the height of three LNBs to receive transmissions from 13°E, 19°E and 28°E on a single 90cm dish.

A Toroidal dish is available in 55cm and 90cm versions that can accommodate up to six LNBs over an arc stretching from 1°W to 28°E.

LNB Switching

A separate coaxial downlead must be installed for each LNB if a separate satellite receiver is to be used for each orbital location. However, several types of switching systems are available if two LNBs are to be connected to a single receiver. These are normally installed at the dish location to reduce the number of downleads:

Keywords

- Multiple LNB Installations

- Torodial

- LNB Switching

Keywords

Power breaker – the switch toggles between the two LNBs whenever the LNB voltage is interrupted.

60Hz tone – the appropriate LNB is selected depending on whether or not a 60Hz tone is present, this tone being generated by a stand-alone generator with an on/off switch (controlled by pin 8 of a SCART plug).

Continuous 22kHz tone – the switch selects the LNB according to whether or not a 22kHz tone is present. This concept cannot be used with universal LNBs since the 22kHz tone is already used to select the LNB oscillator frequency. A stand-alone 22kHz generator can be used if the receiver does not have a 22kHz facility.

Modulated 22kHz tone – known as "simple DiSEqC" or "mini DiSEqC".

DiSEqC •

DiSEqC

"**D**igital **S**atellite **E**quipment **C**ontrol" (**DiSEqC**) is an extension of the 22kHz concept to provide control of multiple devices. Receiver manufacturers are now building DiSEqC generators into their products, and peripheral products are available that can be controlled either directly or via a DiSEqC switch.

The DiSEqC concept is to modulate the 22kHz tone so that it can relay additional information. Any continuous 22kHz tone that is present is interrupted whilst the DiSEqC message is being sent.

Mini DiSEqC •

Mini DiSEqC

This version has only two states - "0" and "1", the "0" being a continuous 22kHz tone and the "1" a sequence of nine tone bursts over a period of 12.5ms.

If two LNBs are connected to a mini DiSEqC switch, a "0" signal from the receiver will select one LNB and a "1" signal the other.

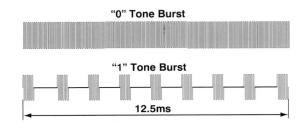

Full DiSEqC •

Full DiSEqC concept

The 22kHz carrier is chopped into time segments as shown:

The "0" data bit corresponds to 1msec of tone followed by 0.5ms of silence, and the "1" data bit 0.5ms of tone followed by 1ms of silence. The end of each DiSEqC message is followed by at least 6ms of silence. Such a system could control a two way switch and most such devices will support both the mini DiSEqC and full DiSEqC concepts.

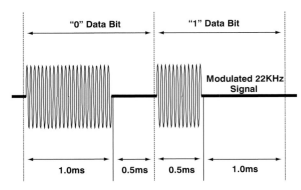

Keywords

• DiSEqC 1

DiSEqC 1

This utilises the full DiSEqC protocol to relay a more complicated set of commands to provide a variety of functions. Messages consist of one or more bytes of data, each followed by a parity bit as shown below:

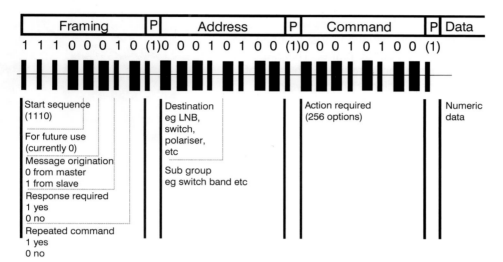

• Framing Byte

The first byte is called the "framing" byte. The first five bits are "11100" to allow listening devices (slaves) to synchronise to the signal. The sixth bit is set to 0 if the message is a command from the master, or 1 if it's a reply from the slave. Bit seven is set to 1 if a response is required, or 0 if not. The last framing bit signals whether this message is a retransmission of a message for which a reply has not been received.

• Address Byte

The second byte is the address byte to indicate which family of devices the message is for. The first four bits indicate the type of device (LNB, switch, positioner etc.) and the second four bits the particular type. In each half of the address byte, a value of 0 means that the message is open to all.

• Command Byte

Next comes the command byte. This actually tells the listening devices what to do. This is followed by one or more data bytes to pass on numbers relevant to the command (such as the angle required from a separate polarotor). Each of these bytes has eight data bits, so up to 28 or 256 different instructions can be accommodated.

There are three versions of DiSEqC 1:

• DiSEqC 1.0 – One way commands from the receiver. A typical application would be to select one of four LNBs.
• DiSEqC 1.1 – As 1.0 but including extra commands.
• DiSEqC 1.2 – As 1.1 but including additional commands for motorised receiver positions.

DiSEqC 2

• DiSEqC 2

This is simply an extension of DiSEqC 1 to provide two way communication between individual components of a complete system. Peripheral devices can acknowledge a command and give status information.

All DiSEqC systems are backwards compatible – for instance, a DiSEqC 2 system would operate on mini DiSEqC and DiSEqC 1 as well.

An external DiSEqC generator can be used if the receiver does not incorporate DiSEqC facilities.

Keywords

Motorised •
Systems

Polar Mount •

Declination •
Angle

7.9   Motorised Systems

It is possible to use a moveable satellite dish antenna to receive all the satellites visible from any location as long as there is nothing in the way to block the incoming signals.

The satellites appear to be lower in elevation as the dish is moved further east or west of due south. Therefore dish elevation must be changed as it moves in the horizontal plane. This happens automatically with a "polar mount" if the axis of rotation of the dish is dish is tilted upwards. The installer therefore has two objectives:

- To make it go up and down by the correct amount.
- To ensure that its highest elevation occurs when the dish is pointing due south.

In order to track all the satellites, the axis of rotation of the dish must be parallel with the earth's axis of rotation. The dish must then be tilted downwards towards the satellites as shown in the drawing below:

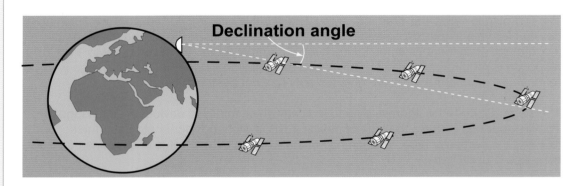

Declination angle

These angles are called modified polar elevation and declination offset angles respectively, and their values change according to the latitude of the receiving site away from the equator. The installation sequence is as follows:

- Rotate the dish on its polar mount so that it is pointing forwards (ie. at its highest elevation).
- Set the polar elevation and declination offset to their correct values.
- Clamp the whole assembly on the pole so that the dish is now pointing due south.
- Check that, as the dish is rotated on its polar mount, the signal level from any satellite is not increased when the dish is stressed upwards and downwards.

In practice an installer would be lucky to achieve this at the first attempt and it is normally necessary to "fine tune" the adjustments until the dish tracks all the satellites perfectly.

Keywords

• Declination
  Offsets

Initial Dish Settings

Check that the mounting pole is exactly vertical. Then mount the dish and polar head on the pole with the dish facing forwards. Set the polar elevation and declination offset according to the site latitude as indicated in the following diagram:

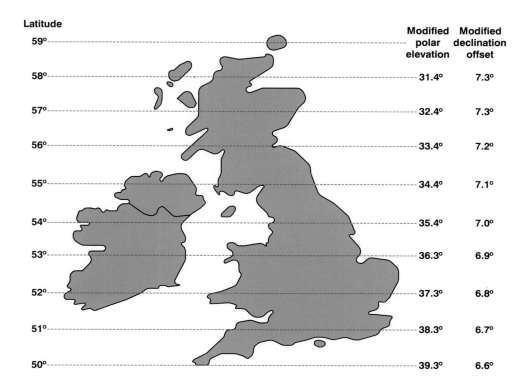

Latitude	Modified polar elevation	Modified declination offset
59°		
58°	31.4°	7.3°
57°	32.4°	7.3°
56°	33.4°	7.2°
55°	34.4°	7.1°
54°	35.4°	7.0°
53°	36.3°	6.9°
52°	37.3°	6.8°
51°	38.3°	6.7°
50°	39.3°	6.6°

The polar elevation is adjusted using an inclinometer or spirit level with an adjustable angle to tilt the axis of elevation upwards from vertical by the angle indicated. The dish face is then tilted further forwards by the amount of the declination offset (plus the offset angle if an offset dish is used – see the previous section for typical offset angle values):

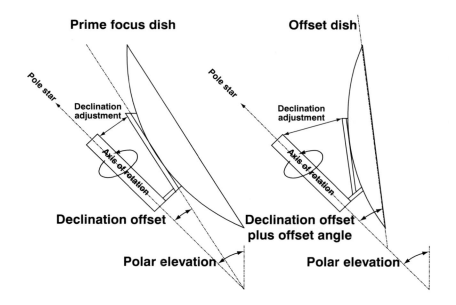

Prime focus dish

Offset dish

Pole star

Declination adjustment

Axis of rotation

Declination offset

Polar elevation

Pole star

Declination adjustment

Axis of rotation

Declination offset plus offset angle

Polar elevation

Keywords

Dish •
Alignment

Signal Measurements

Rotate the dish and polar head on the mounting pole so that the dish points true south and tighten the fixing bolts. This can be done with a compass or by using a spectrum analyser to find Thor/Intelsat 707 at 1°W for locations in central England.

The next step is to rotate the dish on the polar head to find a reference satellite to the east-typically Astra at 28°E. This can be achieved using the motor positioner or by unclamping the motor and moving the dish by hand.

Move the dish east and west to maximise the signal, then slacken the elevation adjustment bolts, peak the signal level and retighten the bolts.

Next, rotate the dish on its polar head to find a satellite to the west and maximise the signal. Then, without loosening the elevation bolts, flex the dish up and down by hand to see if the signal level can be increased. If so, the polar head must be adjusted very slightly on the mounting pole, and the whole procedure repeated until no increase in the signal level can be obtained on either the east or west satellite.

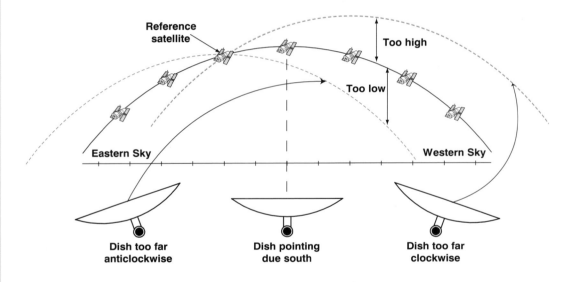

To check that the declination offset is correctly set, move the dish on its polar head to find a satellite as near as possible to due south and check that the signal is still peaked. If not readjust the declination angle setting on the dish very slightly and repeat the whole procedure until the signal level is peaked for all satellites. The adjustments are all interdependent and setting up a motorised dish can be quite time consuming.

Equipment Choice and Location

The size of the dish will depend on the strength of the signals from the weakest satellite that is required. Its location will depend on physical constraints such as signal blockage from trees and nearby structures, access for installation and maintenance, and aesthetic considerations. Check with the local authority as to whether or not planning permission is necessary.

Smaller dishes are usually of the offset type whilst those bigger than 1.8M are of prime focus or cassegrain design. Offset dishes are less versatile if C band feeds or circular-to-linear polarisation conversion is required.
The dish must be connected to the main building earth terminal (PME) using a 4mm^2 copper conductor, and to the lightning protection system if one exists.

A universal LNB will cover the whole of the Ku frequency band – use a C120 version with a separate feedhorn for a prime focus dish.   The only drawback to using universal LNBs is that there is no polarisation adjustment. If adjustable "skew" is required for each satellite, a separate polarotor is needed, together with an LNB with a WR75 flange. Such LNBs use voltage switching to select high/low band and the most common version has local oscillators of 9.75GHz and 10.75GHz.

There are three main types of motor actuator:

- **Linear** This has a telescopic shaft which moves inside a fixed external tube, driven via a gearbox from a 36V DC motor. Versions are available with a linear movement of between 8" and 36" although the arc through which the dish can move is normally limited to about 60°.
- **Horizon-to-horizon (H to H)** This uses the same type of motor which is an integral part of the polar head. It can usually cover a bigger arc than the linear type but cannot be used on larger dishes. In the event of a fault condition, the whole assembly must be changed.
- **DiSEqC** This is a version of the H to H mount which is controlled via the coaxial cable by a receiver equipped with DiSEqC1.2 software. It is normally used with small offset dishes up to 1.2M.

Ensure that the dish movement is restricted so that it cannot hit a wall or other adjacent structure. Most linear and H to H motors incorporate limit switches which should be set as part of the installation procedure.

It is important to ensure that the motor fixings are rigid and that there is no mechanical backlash or play at all, otherwise the dish will not position correctly when approaching from both directions.

Linear and H to H motorised systems need a separate cable link to the receiver. This normally comprises two heavy duty wires for the motor, and two or three feedback wires which must be contained within a metallic screen to prevent the motor current from introducing spurious interfering pulses. Polarotor connections also need a metallic screen and "ribbon" cables are available that incorporate all the necessary circuits.

Most new motorised installations incorporate a digital receiver. A fixed receiver incorporating DiSEqC 1.2 software can also be used for motorised systems.

Types of Motor Feedback

There are several methods of providing feedback to tell the receiver the orientation of the dish in the horizontal plane and the two most common types are as follows:

- Polarotor
- Motor Actuator
- Motor Limit Switches
- Backlash
- H to H Motors
- Motor Feedback

175

Keywords

Reed Feedback •

Reed type A magnet is attached to a rotating shaft connected to the motor that moves the dish in the horizontal plane. A small reed switch is mounted next to the magnet incorporating two contacts inside an evacuated glass bead. Each time that the magnet completes one revolution, it causes the reed switch to open and close. Two wires connect the reed switch to the receiver which "counts" the number of switch operations to determine how far the dish has moved. The receiver applies power to the motor until a pre-determined number of operations has been received. A total of four wires are required, two for the motor and two for the feedback.

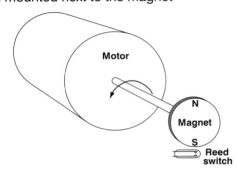

Optical Feedback •

Optical type A disc with holes is used instead of the magnet. A small lamp is positioned behind the disc and a photo-sensitive cell in front of it. Each time that the light shines through a hole in the rotating disc, it changes the characteristics of the cell. The sequence is monitored by the receiver which counts the changes to determine the direction of orientation of the dish. Five wires are required, two for the motor and three for the feedback.

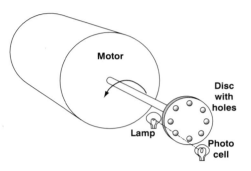

Types of Polarotor

A polarotor is inserted between the feedhorn and LNB to give polarity selection of either horizontal or vertical signals, together with a fine polarity (or "skew") adjustment.

Unless incorporated as an integral part of the feedhorn, the input is a circular C120 waveguide supporting both polarisations and the output is a rectangular WR75 waveguide supporting the selected polarity only.

Polarity selection is achieved by either rotating a pick-up probe or using a magnetic field to twist the signal. In either case, the electromagnetic signal is then reradiated to a probe inside the LNB.

Mechanical •
Polarotors

Mechanical

A small hook-shaped probe inside the circular waveguide is connected to the shaft of a motor and can be rotated in either direction.

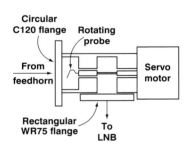

In practice, a "servo" motor is used to eliminate the need for feedback to tell the receiver the orientation of the pick up probe. A control pulse is generated by the receiver whose width is variable (this is called the mark-space ratio) depending on the required angle of orientation.   This is normally applied for just enough time

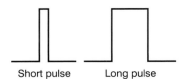

Short pulse   Long pulse

Keywords

for the servo motor to position itself (in practice, about 5 seconds) and then removed to prevent the motor from "chattering".

The skew setting is independent of frequency so one setting on each polarity will suffice for all the transponders at a particular orbital location.

Three wires are required:

    Red = +5V   White = pulse   Black = ground

Magnetic

These devices have no moving parts. The electromagnetic signals from the feed horn are passed through a coil of wire through which a current is passed generating a magnetic field which "twists" the signal, thus changing its polarisation. The more the current, the more the twist but the current must be applied continuously. The amount of skew also depends on the frequency, so the current (or skew setting) may have to be adjusted for each channel frequency.

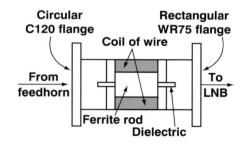

• Magnetic
Polarotors

Only two wires are required. Magnetic polarotors generally have lower insertion losses than mechanical versions, typically 0.1-0.3dB. Versions are available which also convert circular to linear polarisation but these degrade the cross-polar discrimination to values as low as 15dB.

Dish Mountings

Most large satellite dishes are mounted on a vertical pole, or "King Post". The recommended King Post sizes are as follows:

Dish size	Pole length	Pole diameter	No of anchors
Up to 88cm	90cm	50mm	Tray or flat plate
90 – 120cm	100cm	75mm	3
150 – 180cm	140cm	114mm	6
240cm	180cm	168mm	8

• Dish Mountings

The anchors normally comprise 50cm lengths of 19mm galvanised studding with very large plate washers on the bottom end. These are cast into the concrete base and protrude through the top by some 75mm, again with large plate washers.

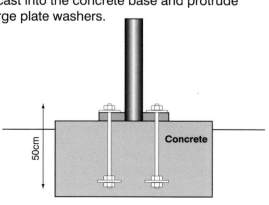

Keywords

Dish •
Assembly

Large Dishes

Many large dishes are delivered in kit form for assembly on site. A typical assembly procedure for a petalised dish would be as follows:

Locate a suitable flat and accessible site where the dish can be built, and erect a temporary ground base.

Mount the central hub on the ground base.

Fit the radial arms to the central hub

Mount the outer ring on to the radial arms

Fit the first petal on to the frame

Fit the remaining petals loosely, then tighten the petal fixings cyclically working from the centre of the dish outwards

Erect the ground base at the permanent dish location

Lift the dish into position

Fit the dish to the permanent ground base and align to the required satellite(s).

Keywords

7

VISION®

Choice of Power Sources
Power can be supplied from
any part of the network

Signal Level Setting
Adjust both high band
signals with one control

Optimal Signal Levelling
Stepped Gain on outputs
for differing cable lengths

Factory Fitted Earthbars
Save time and money

Independently Variable Gain
On Terrestrial TV/Radio input

Rec.2   Rec.4   Rec.6   Rec.8
92dBμV 92dBμV 90dBμV 90dBμV

MAX. OUTPUT TERR
SAT/TERR GAIN

12/10dB 12/10dB 10/8dB 10/8dB

Terr.TV

Colour Coded
Inputs and outputs to
industry standard.
Matching cable available

VISION™

Multiswitch V5-508   CE

Frequency Range	SAT	950-2400MHz
	TERR	47-862MHz
Maximum Output	SAT	93dBμV
Maximum Consumption		18V 80mA

CE Compliant
For safety and
peace of mind

V,Hi

V,Lo

AUX
+ ↑
18V

H,Hi

DC Power Input
For line powering
the system

12/10dB 12/10dB 10/8dB 10/8dB

SAT/TERR GAIN
MAX. OUTPUT TERR

92dBμV 92dBμV 90dBμV 90dBμV
Rec.1   Rec.3   Rec.5   Rec.7

H,Lo

Signal Level Setting
Adjust both low band
signals with one control

High Quality Connectors
Used throughtout for
unrivaled digital performance

**Superior Performance
Guaranteed**
V5 specifications are not
deteriorated by earth-bars
thanks to top quality
connectors. Every unit
100% tested in production

Compact Size
Enables network to be fitted in
approximately two-thirds the
space of legact systems

Features will vary across the range from model to model

Also Available In The Vision Reception Range

Satellite
Dishes

Amplifiers &
Splitters

V75
Multiswitches

V9 Satellite
Distribution

V4 Satellite
Distribution

www.vision-products.co.uk

8.1 Distribution in the Home

Keywords

• Sky TV Distribution

The BSkyB satellite receiver has two UHF outputs, the first of which is linked via the VCR (or DVD player) to the UHF aerial socket on the adjacent TV receiver. Additional Scart connections will give improved performance and also allow a satellite programme to be recorded whilst watching another UHF programme on the TV receiver. The second UHF output enables a TV receiver in another room to watch any UHF programme or the selected Sky channel:

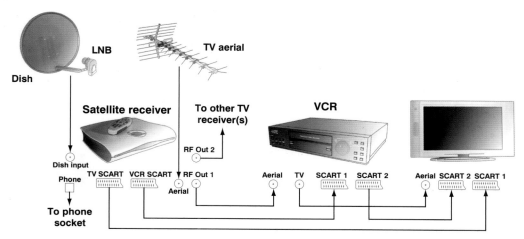

The second output can also receive handset commands in the reverse direction, making it possible to change the satellite channel from other rooms. It is necessary to fit a "remote eye" in each of these rooms to receive the infra-red commands from the receiver handset. Each "eye" needs a 9V DC power supply which is supplied by the receiver – it must be switched on in the "RF outlets" section of the installer's menu. Any components in circuit must be able to pass the dc voltage and the remote eye commands.

• Remote Eye

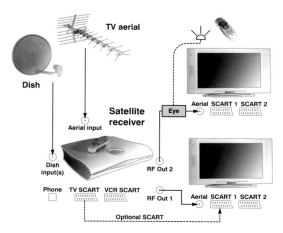

Keywords

Many people prefer to locate their Sky receiver in the loft and controlled using a remote eye in the living room. This eliminates the need for unsightly cables downstairs, but a mains power socket will be required in the loft – this can be a fused spur connected to the lighting circuit if necessary. It also means that Scart connectivity is not possible.

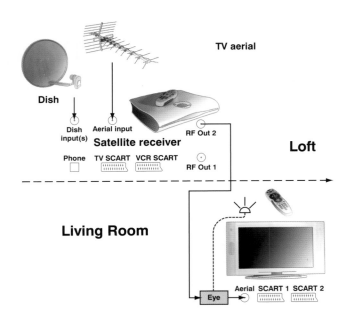

Remote Control •
of other
Equipment

Attachments are available to use the same remote eye to control other infra-red controlled equipment such as a VCR or DVD player, as shown below:

TV Link Plus •

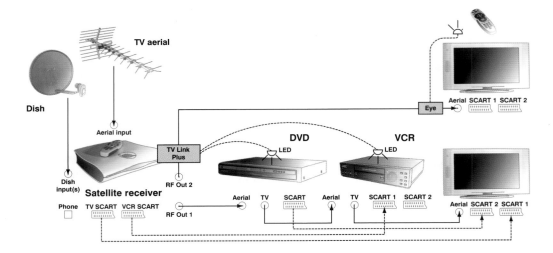

The remote eye concept can be extended to other rooms by using a UHF distribution amplifier with "remote eye pass" in the reverse direction. Some versions of these are powered by the Sky receiver:

Keywords

- Multiple Remote Eyes

- Loft Box

Amplifier

TV aerial

Dish

Eye   Aerial SCART 1 SCART 2

Eye   Aerial SCART 1 SCART 2

Eye   Aerial SCART 1 SCART 2

Eye   Aerial SCART 1 SCART 2

Dish input(s)   Aerial input   RF Out 2

Satellite receiver

Phone   TV SCART   VCR SCART   RF Out 1

Aerial SCART 1 SCART 2

Optional SCART

8

It is also possible to integrate the distribution of various services to several viewing locations using a **"Loft Box"**. This requires a separate coaxial cable from the Loft Box to each viewing location, except for the link to the Sky receiver, which requires two such coaxial cables:

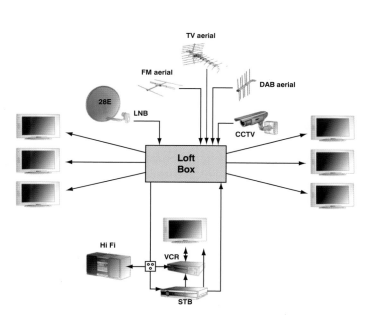

TV aerial

FM aerial

DAB aerial

28E   LNB

CCTV

Loft Box

Hi Fi

VCR

STB

Integration of •
Sky Plus / Sky HD

Some versions can
accommodate Sky Plus
and Sky HD services without
adding additional cables,
although a special integrated
faceplate is required at the Sky
receiver location.

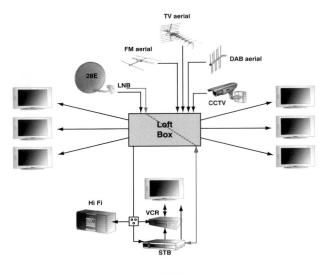

Integration of •
Sky "Multiroom"

Other versions are
available to create a fully
integrated system with
independent Sky receivers at
additional locations, again without
adding additional coaxial cables.

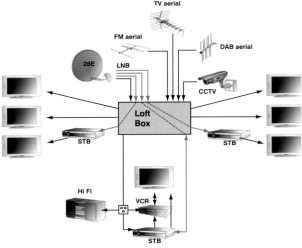

Alternatively, the third and fourth dish inputs could be connected to a separate dish
on a different satellite, and the additional set top boxes could be conventional digital
satellite receivers instead of Sky receivers, thus providing services from another satellite
in these rooms.

Multiple Sky •
Installations

8.2   Multiple Sky Installations

A basic Sky reception system consists of an offset dish with a
universal LNB and a single coaxial cable link to the Sky receiver.

It is not possible to split the cable link to feed two Sky receivers because the LNB could
receive conflicting commands from the receivers. For instance, if one receiver selects a
horizontally polarised channel by sending 18V to the LNB, and the other selects a vertical
channel by sending 12V, this would be impractical because a single LNB cannot receive
both polarities simultaneously. The same situation could occur if a Sky Plus or Sky HD
receiver tries to access both polarities at the same time.

Keywords

• Twin LNB

• Quad LNB

• Octo LNB

• LNB "States"

The solution is to fit a "twin" LNB – this has two independent outputs with separate coaxial cable links to the connected to each receiver, or to the two inputs on a Sky Plus or Sky HD receiver. Installers often swap a single universal LNB for a twin version and install a second cable link when upgrading a customer from basic Sky to Sky Plus.

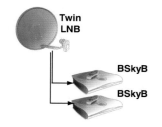

This concept can be extended further. A "quad" LNB has four independent outputs to accommodate up to four standard Sky receivers or two Sky Plus (or Sky HD) receivers.

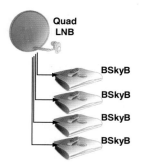

There is even an "octo" LNB with eight independent outputs. All these LNB versions can be fitted on a standard zone 1 or zone 2 Sky dish.

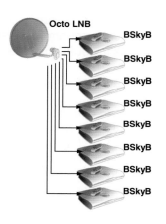

Integrated Reception Systems

For more than eight LNB outputs, a different approach must be adopted. An LNB can have four separate "states":

- Low band vertical   12V
- High band vertical   12V + 22kHz
- Low band horizontal   18V
- High band horizontal   18V + 22kHz

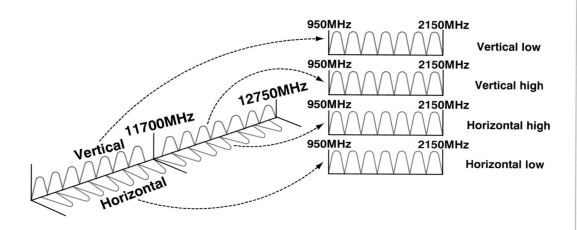

Keywords

Each of these states is relayed, one at a time, to the receiver in the frequency band 950 – 2150MHz.

Quattro LNB •

An LNB that produces these four states simultaneously is known as a "Quatro" LNB. Such devices will always produce these four states, irrespective of what voltage or tone command they are receiving – they need a voltage (12V or 18V) from a receiver or power supply on at least one of their output ports, and the "horizontal high" connector is normally used for this purpose.

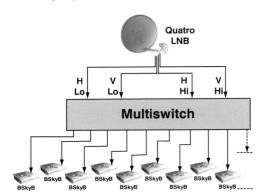

A Quatro LNB cannot operate a receiver directly – it needs an interface switching box under the control of the receiver, to select the required state. This interface is known in the trade as a "multiswitch". Such a device will utilise the voltages and tone commands from the receiver to operate a four-way switch to select the required state. The multiswitch is therefore "transparent" to the system because the receiver controls the switch in the same way as it would control an LNB directly.

Multiswitch •

Several switches can be wired in tandem to provide additional outlets.

Star-Wired •
Network

A system of this type needs a "star-wired" coaxial cable network with a separate coaxial cable to each outlet location. Such networks often exist in multi-dwelling units and have been relaying VHF and UHF TV signals for many years. In principle, it is possible to use this same cable to relay Sky signals as well by using Satellite/TV diplexers as described in section 7.7. This would result in some or all of the following services being relayed to each outlet on the same coaxial cable:

Services Relayed •

• FM radio
• Digital Audio Broadcasting (DAB)
• UHF analogue terrestrial TV channels
• Additional UHF analogue TV services (CCTV door camera, VCR etc.)
• UHF digital TV multiplexes
• Satellite IF digital TV multiplexes

This technique can only be used if the existing coaxial cable is double screened and of the highest quality. Unfortunately, this is usually not the case. However, the same principles can be adopted for all new installations, as long as benchmarked cables are used throughout the network.

Keywords

• IRS Terrestrial Input

• Integrated Reception Systems (IRS)

• Multiswitch Capacity

• Multiswitch Powering

• Five Cable Backbone

This diagram shows the concept of introducing the terrestrial signals into the system by using a fifth signal input on the multiswitch. This is superimposed on to all the other four inputs so that, whichever satellite state is selected, each viewer has access to all the terrestrial services as well:

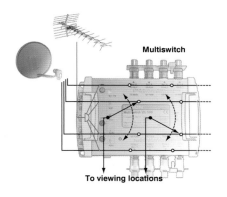

Systems of this type are known as Integrated Reception Systems (IRS).

Multiswitches are available with between 4 and 24 outputs. Such a device with 5 inputs and 8 outputs is referred to as a 5x8 switch. Switches without a terrestrial input are sometimes powered by the LNB voltage from the Sky receivers connected to their outputs, so they do not need a separate mains power supply.

A system where each switch has 5 inputs is referred to as having a five cable backbone. Some multiswitches can be daisy-chained, having 5 inputs and 5 outputs; other versions are fed using "taps" from the 5 cable backbone.

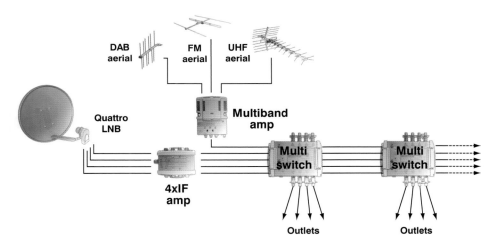

Systems can have just one or several backbone cables. A four backbone cable splitter is shown below.

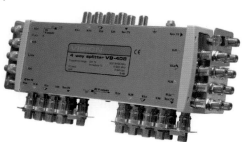

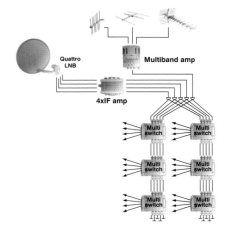

Keywords

IRS Outlet Plates •

Diplexed Outlet •

Triplexed Outlet •

Multiservice •
Outlet

Outlet Frames •

8

Quad Outlet •

Nine Cable •
Backbone

IRS Outlet Plates

Different types of outlet plates are available to cater for the various services:

- A "diplexed" Radio/TV plate where a separate satellite receiver is not required (eg bedrooms)

- A "triplexed" Radio/TV/Satellite plate to allow for the connection of a satellite TV receiver

- A "multiservice" plate which includes a UHF return feed for connection to other rooms, and an RJ11 telephone socket

Some manufacturers offer single gang or double gang flush outlet frames for mounting a choice of input / output modules:

Sky Plus and Sky HD receivers have the ability to record two different programmes simultaneously and therefore require two IRS input cables. "Quad" outlet plates are available to provide these facilities.

Multi-Satellite Systems

It is also possible to integrate services from two or more satellite locations on to an IRS network using the DiSEqC switching techniques described in section seven. For instance, signals from the Astra satellites at 28.2°E and the Hotbird satellites at 13°E can be relayed on a nine cable backbone to switches with nine inputs. Such systems normally default to the Astra services and will change to the Hotbird services on receipt of a DiSEqC command from the satellite receiver.

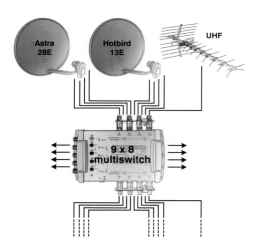

Keywords

• Seventeen
  Cable
  Backbone

• Single Cable
  Router

• IF Stacker

Networks with a seventeen cable backbone will provide reception from four different satellites, again selected using DiSEqC commands, as shown alongside:

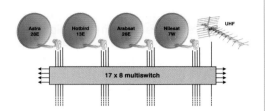

Single Cable Router (SCR)

As stated previously, Sky Plus and Sky HD receivers require two separate satellite IF feeds. Where it is not physically possible to provide more than one separate cable input, a "single cable router" can provide up to four independent feeds on <u>one</u> coaxial cable.

The concept is illustrated alongside. Instead of relaying all the multiplexes simultaneously, just four programmes are relayed on individual frequencies, one for each Sky receiver (or two for each Sky Plus / Sky HD receiver). Each Sky receiver sends data commands to the router requesting a specific programme, which is then relayed to the receiver on its unique frequency.

Such systems require the following:
• Four independent outputs from a multiswitch or Quad LNB
• Sky receivers with the appropriate software (eg Pace PVR V3 TDS470N with software version 9F2211xxx or higher NDS version with PR6 software)

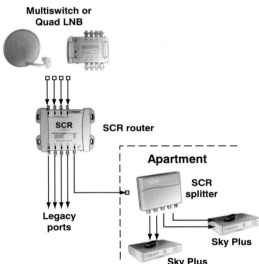

The router is located adjacent to the multiswitch or Quad LNB and the splitter connects the incoming single coaxial cable to the four drop-in cables. The router also has four "legacy" output ports for connection to other IRS outlets in the building.

The IF "Stacker"

Another way of providing two satellite IF feeds for a Sky Plus or Sky HD receiver on a single coaxial cable is to stack the frequencies side-by-side:

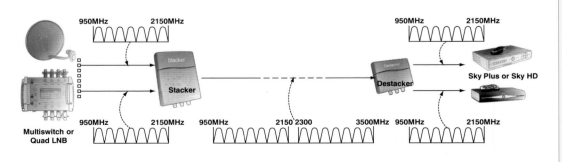

Keywords

The "stacker" receives two independent IF satellite feeds from a multiswitch or Quad LNB, and converts one of them to a higher frequency band. Both frequency bands are then relayed on a single coaxial cable to the viewing location where a "destacker" reverses the process, providing the two independent feeds.

The range of frequencies being relayed on the distribution system is greater, resulting in even greater signal losses at the higher frequencies, so it is essential that only the very best quality of coaxial cable is used, and its length should be kept as short as possible. Some such systems have been known to suffer interference from nearby Wi Fi systems in the 2,4GHz frequency band.

Fibre Optic Systems

Fibre-Optic •
Distribution

It is also possible to feed several Sky receivers on one cable by installing a single fibre cable.

The subject of fibre optics is covered in detail in Part Ten. However, one of the principle advantages of utilising fibre is its enormous bandwidth – enough to accommodate all four IF states side-by-side on a single fibre optic cable:

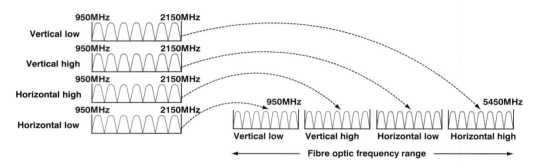

Such systems consist of the following:

- An optical LNB or multiswitch to convert the incoming signals into a beam of light modulated with the four satellite IF frequency bands.
- A fibre optic cable network linking this source to the receiver location(s).
- An optical receiver to convert the modulated light beam back into one or more satellite IF feeds, the required "state" being selected in the normal way using the 12/18V and 22KHz on/off commands.

8.3   System Concepts

Establishing compliance with a specification

The IRS concept is now widely used in the UK to distribute TV services throughout multi-dwelling units. Most big projects are normally put out to tender. Those for MATV and IRS systems often refer to the latest edition of the following documents:

IRS •
Specifications

- Code of Practice for the Installation of Terrestrial and Satellite TV Reception Systems.
- Specification for an Integrated Reception System, published by Sky Homes.

This eliminates the need to list all the technical parameters of the proposed system. All the specifications given in this publication comply with those in the above-mentioned documents.

Keywords

It is important that a tenderer understands the basic system specified in the tender documents and what equipment will be required to achieve the specified system performance. It is sometimes necessary to deviate from the specification, especially if the tender documents were prepared by a non-technical person. The tenderer should, as far as possible, comply exactly with the specification given, and highlight any deviations separately as changes to his tender price.

Design and Layout Considerations

Property developers are not (usually) experts in IRS layout concepts, and what facilities they should design into the building fabric to enable the installer to provide the required services at a minimum cost.

• IRS Layout Concepts

On new buildings, the installer will need to work in close co-operation with the electrical contractor who will provide the cable containment (and often install the network coaxial cables as well). If the installer can advise the developer whilst the building is in the design stage, he can make his own job a whole lot easier when the time comes to install the system.

On existing buildings, consider whether the system relay cables should be routed internally (and how to hide them) or externally (with the consequent lack of accessibility).

Site Survey

A site survey and field strength test will be required in order to determine the services available at any particular location. It will be necessary to consider the following:

• Site Survey

- The signal strength of the relevant services. It is vital to get the best possible signals from the aerial or satellite dish. 2dB more signal means 2dB more C/N ratio throughout the system. A separate satellite dish is preferable for each orbital location, instead of multiple LNBs on one dish.
- Possible sources of interference include vehicles on a nearby main road, neighbouring TV transmitters, cellphone and Tetra relay stations and microwave transmitters. It may be necessary to consider the use of an aerial with a good front-to-back ratio or a dish location such that a nearby structure will provide screening against interference.
- Access to the aerial location – the builder's scaffolding wont be there after the building has been completed, so what about subsequent maintenance?
- Access during the installation of the network relay cables – is the ground flat enough for a scaffold tower to be erected or a "cherry-picker" used, and how can they be secured overnight?
- An assessment of the risks involved during the installation phase of the project.
- A record of any existing damage to the fabric or fittings of the building.
- Does the building have a lightning protection system and is the downconductor made of copper or aluminium?

Planning Permission

Check with the local council regarding planning regulations – these can be quite onerous, especially in areas of "outstanding natural beauty".

• Planning Permission

Most local councils interpret the regulations as follows:

- A single domestic dwelling can have one dish of not more than 90cm (in any direction), or not more than 50cm if it is on the chimney, without the need for planning permission – a BSkyB zone 1 dish has one dimension of more than 50cm!
- A multi-dwelling unit can have up to two dishes, each no more than 90cm, without permission – some councils specifying that a multi-dwelling unit must be more than 15m high!

Keywords

IRS Services •

Network Layout •

Aerial / Dish •
Location

Head-end •
Equipment
Location

Services to be provided
The customer must define exactly what services are required and in which locations.
For instance:
- Do they want Sky or Sky Plus, and in which rooms?
- Will there be an integrated wall plate for all services, including the telephone connection?
- Do they want remote control of the Sky receiver from other rooms?
- Do they want services from other satellites?
- What other services do they want – terrestrial radio (FM/DAB), terrestrial TV (analogue/ digital), CCTV etc., and in which rooms?

Network Layout
IRS backbone cables are usually installed in vertical risers or horizontal ducts that are shared with other services, which could include plumbing or electricity, communication or security system cables. It is important that the IRS cables are located as far away as possible from mains power cables, especially if the electricity cables are to carry heavy currents.

The ideal solution is for the developer to supply a separate metal cable tray for the IRS backbone cables, the various lengths being earth-bonded together and connected to a good earth. The coaxial cables can then be attached to the tray using cable ties. IRS signals are most vulnerable to the pick-up of interference on the drop-in cables between the multiswitches and each viewing location, when they are at their lowest levels. It is therefore important that the multiswitches are located to keep the drop-in cables as short as possible. The suggested maximum length is 40m wherever possible. This may entail the use of more than one riser in the building.

Aerial / Dish Location
The terrestrial aerials should be mounted outdoors with an unobstructed view in the direction of the transmitters. Several aerials can be mounted on a single pole as long as they are at least 1m apart, the TV aerial normally being mounted at the top. If two different TV transmitters are to be received, it will be necessary to use two aerials with the one receiving the weakest signals at the top. All this assumes that the pole is securely fixed and strong enough to withstand wind speeds of at least 100mph. Aerials mounted further up the pole will exert a greater moment of force on the pole fixings.

The building structure should be checked to ensure that it is strong enough to take the extra load exerted by the aerial array (particularly important if the aerial is to be mounted on a chimney). Aerials should not be positioned over pavements or public walkways. The aerial location must be accessible for subsequent maintenance and free of hazards such as radiation from a nearby cellphone relay site. The mast must be bonded to the building's lightning protection system, if one exists, using a downconductor with the appropriate cross sectional area.

Head-end Equipment Location
The relay equipment must be housed in an accessible, secure, well ventilated location. This could be a waterproof kiosk on the roof, a plywood board in the loft (as long as it doesn't get too hot in summer), a cupboard, or even the top floor riser if it is big enough.

A lift motor room is not preferred for several reasons:
- Some of the lift equipment could be unprotected
- Lift companies don't like sharing space!
- Lifts create intermittent loads on the electricity supply, which can cause electrical interference on equipment connected to the same mains power source.

Keywords

The following will be required at the Head-end location chosen:

- A clean mains power supply with a current rating of at least 3 amps.
- A 4mm^2 earth wire connected to a "good" earth, preferably the building's PME (primary multiple earth).

Multiswitch Locations

It would be preferable to route all the drop-in cables to a single central multiswitch at the Head-end location if their lengths do not exceed 40m. Otherwise, it would be necessary to locate the multiswitches in various risers or corridors, in order to minimise the drop-in cable lengths – in such cases, the multiswitches would be linked together using (typically) five backbone cables.

Multiswitches are normally located in risers if indoors, or in surface mounted weatherproof boxes if outdoors.

- Multiswitch Locations

Drop-in Cable Containment

The cables between a multiswitch and the viewing location should preferably be enclosed in a dedicated PVC or metal conduit or trunking, or fixed to a metal cable tray. They can also be loose laid in false ceilings or cavity walls, but they must be supported at regular intervals to ensure that they will not stretch or become damaged. Several coaxial cables can be contained in a single conduit. Cable lengths must be continuous, and joints are not acceptable.

- Drop-in Cable Containment

Services Required in each Apartment

All the services being relayed on an IRS system are normally made available on a flush mounted multi-service plate in the main living area of each dwelling unit. There are two different concepts for distributing signals to other rooms within the same dwelling unit:

- IRS Services Required

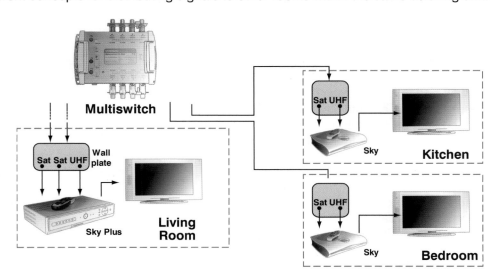

- To duplicate the same services to each of the other rooms – this requires several multiswitch outputs for each dwelling unit (one for each Sky receiver and two for each Sky Plus receiver):

or

- To utilise two multiswitch outputs to a multiservice plate in the main living room, and to relay the UHF output 2 of the Sky Plus receiver via a line-powered UHF amplifier to TV outlets in the other rooms:

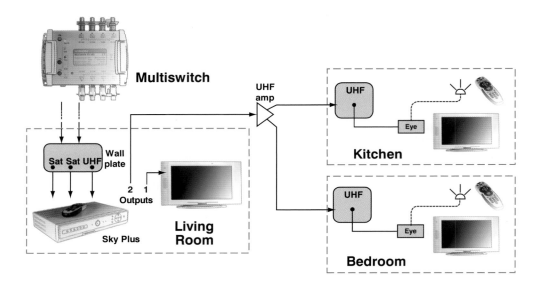

This enables the Sky Plus programme to be selected from the other rooms (using "remote eyes") – the selected channel can then be viewed in all rooms. The disadvantage of this system is that, if the Sky Plus receiver is removed (or if it was never installed), all the other rooms lose their TV pictures unless a coaxial bridging link is fitted on the master wall plate.

Telephone •
Sockets

It is possible to integrate a BT phone socket on the multiservice wallplate, in which case the phone conduit must also terminate in the multiservice conduit box.

Electrical Safety •

8.4 System Electrical Safety

It is now a criminal offence to leave a TV system in an unsafe condition in the UK.

Code of •
Practice

A **C**ode **of P**ractice **(COP)** will be issued in due course, covering electrical safety requirements for signal reception systems. This is a summary document based on the recent British and European safety standards. Its purpose is to prevent serious injury either to a system user or to any maintenance personnel, due to the risk of hazardous voltages becoming present on a distribution system. Such a fault could be generated by either a faulty TV receiver or some other mains operated equipment being connected to the system, thereby passing hazardous voltages around the system unless some electrical protection is provided.

Hazardous •
Voltages

Two aspects must be considered:
- **Earthing** provides safety by limiting the **duration** of a "touch" voltage.
- **Equipotential bonding** provides safety by limiting the **magnitude** of a touch voltage.

All new systems must be electrically bonded to the building's **M**ain **E**arth **T**erminal **(MET)**, or **P**rimary **M**ultiple **E**arth **(PME)**, using either earth bars or a direct connection to the metal case of each unit. In the latter case, a temporary bond must be fitted before such equipment is removed. Bonding conductors must have a minimum cross-sectional area of

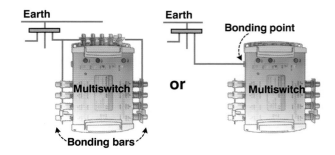

Keywords

• Equipment
Potential
Bonding
• MET
• PME

• Class 1
Equipment
• Class 2
Equipment

• Lightning
Protection

$4mm^2$. Where a route back to the PME is difficult to achieve, it is acceptable to use other bonded metalwork only provided that it is connected back to the PME in a robust, permanent and continuous manner. The path must have adequate current carrying capacity – bonding to the ring main earth via a mains plug is not allowed. All earth bonding points must be labelled "Safety earth connection – do not remove".

Ensure that the fuse rating for each item of electrical equipment is adequate but not excessive, and less than the rating of the mains power cable.

The COP refers to two classes of equipment:

Class 1 which has an integral earth wire in the mains power lead, and

Class 2 which has only a two-wire mains lead and relies on double insulation for protection.

The only relaxation permitted is for small systems in single dwelling units to which not more than seven items of "class 2" equipment will be connected, in which case the earth bonding is not compulsory. For more than one viewing location or more than seven class 2 connections, such small systems must however be connected to a "functional earth" somewhere on the system. An example of this would be a $2.5mm^2$ conductor to the earth terminal of a lighting circuit.

The above information has been interpreted by the author from the draft code of practice. All system designers and installers should familiarise themselves with the detailed requirements for earth bonding a system, as described in the Code of Practice.

The photograph alongside shows a small IRS head end with all the incoming and outgoing coaxial cables routed via earth bars, which are connected via a $4mm^2$ down conductor to the PME.

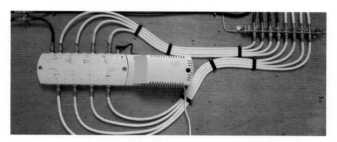

If the building has a lightning protection system, outdoor aerials and dishes should be earth bonded to it using a down conductor with a cross sectional area of at least $16mm^2$ copper or $25mm^2$ aluminium. This work should be carried out by a "competent" person. The photograph shows a pvc covered 25 x 3mm copper down conductor from the mast bonded on to an existing horizontal lightning down conductor of similar material

Keywords

Copper •
Conductors

Copper conductors must not be allowed to come into direct contact with aluminium – in such cases, the end of the copper can be plated with solder using a soldering iron.

Earth Mat •

If the aerial is installed at ground level in an exposed location (such as on top of a hill), lightning protection can be provided by bonding the pole to an earth mat comprising radial aluminium or copper conductors buried in the ground, as shown in the adjacent picture.

Thatched Roof •

In view of the increased hazard from lightning, it is prohibited to fix an aerial to any building with a thatched roof.

IRS Network •
Planning

8.5   Network Planning

The system must be designed to deliver the required signal levels to each apartment.

The suggested planning procedure is to assume the use of 7mm diameter cable (WF100 or equivalent) and to calculate the required UHF TV and satellite IF system input levels to achieve the desired performance at each outlet plate. If this cannot be achieved, possible solutions could include the fitting of satellite IF and terrestrial amplifiers in the backbone cables, or using lower loss backbone cables (WF125, WF165 or similar).

Terrestrial •
Filtering

Try to incorporate some form of filtering on the terrestrial input. Bandpass filters can ensure that unwanted interference does not enter the system via this route.

Whilst six or eight multiswitches can be cascaded, it is good practice not to have more than (say) three multiswitches in tandem, wherever possible.

CTB •

The factor that usually limits the "reach" of an IRS system is usually the maximum output level of the terrestrial TV head-end amplifier. Setting its analogue level too high will cause a form of third-order intermodulation distortion, known as "composite-triple-beat" (CTB), which will degrade the BER (this was discussed in part 7). It is always necessary to check the required analogue launch level against the amplifier specification when planning a system. Check also that the FM and DAB launch levels do not exceed those of the analogue TV signals.

Fibre Optic •
Links

For larger community systems it may be advantageous to use fibre optic links between remote sites to relay signals from a central head-end location to two or more independent IRS systems, each covering a smaller area.

Cable Types

IRS Cables •

It is most important that only benchmarked cables are used for IRS networks wherever possible. The most common types are 7mm diameter with either a foam or a semi air spaced dielectric and a longitudinally applied copper tape and a thickly woven copper braid, all contained in an overall PVC outer sheath.

PVC Sheath •
Polythene •
Sheath

PVC is not totally waterproof, so cable in underground ducts should be specified to have an alternative polythene sheath. However, on no account should polythene be used indoors because of the consequent fire risk – polythene is inflammable since it will support combustion. PVC will give off chlorine gas when exposed to a naked flame, but it will not catch fire. Some property developers specify the use of a totally "fireproof" cable with a low smoke / zero halogen outer sheath – this is known in the trade as LSOH cable.

196

Keywords

• LSOH Cable

• IRS Network Schematic

It is possible to purchase coaxial cables with a thicker outer sheath (for use in ducts or for direct burial in the ground), or with an integral catenary wire. When specifying the use of these alternative cables, check their overall dimensions to ensure that the appropriate sizes of connectors are used.

Network Schematic

Draw a schematic diagram of the proposed system, showing the following:

• The expected digital terrestrial signal levels at the aerial location (it may be necessary to carry out a site test to determine these levels).

• The proposed dish sizes and satellite(s) to be received – use at least a 78cm dish for Sky in Southern England and a correspondingly larger size for other locations and weaker satellites.

• The types of equipment used. The equipment interconnections and the estimated cable lengths .

A typical schematic diagram is shown alongside. This example is for a four storey building with two flats per floor, each requiring Sky Plus and all the terrestrial services.

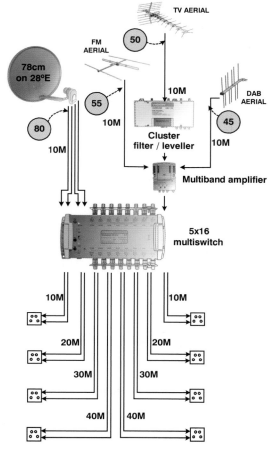

Digital levels inside circles are in dBµV

Prepare a table showing the maximum gains of each item at 860MHz (DTT) and 2150MHz (Satellite IF). Typical values are as follows:

• Network Gains / Losses

	DTT gain (max)	Satellite IF gain (max)
Cable 100 type	-2dB/10m	-3dB/10m
125 type	-1.5dB/10m	-2.5dB/10m
165 / 167 type	-1dB/10m	-2dB/10m
Outlet plate - single	-1dB	-1.5dB
- Diplex/triplex	-1.5dB	-2dB
Cluster filter / leveller	-2dB	
Multiband amplifier	+34dB	
5 x 16 multiswitch	-1dB	-1dB

Keywords

Outlet Signal •
Levels

Specify the minimum and maximum signal levels for terrestrial analogue, terrestrial digital and satellite IF signals, allowing a safety margin of at least 5dB for the minimum levels – suitable target values are as follows:

	Terrestrial analogue	Terrestrial digital	Satellite IF
Minimum	65dBµV	55dBµV	55dBµV
Maximum	80dBµV	80dBµV	75dBµV

Planning •
Sequence

Make two further copies of the schematic drawing, one for DTT levels and the other for satellite IF levels, and mark the gains/losses of each item on the appropriate drawing. Identify the outlet location where the signal will be weakest (the one with the longest cable run) and record the appropriate minimum signal level on each drawing.

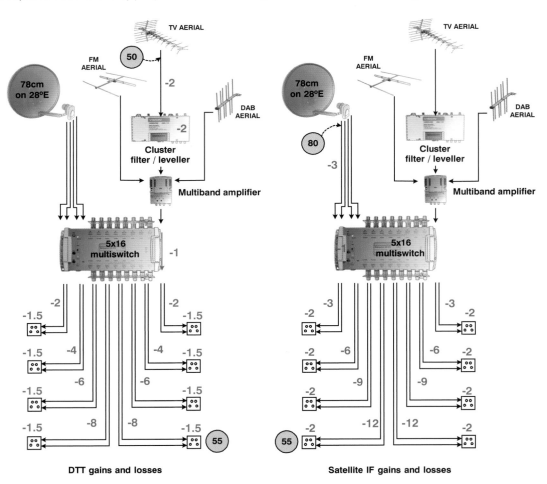

DTT gains and losses   Satellite IF gains and losses

The final step is to calculate the actual signal levels into the multiswitch, and the required output levels from the multiswitch in order to achieve the required minimum signal levels at each outlet, as shown on the next page:

Keywords

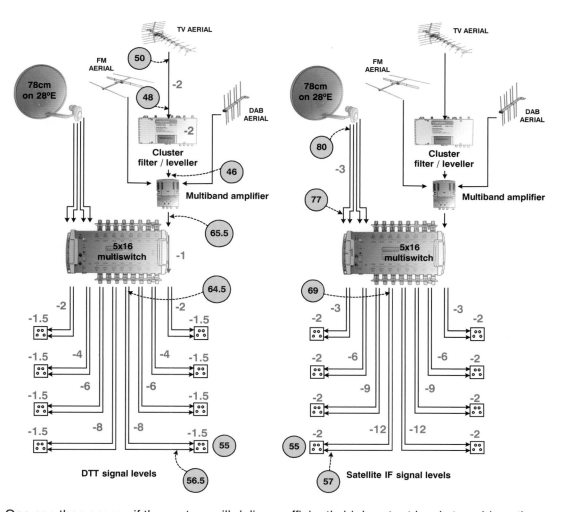

DTT signal levels

Satellite IF signal levels

One can then assess if the system will deliver sufficiently high output levels to achieve the minimum signal levels required at the furthest outlet location. In this example, the following conclusions can be drawn:

- For DTT, the input level to the multiband amplifier will be 46dBμV; the necessary output from the amplifier is 65.5dBμV so the required gain is 19.5dB. The amplifier has a maximum gain of 34dB so the gain can be turned down by 14.5dB.
- For satellite, the input level to the multiswitch will be 77dBμV; the necessary output from the multiswitch is 69dBμV so the level control can be turned down accordingly.

It is also necessary to check that the FM, DAB and analogue UHF levels will be within their correct operating windows at each outlet location and at the output of the amplifier and multiswitch. These levels are summarised in the chart on the next page. The analogue UHF levels are of particular importance – they are typically 20dB higher than the digital levels, so check that the analogue levels from the multiswitch do not exceed its maximum rated output after the amplifier derating rules have been applied.

Keywords

It is recommended that, when planning a system, you build in some flexibility. If an amplifier has adjustable gain, use a planning gain of 6dB less than the maximum, to give room for adjustment when commissioning the system.

It is most important to ensure that the signal levels of all the TV channels are similar, unless some pre-emphasis of the higher channels is required. Individual channels that are abnormally low or high will severely reduce the window of operation of the entire system.

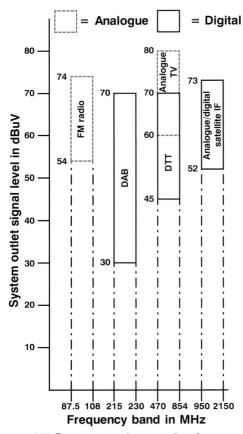

IRS operating windows

Larger Planning • Example

Planning Larger Systems

The same principles apply for larger systems, except that the multiswitches are distributed throughout the property in order to keep the drop-in cables as short as possible. These switches powered down the backbone cable from a launch amplifier at the head-end location. Careful planning is required to ensure that the levels at every outlet location are within their windows of operation.

The following worked examples show the proposed layouts and network level calculations using equipment from different manufacturers.

Sixteen flats over four floors

This four storey building has two blocks, each with eight flats requiring UHF TV and Sky Plus facilities. Each block has a flat roof and the dish/aerials had to be located at the rear of the property.

A 5 x 16 multiswitch was located on the flat roof of each block, with the drop-in cables run down the front of the building and through the wall to a surface-mounted Quad outlet plate in each lounge.

Keywords

The layout of the equipment and cables on the flat roof is shown alongside.

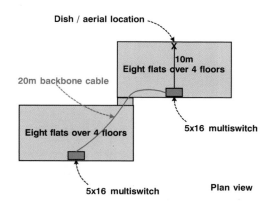

Dish / aerial location

10m
Eight flats over 4 floors

20m backbone cable

Eight flats over 4 floors

5x16 multiswitch

5x16 multiswitch

Plan view

Using Fracarro equipment, the planning parameters can be obtained from the relevant data sheets and are as follows:

• Fracarro Example

- Signal levels measured from UHF TV aerial – analogue 70dBμV
- DTT 50dBμV
- Signal levels from Quatro LNB – 80dBμV
- UHF programmable equaliser/filter FIL261000 – gain 5dB
  - Max output level 75dBμV
- Multiband amplifier, MBJ2356 - Gain FM 21dB
  - DAB 19dB
  - UHF 22dB
  - Max UHF output level 112dBμV
- Satellite launch amplifier, AMP9254A – satellite gain 32dB
  - UHF gain -1dB
  - Max satellite output level 116dBμV
- 5x16 multiswitch, SWI8516PLUS, Satellite gain – through -4dB
  - side -3dB
  - UHF gain – through -3dB
  - side -5dB
  - Max output level – Satellite 110dBμV
  - UHF 100dBμV
  - Current consumption 720mA
- Power supply unit, AMP8331 – maximum current 3amps
- Quad plate gain – UHF -1.5dB
  - Satellite -2dB
- Cable gain, CT100 type, per 10m - UHF -2dB
  - Satellite -3dB

The drawings on the next page show the gains and losses of each item, and the calculated signal levels throughout the network, for both DTT (860MHz) and satellite IF (2150MHz). The UHF analogue signal levels will be 20dB higher than the DTT levels.

Each multiswitch consumes 720mA of current, so a single AMP8331 power supply unit will suffice, its maximum output being 3 amps.

Keywords

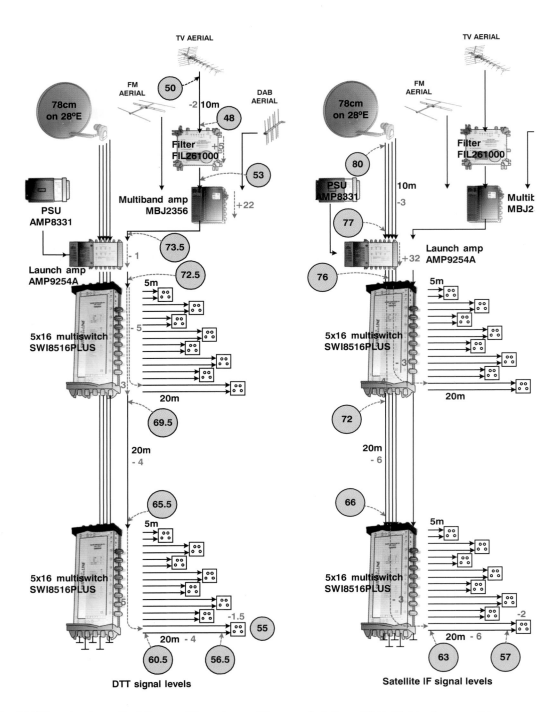

DTT signal levels

Satellite IF signal levels

The DTT levels show that the multiband amplifier must deliver 73.5dBμV, whereas it is capable of producing 75dBμV, giving 1.5dB in hand.

The satellite IF levels show that a launch amplifier is not really required in this case, since no gain is required at all for such a small system. If no launch amplifier is used, the voltage from the AMP8331 power unit must be connected via a DC power inserter.

Keywords

• Triax Example

A typical **Fracarro** multiswitch is shown alongside. These units are designed for end-mounting, making it easier to connect and remove drop-in cables during subsequent service work. The system can be powered from anywhere on the network.

The same system could be installed using Triax equipment. The relevant planning parameters are as follows:

• Signal levels measured from UHF TV aerial –		analogue	70dBµV
		DTT	50dBµV
• Signal levels from Quatro LNB –			80dBµV
• Programmable multiband amplifier, TMB 10C - Gain		FM	45dB
		DAB	45dB
		UHF	45dB
	Max UHF output level		124dBµV
• Satellite launch amplifier, TMM 44AMP –		satellite gain	40dB
	Max satellite output level		115dBµV
• 5x16 multiswitch, TMM 5x16,	Satellite gain – through		-2.5dB
	side		-12dB
	UHF gain – through		-3dB
	side		-12dB
	Max output level – Satellite		95dBµV
	UHF		85dBµV
	Current consumption		95mA
• Power inserter, TMM PSI, gain -		UHF	-1.5dB
		Satellite	-2.5dB
• Quad plate gain –		UHF	-1.5dB
		Satellite	-2dB
• Cable gain, CT100 type, per 10m -		UHF	-2dB
		Satellite	-3dB

The drawings on the next page again show the gains and losses of each item, and the calculated signal levels throughout the network, for both DTT (860MHz) and satellite IF (2150MHz). The UHF analogue signal levels will be 20dB higher than the DTT levels.

This system can also be powered from anywhere on the network.

This photograph shows a typical **Triax** multiswitch. The amplifiers have controls for both gain and slope and each switch has input level controls. The switches are end-mounted, for ease of adjustment. Voltage is relayed via the terrestrial backbone cable to power the terrestrial amplifier in each switch, the satellite amplifier being powered from the satellite receiver at the viewing location.

Keywords

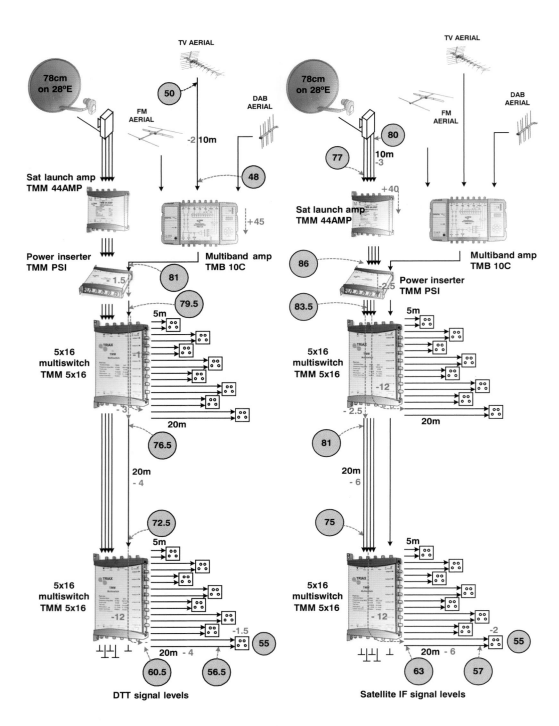

DTT signal levels

Satellite IF signal levels

Once again, there is plenty of gain in hand. The DTT levels show that the multiband amplifier must deliver 81dBμV, whereas it is capable of producing 93dBμV, giving 12dB in hand. The satellite IF levels show that a launch level of only 86dBμV is required so the gain of the launch amplifier must be turned right down.

Keywords

Here is the same project using **Vision** V5 equipment.

Levels are shown in BLACK for UHF digital TV and in *RED* italic for digital satellite.

The DTT levels show that the masthead amplifier (27dB gain) must deliver 65.1dBµV whereas it is capable of delivering more than 80dBµV assuming that the analogue level is some 20dB higher. The masthead amplifier is powered via a power supply in the terrestrial downlead.

The satellite levels form the LNB are adequate to drive the network without the need an expensive launch amplifier since little or no gain is required except that provided by the multiswitches. As no launch amplifier is employed powering is made via a V5-024 power supply plugged into the auxiliary DC socket in one of the multiswitches.

Each multiswitch 80mA of the current, so a single V5-024 power supply will suffice, its maximum output being 2.2A

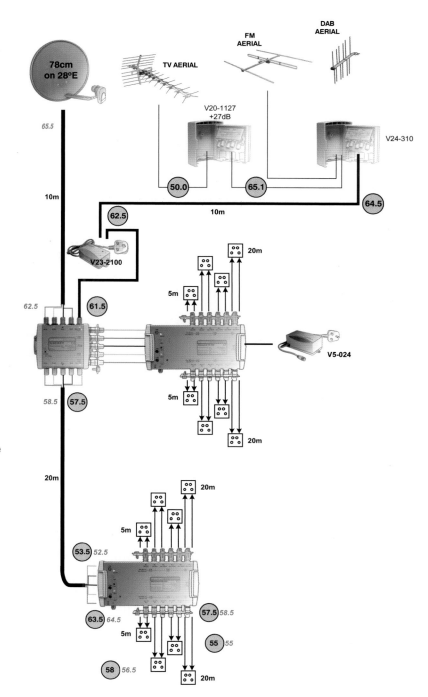

Keywords

The next example is for the same buildings using **Spaun** equipment, but with a nine cable backbone to provide both the Astra and Hotbird satellite signals at 28°E and 13°E respectively. The following system parameters were used:

The calculations show that a DTT level of 59dBμV is required into the launch amplifier in order to receive 55dBμV at the weakest point on the network. The multiband amplifier will deliver 68dBμV, so an adjustable attenuator must be fitted and adjusted to lose 9dB.

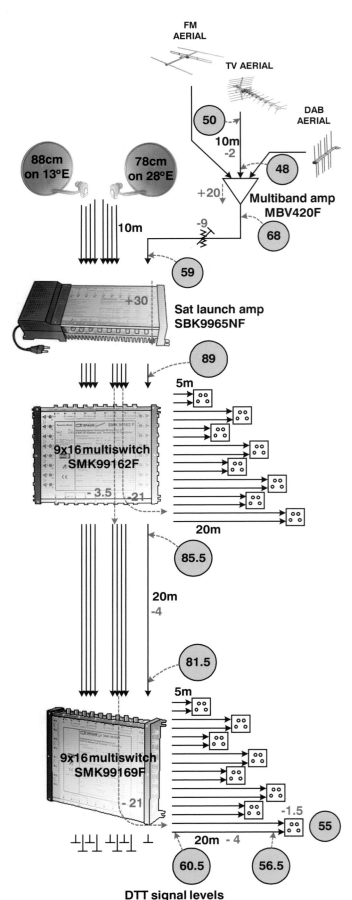

FM AERIAL

TV AERIAL

DAB AERIAL

50

10m
-2

48

+20

Multiband amp
MBV420F

-9

68

59

+30

Sat launch amp
SBK9965NF

89

5m

9x16 multiswitch
SMK99162F

- 3.5   -21

20m

85.5

20m
-4

81.5

5m

9x16 multiswitch
SMK99169F

- 21

-1.5

55

20m - 4

60.5   56.5

DTT signal levels

These calculations show that the satellite IF launch amplifier must deliver 89dBµV for the system to operate satisfactorily at the furthest point on the network. It is predicted that the input level from the LNB will be 77dBµV, so the gain of the launch amplifier must be reduced by 19dB.

These nine cable backbone systems are normally set to default to the Sky programmes and a Hotbird receiver must be programmed to send a DiSEqC switching command to access the Hotbird channels.

The Spaun range of products includes a DiSEqC tone burst generator type SUG2201F for use to switch between satellites if the satellite receivers do not incorporate such a facility.

Spaun also offer a seventeen cable backbone system which is capable of accessing four satellites when given the appropriate DiSEqC commands.

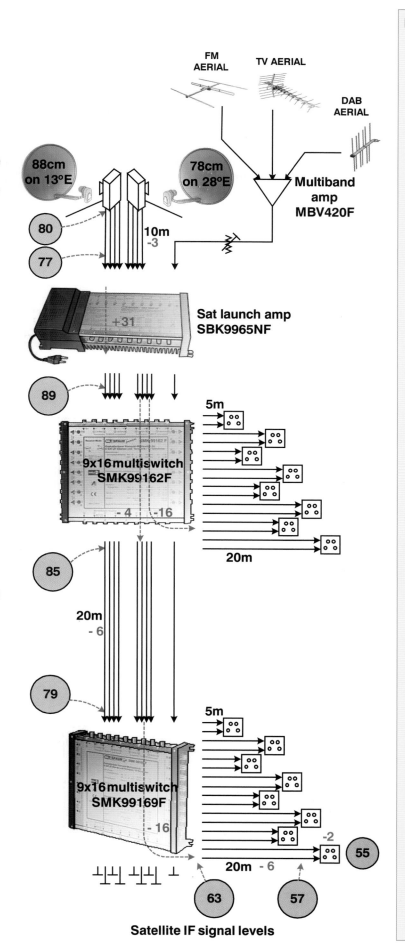

Satellite IF signal levels

Keywords

- DiSEqC Tone Burst Generator

- Seventeen Cable Backbone

Keywords

Vision Example •

This calculation is for an eighteen storey block of flats with 6 flats per floor, each requiring radio, UHF TV and Sky Plus facilities.

Vision equipment is used for this example. A total of nine 24 way switches are installed, each serving two floors. This equipment uses system taps to feed each multiswitch and the switch has a significant dB gain (as opposed to a loss in the previous examples).

Voltage is relayed via the "horizontal high" backbone cable to power the terrestrial amplifier in each switch, the satellite amplifier being powered from the satellite receiver at the viewing location.

The relevant parameters are as follows:

• Signal levels measured from UHF TV aerial –	analogue	70dBµV
	DTT	50dBµV
• Signal levels from Quatro LNB –		80dBµV
• Programmable Varifilter, V90-110 - Gain	FM	40dB
	DAB	40dB
	UHF	40dB
	Max UHF output level	119dBµV
• Satellite launch amplifier, V5-100T, satellite gain		22dB
	UHF gain	17dB
	Max satellite output level	110dBµV
	Max UHF output level	114dBµV
	Maximum current	2 amps
• 5x24 multiswitch, V5-524,	Satellite gain	14dB
	UHF gain	10dB
	Max satellite output level	93dBµV
	Max UHF output level	90dBµV
	Current consumption	160mA
• Quad plate gain	UHF	1.5dB
	Satellite	-2dB
• Cable gain, CT100type /10m	UHF	-2dB
	Satellite	-3dB

• Tap losses (UHF and Sat.):	Through	Side
V5-204	4dB	4dB
V5-210	2dB	10dB
V5-220	1dB	20dB

Keywords

These drawings show the calculated signal levels throughout the network. In this case, the required DTT launch level is 78.5dBµV. Since the Varifilter output is higher than this, this gains must be reduced.

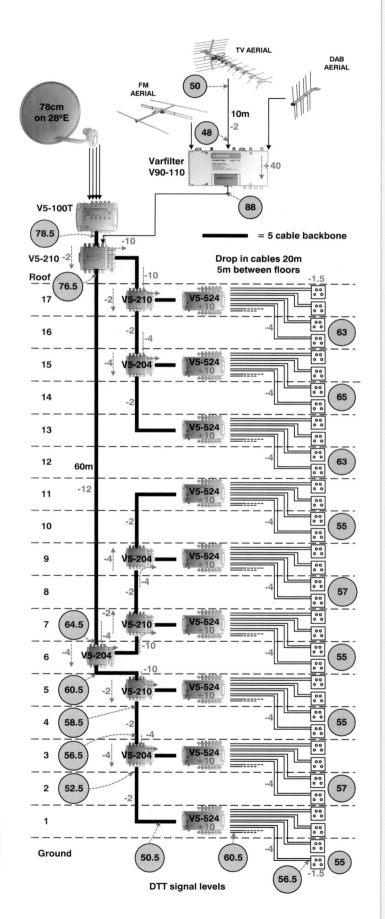

TV AERIAL

FM AERIAL

DAB AERIAL

78cm on 28°E

50

10m
-2

48

Varfilter V90-110

+40

88

V5-100T

78.5

= 5 cable backbone

-10

V5-210 -2

Roof 76.5

Drop in cables 20m
5m between floors

-10

-1.5

17   -2   V5-210   V5-524 +10

16   -2   -4   63

15   -4   V5-204   V5-524 +10

14   -2   -4   65

13   V5-524 +10

12   60m   -4   63

11   -12   V5-524 +10

10   -2   -4   55

9   -4   V5-204   V5-524 +10

8   -2   -4   57

7   64.5   -2   V5-210   V5-524 +10
         -4

6   -4   V5-204   -10   -4   55

5   60.5   -10   -2   V5-210   V5-524 +10

4   58.5   -2   -4   55

3   56.5   -4   V5-204   V5-524 +10

2   52.5   -4   57
         -2

1   V5-524 +10

Ground   50.5   -4   60.5   55
                    56.5   -1.5

DTT signal levels

Keywords

The required satellite IF signal level into the cable network needs to be 85dBµV so the gain of the launch amplifier will need to be reduced accordingly.

V5 multiswitches have stepped outputs so the outlets with longer drop-in cables can be connected to the higher level outputs.

Vision offer a free system design service for all new IRS projects.

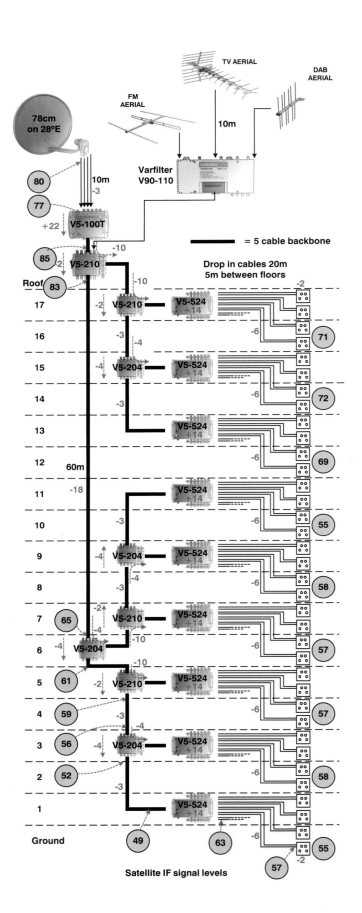

Keywords

• Four Cable Backbone

• Satellite IF Amplifiers

Systems with Four Cable Backbones

Some apartment blocks already have a satisfactory MATV system distributing terrestrial radio and UHF TV services to each apartment. When these are upgraded to provide satellite services, it may be necessary to provide only a four cable backbone system. Most manufacturers offer multiswitches with four satellite IF inputs – these usually do not require a mains voltage input, the power being provided by the satellite receivers. However, such systems must still be bonded to a proper earth as detailed in part 8.4.

Satellite IF Amplifiers

For both domestic installations and IRS projects, it is sometimes necessary to fit satellite IF line amplifiers on long cable runs, to ensure that the signals do not drop below their minimum required levels. In such cases, care must be taken to ensure that the amplifiers do not operate above their rated maximum output levels and the overall C/N of the system is not degraded, as illustrated in the following example:

Assume that the satellite IF signal level is 80dBµV at the LNB output, and that the minimum signal level into the satellite receiver is 47dBµV.

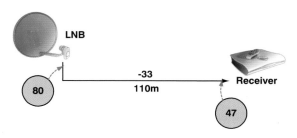

Using WF100 type cable, the signal loss is 3dB per 10m at 2150MHz.

The maximum permitted attenuation is 80 − 47 = 33dB, so the maximum cable length will be 110m. For longer cable lengths, an IF line amplifier must be fitted. The version shown alongside has a gain of 22dB at 2150MHz, extending the system reach by just over 70m. These amplifiers are normally powered by the 12/18 volts being relayed to the LNB. For IRS networks with Quatro LNBs, four such amplifiers would be required.

The specified maximum output level of the amplifier is 93dBµV (after derating, to allow for the number of multiplexes being relayed). Therefore, it cannot be located adjacent to the LNB because its output level would be too high.

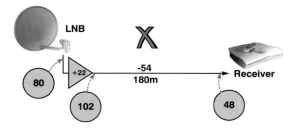

If it were fitted at the input to the receiver, its input level would be well below the required minimum level, severely reducing the C/N ratio.

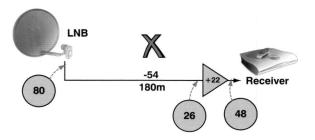

• Amplifier Location

Keywords

The best location is where the output of the amplifier is at its maximum rated level – in this case, 30m from the LNB.

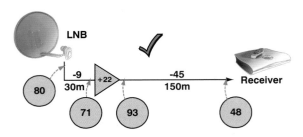

As a general rule, measure the carrier levels at the LNB output and calculate the length of cable required to attenuate the signal down to the maximum input level of the IF amplifier (this is its maximum output less its gain) – the amplifier should then be fitted at, or slightly beyond, this distance from the LNB. IF amplifiers should generally be located nearer to the LNB than to the receiver.

8.6   Installation Techniques

Network Layouts

Internal IRS •
Cable Routes

New blocks of flats are always wired internally. The usual method is to install the equipment and backbone cables in the service risers, with the drop-in cables either loose laid or contained in 20mm PVC conduit, terminating in a single or double gang flush box at each receiver location.

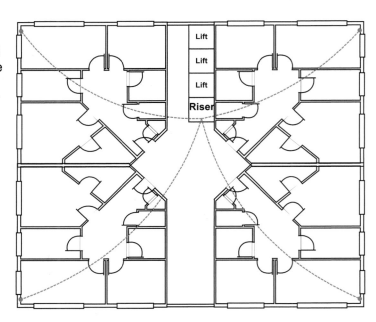

Existing blocks are normally wired either through the loft spaces, or externally. Drop-in cables are run vertically down the outside walls, entering each apartment through a hole and terminating on a surface mounted outlet plate.

External IRS •
Cable Routes

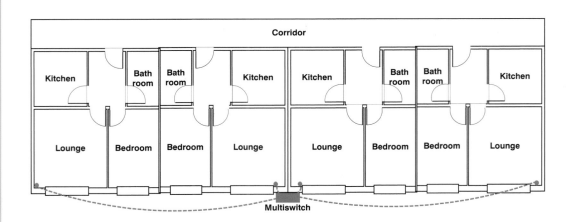

Keywords

If a satisfactory MATV system already exists, satellite services can be added by installing an IRS network with just a four-cable backbone, the fifth coaxial cable (for terrestrial TV) not being required.

For buildings with up to three stories, the external horizontal cables would normally be routed under the eaves, thus providing some protection against rainwater.

The problem with taller buildings is that a ladder is not a safe working platform above the third storey, so other means of access must be found.

For the block of flats shown alongside, each lounge had an outside balcony and the multiswitches were located in the lofts. It was then possible to install the drop-in cables fixed vertically between the balconies, using just a stepladder on each balcony.

There were no balconies on this block but the grass around the building was flat with no hedges. It was therefore possible to use a portable scaffold tower to fix the trunking containing the vertical drop-in cables; the multiswitches were housed in metal outdoor cabinets on the inside parapet wall of the flat roof.

This building has a sloping tiled roof and large lofts accessible through hatches in the stairwell ceilings. The multiswitches were located in the lofts and a cherry-picker was needed to install the vertical drop-in cables, since access was not available for a portable scaffold tower on two sides of the building.

This building was also wired on the outside, using a 3 section ladder for the three lower floors. Since each lounge had a large picture window that opened fully, it was possible to fix the vertical cables to the upper floors by leaning out of the windows. The flat roof provided easy access for the roof connections to the multiswitches.

The building shown alongside was wired using the balconies on each floor to fix the vertical drop-in cables between floors. The photograph shows all the BSkyB dishes that were replaced by a single dish on the flat roof and connected to all the apartments using an IRS cable network.

Keywords

Lack of access sometimes means that it is just not possible to fix drop-in cables to the outside of the building, and they have to be routed internally. The multiswitches would then be located in a vertical riser on every floor (or every second floor), the drop-in cables being contained in 16mm² self-adhesive PVC trunking.

**Loft Box •
Location**

Larger apartments may require the additional facilities provided by the "loft box" concept, as described in part 8.1. The ideal conduit requirements for such facilities are shown alongside, the loftbox being located in a utility cupboard and requiring a mains power socket and a good earth.

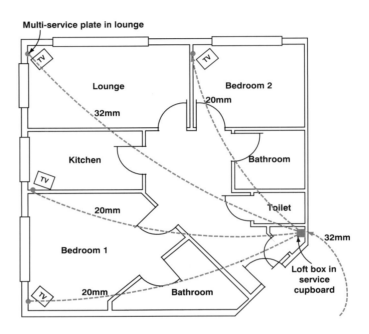

Tall Buildings •

Tall buildings give rise to the following additional considerations:

- Being exposed to very high winds, great care must be taken to ensure that the aerial mast and satellite dish on the roof are fixed very securely.
- Any cellphone relay equipment sharing the same roof must be switched off whenever personnel are working on the roof – the relevant contact telephone number is always displayed.
- Because of the increased risk of lightning strikes, it is recommended **Surge Arrestors •** that surge arrestors are fitted to all coaxial cables incoming from the roof – the photograph alongside shows a bank of these arrestors.

**Equipment •
Cabinets**

Equipment Cabinets

Wall mounted equipment is often mounted on a plywood board enclosed in a cabinet. This can be a metal frame around the equipment with a lockable front panel, or a complete unit.

IP Rating •

Outdoor cabinets are graded using an "IP" rating. IP protection conforms to Standard BS 5490 and is a two digit number used to define protection against solid objects and liquids, as follows:

Keywords

First digit – protection against solid objects:

0	No protection
1	Up to 50mm eg touch by finger
2	Up to 12mm eg touch by tools
3	Up to 2.5mm eg tools/wires
4	Up to 1mm eg small wires
5	Dust limited ingress
6	Dust protected

Second digit – protection against liquids:

0	No protection
1	Vertical water drops eg condensation
2	Direct sprays up to 15° from vertical
3	Direct sprays up to 60° from vertical
4	Water sprayed from all directions
5	Low pressure water jets
6	Strong water jets
7	Immersion between 15cm and 1m
8	Long periods of immersion

Most outdoor enclosures used in the TV industry are specified to IP56 or better, although the lack of ventilation holes in such cabinets may cause a build up of heat inside the enclosure.

Multiswitches can be either end-mounted or flat mounted. End mounting makes the connectors more accessible for servicing, whereas flat mounting makes it easier to dress the cables neatly.

- Multiswitch Mounting

Cable Networks

Many electrical contractors install slotted metal trays in service risers for electrical and communication cables. A more convenient solution for IRS networks (especially where a cable tray is not available) is to use composite cable sheaths containing four or five individual coaxial cables which can be fixed directly to a riser wall using "P" clips.

- Composite Coax Cables

- P Clips

Take care not to cross-connect the IRS backbone cables. A recent innovation is the use of coloured backbone cables and the following colour code is now used:

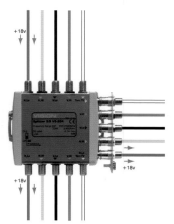

- Backbone Cable
- Colour Code

Service	Colour
Horizontal low band	Green
Horizontal high band	Yellow
Vertical low band	Black
Vertical high band	Red
Terrestrial services	White

Some manufacturers have also colour-coded the backbone

Keywords

connectors on their equipment, so that each coloured cable is connected to the connector with the same colour.

Cables on •
Flat Roofs

IRS cables must not be laid directly on flat roofs. Metal cable trays should be installed and the cables attached with plastic ties. The trays must be supported at regular intervals with short sections of 50x50mm slotted tray, or breeze blocks. Since roofing felt becomes soft in hot weather, the load should be spread using a small piece of felt, an offcut of marine-grade plywood, or even a piece of polystyrene sheet. The metal tray should be electrically bonded to the lightning protection system, if one exists.

This photograph shows the flat roof of a four storey block with the drop-in cables tied on trays – the cables are then routed over the low parapet wall and down the outside of the building to each apartment.

External Vertical •
Cables

The exterior vertical cables can be contained in pvc or metal trunking with clip-on covers, or cable-tied to a vertical catenary wire, this being attached to the building with eye bolts at the top and bottom, as shown alongside.

Another method is to install false vertical rainwater drainpipes, into which the cables are inserted!

Keywords

• Non-Penetrating
  Roof Mount

On flat roofs, it may be necessary to mount the aerials and dish(es) on a non-penetrating mount, this being held in place with dense concrete blocks.

Earthing

The mandatory requirement to earth all systems is often achieved by fitting earth bars on the inputs and outputs of each unit. Several manufacturers now supply equipment with the earth bars already fitted. Alternatively, the earth bars can be fitted separately and connected to the equipment with F-F leads.

• Earth Bars

Another new innovation is the use of push-on F connectors with earth lugs.

• Earth Lugs

Other versions have push-on F connectors connected together with flexible copper braid.

A recent document now allows for the metal case of each unit to be earthed instead of the input/output connectors, as detailed in section 8.4. In such cases, special precautions must be taken when changing a unit to preserve the integrity of the earthing system.

Keywords

Equipment •
Cabinets
Wall Panels •

Equipment Mounting

Equipment can be mounted either in 19" equipment cabinets, or on wall panels as shown below:

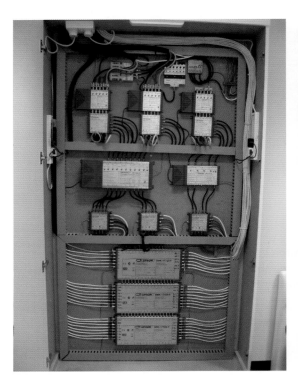

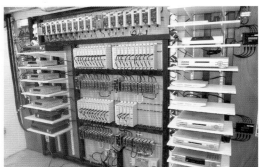

Keywords

- Signal Measurements

- Crystal Palace UHF Channels

- UHF PAL I Channel

9.1   The Frequency Spectrum

The procedure for measuring signal parameters consists of two steps:

1. Select the required range of frequencies over which the measurements are to be carried out.
2. Perform the required measurements on the selected frequency range.

The relevant frequency ranges are as follows:

UHF analogue and DTT	470 – 854MHz
Satellite IF	950 – 2150MHz

The UHF frequency spectrum is divided into channels 21-68, each 8MHz wide. Each transmitter location broadcasts analogue and/or digital programmes – the channel allocations for the Crystal Palace channels prior to the termination of the analogue transmissions are shown below:

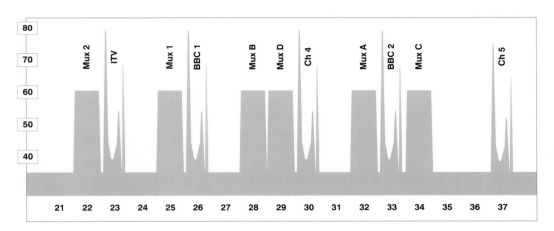

Analogue signal level measurements on UK channels are always carried out on the picture (luminance) carrier frequency, which is 1,25MHz above the start frequency of the 8MHz channel, because this is where most of the power is concentrated. The measurement is usually the RMS value at the peak of the sync. pulses. This represents the peak power transmitted – if the sync. pulse is ignored, the measurement would be some 5dB lower. Network equipment, such as amplifiers, have their distortion performance measured against the equivalent peak sync. levels. The measurement (resolution) bandwidth is usually between 100KHz and 250KHz – corrections are not necessary to allow for the power contained in the sub-carriers because they are significantly lower.

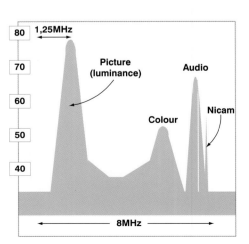

Keywords

DTT Level •
Measurements

Interpolation •

Integration •

Digital signals are different. The digital information is contained in many carrier frequencies spread across nearly all of the 8MHz channel bandwidth and it is necessary to measure the average power of all these carrier frequencies together.

The measuring device is normally set to the centre frequency of the 8MHz channel although most meters do this automatically when the channel number is selected. Basic meters measure the centre frequency and interpolate the power of the whole multiplex, whereas the more sophisticated versions measure the power of all the carriers and integrate them together:

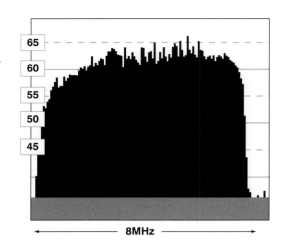

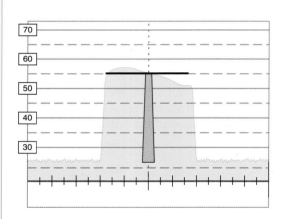

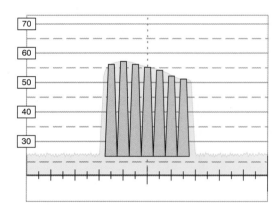

The table on the next page lists the frequency band for all the UHF channels, together with the analogue vision carrier frequency and the digital multiplex centre frequency:

Satellite •
Digital Level
Measurements

Satellite IF digital signal levels are measured in the same way. Some meters have an adjustable bandwidth and this should be set to the bandwidth of the signal being measured (normally 30MHz or 40MHz). The meter should then be tuned to the centre frequency of the multiplex and the digital signal levels recorded.

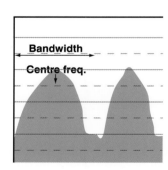

Keywords

- UHF Channels

9.2 Analogue TV Measurement Parameters

The UHF channel frequencies are as follows:

Ch	Analogue Vision Freq. MHz	Digital Centre Freq. MHz	Ch	Range MHz	Analogue Vision Freq. MHz	Digital Centre Freq. MHz
21	471.25	474	45	662-670	663.25	666
22	479.25	482	46	670-678	671.25	674
23	487.25	490	47	678-686	679.25	682
24	495.25	498	48	686-694	687.25	690
25	503.25	506	49	694-702	695.25	698
26	511.25	514	50	702-710	703.25	706
27	519.25	522	51	710-718	711.25	714
28	527.25	530	52	718-726	719.25	722
29	535.25	538	53	726-734	725.25	730
30	543.25	546	54	734-742	735.25	738
31	551.25	554	55	742.750	743.25	746
32	559.25	562	56	750-758	751.25	754
33	567.25	570	57	758-766	759.25	762
34	575.25	578	58	766-774	767.25	770
35	583.25	586	59	774-782	775.25	778
36	591.25	594	60	782-790	783.25	786
37	599.25	602	61	790-798	791.25	794
38	607.25	610	62	798-806	799.25	802
39	615.25	618	63	806-814	807.25	810
40	623.25	626	64	814-822	815.25	818
41	631.25	634	65	822-830	823.25	826
42	639.25	642	66	830-838	831.25	834
43	647.25	650	67	838-846	839.25	842
44	655.25	658	68	846-854	847.25	850

It is important to ensure that the analogue signal level does not drop below 60dBμV anywhere on the system, otherwise the picture quality will be degraded by noise.

One should also ensure that none of the system electronics is overloaded, otherwise the picture quality will be degraded by intermodulation and cross modulation distortion. The signal levels at the input to an analogue TV receiver should not exceed 80dBμV. Amplifier outputs should not exceed their maximum rated values, these having been derated in accordance with the rules given in section 5.4.

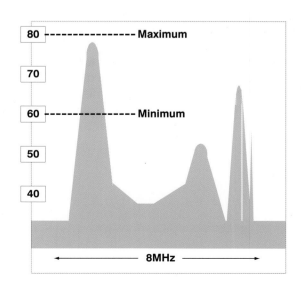

- Analogue Signal Level Limits

Keywords

The analogue picture quality should also be visually assessed using the CCIR impairment scale, and the cause of any downgrading recorded (eg ghosting, patterning, co-channel interference, intermodulation distortion etc).

It is important to examine the signal levels, not just for one UHF channel, but for all channels across the UHF frequency band. Cable losses increase with frequency so the signal levels will be less on the higher channels. Some channels may have extraneous interference from sources such as microwave towers, radar and TETRA relay sites, all of which may degrade the TV signals. It is also advisable to check any associated FM or DAB signal levels, to ensure that they will not overload any TV amplifiers.

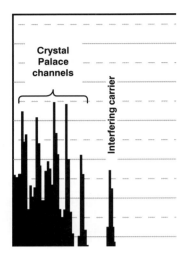

Noise levels and signal-to-noise ratios are not generally measured for analogue TV, but can be directly related to the received signal strength measured at the aerial. The easiest way to determine if the S/N ratio is adequate is to observe the picture quality. As a general guide:

60dBμV	CCIR Grade 5	equivalent S/N 46dB or better
54dBμV	CCIR Grade 4	equivalent S/N 43dB
48dBμV	CCIR Grade 3	equivalent S/N 40dB or worse

A very poor S/N ratio can be identified using a spectrum analyser. However, some spectrum analysers have a poor noise figure and will therefore contribute a reasonable proportion of noise to the measured signals.

S/N ratio is the term normally applied to the analogue baseband video signal-to-noise ratio ie the demodulated signal.

9.3   Digital TV Measurement Parameters

Signal Levels

DTT Level •
Limits

The signal levels into a DTT Freeview receiver must be between 45 – 65dBμV. The upper limit is because analogue signal levels are typically 20dB higher than the digital levels, and an analogue level of 85dBμV will overload a DTT receiver – the 65dBμV upper limit for digital levels may be increased in due course when the analogue transmissions are terminated.

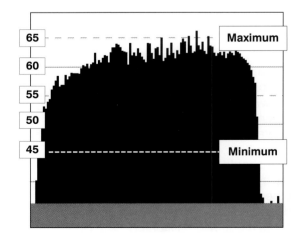

Keywords

Carrier to Noise Ratio

Data can be relayed by varying the phase and amplitude of each cycle of a carrier wave.
The rotating vector represents the "1" and "0" data bits in sequence.

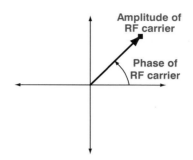

This 16QAM drawing shows sixteen different "states" per cycle.

• 16QAM Display

16 QAM - 4 bits per cycle

If each of the 16 states is a single dot, this indicates a clean (and therefore robust) digital signal. Noise or distortion on a data symbol will cause changes to the amplitude and/or phase of the rotating vector. If the dots are dispersed, the symbol is more likely to be wrongly interpreted, causing errors.

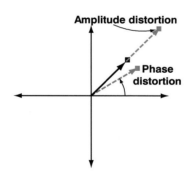

• Effect of Noise and Distortion

As long as each "hit" stays within the amplitude/phase boundary representing a particular binary number, the receiver will interpret the data correctly.

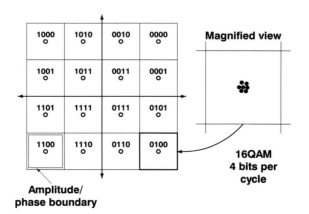

Keywords

Digital Errors •

If the distortion becomes more severe, the dots spread out, until, eventually, they fall into an adjacent boundary - the digital receiver will then interpret the information wrongly, causing an error. The greater the noise, the more likely it is that this will occur.

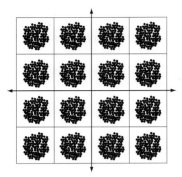

Constellation •
Diagram

These drawings are known as **"constellation diagrams"** which can be displayed on some makes of spectrum analyser. They provide a very useful indication of the robustness of a data signal.

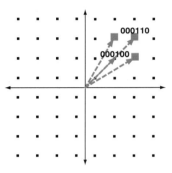

Carrier-to-Noise •
(C/N) Ratio

It is therefore most important to measure the amplitude of any noise induced on to the received signal, in relation to the amplitude of the carrier wave – this is known as the **C**arrier-to-**N**oise ratio **(C/N).**

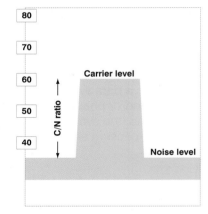

The higher the C/N ratio, the better. The minimum C/N ratio required depends on the type of modulation used and the amount of error correction applied to the received signal, as described earlier in this document. The minimum DTT C/N ratios are as follows:

DTT C/N Limits •

| 16QAM (FEC 3/4) | 22dB |
| 64QAM (FEC 2/3) | 26dB |

Noise •
Measurements
Location

Ideally, the noise level should be measured in the same UHF channel as the received signal. Since this is clearly not possible, the noise measurement should be made at a frequency as close to the UHF channel as possible and where no other UHF signal is present – this is known as a "near noise" measurement. If there are occupied channels on either side of the one being measured, it will be necessary to make a "far noise" measurement on a nearby unoccupied UHF channel:

9

Keywords

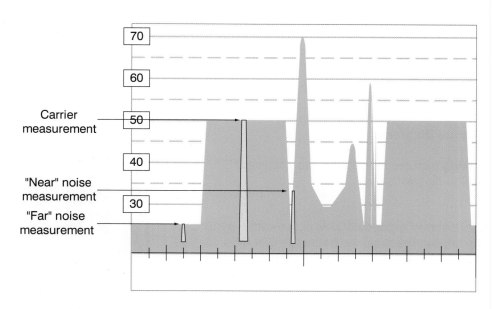

Carrier measurement

"Near" noise measurement

"Far" noise measurement

Some spectrum analysers allow the user to define the frequency at which the noise measurement is made. This should be as close as possible to the channel being evaluated, since the noise level can vary over the UHF frequency band.

Bit Error Ratio (BER)

BER measurements can be made at various points in the reception chain:

- Before any error correction is applied – this is known as the "channel BER" or CBER.
- After Viterbi and before Reed Solomon error correction – called the "post- Viterbi BER" or VBER.
- After all the error correction has been applied (LBER). At this point, there should of course be no errors at all.

- BER Measurement
- CBER
- VBER

- LBER

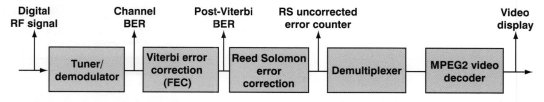

Digital reception - measurement locations

Some spectrum analysers can display the BER at all these locations, and even provide a running count of how many errors have occurred at the MPEG2 video decoder over the entire time period since the analyser locked on to the incoming data stream.

- BER Locations

BER measurements are normally made "post-Viterbi" and "pre-Reed Solomon", where the maximum permitted number of errors for both DTT and satellite IF measurements is 2 errors in every 10 000 bits of data received – this will result in fewer than one non-correctable error for every transmission hour, which is known as **Q**uasi-**E**rror **F**ree **"QEF"**. The amount of Viterbi correction depends on the FEC applied by the broadcaster, but it can be very substantial. BER measurements cannot easily be made post-Reed Solomon because the errors occur so infrequently.

- BER Limit

- QEF

Keywords

The BER is normally quoted in the form **X.X** E - **X** (scientific notation) eg. 3E -4

This is interpreted as 1 part in 3×10^4 = 1 part in 30 000.

Similarly, 3E-7 = 1 part in 3×10^7 = 1 part in 30 000 000.

Constellation •
Diagrams

Constellation Diagrams

The following pictures indicate how to analyse DTT constellation diagrams:

This picture shows a good 64QAM signal with a 30dB C/N ratio. The smaller the dots, the better the C/N ratio.

This is what happens when the signal does not lock.
The receiver is unable to recognise the data being received.

Here, the constellation has locked, but the C/N ratio is very marginal.

Phase noise is visible on this display. This is a circular effect that is most pronounced at the perimeter.
Phase noise is most likely due to the head-end equipment and is not caused by normal transmission along a network.

This has been named the "polo mint" effect. It is caused by an "in-channel" spurious analogue signal approximately 25dB less than the QAM signal. The digital picture would still be perfect but the offending signal should be traced before it causes trouble.

Keywords

This display shows a DTT channel from the Crystal Palace transmitter. The digital picture quality on a TV receiver is perfect, but the system is about to fail because the C/N ratio is only 19dB.
The constellation diagram clearly shows that there is a problem that must be solved!

Modulation Error Ratio (MER)

This is the power of the carrier level, compared to the power of the noise present in the constellation. In effect, it is the C/N ratio with the noise measured within the multiplex. Some meters will measure this for specified individual carriers within a COFDM multiplex.

The minimum MER values depend on the amount of error correction applied and are as follows:

DTT –	FEC	Limit		Satellite IF –	FEC	Limit
	2/3	25dB			2/3	9dB
	3/4	20dB			3/4	12dB
					5/6	13dB

Some meters also indicate the noise margin. This indicates the safety margin in dB above the MER limit at which the BER would be at its recommended minimum value.

9.4   Signal Level Meters

Terrestrial

Many installers still use a tuneable signal level meter for the alignment of terrestrial aerials. The measurement procedure is as follows:

- Tune the meter to the required channel or multiplex.
- Adjust the fixed attenuators to suit the signal level.
- Adjust the frequency to peak the reading.
- Measure and record the signal level in dBμV or dBmV.

Terrestrial measurements are usually taken for each channel that is required. It is usually best to peak the aerial on the weakest channel so as to obtain equal signal strength on all channels, rather than the maximum signal on the strongest channels.

Digital measurements should also include C/N ratio and BER.

This meter displays the levels of a number of channels simultaneously. For digital measurements, it also gives an indication of BER by a Pass (P) or Fail (F) for each multiplex.

Keywords

- Modulation Error Ratio (MER)

- MER Limits

- Noise Margin

- DTT Meters

Keywords

Satellite Digital •
Meters

Spectrum •
Analysers

Satellite

The procedure is much the same. Satellite measurements should be taken on sample multiplexes at the bottom, middle and top of each of the four satellite IF frequency bands.

This meter also has a spectrum display.

9.5 Spectrum Analysers

A spectrum analyser displays the instantaneous amplitude of an incoming signal over a specified range of frequencies:

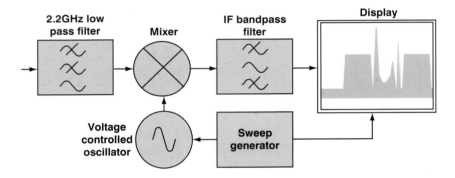

Analysers are battery-powered, mostly with rechargeable batteries. The display device used to be a cathode ray tube (CRT) although modern versions tend to use an LCD display which is lighter, less bulky and consumes less power. Versions are available for terrestrial or satellite applications, or both.

Most modern spectrum analysers are sophisticated instruments that can provide a wealth of information not previously available, to assist the installer and make his job a lot easier. A more detailed schematic layout of such a unit is shown below:

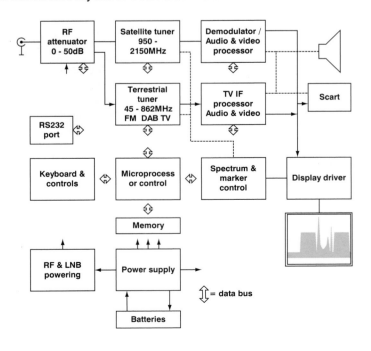

Keywords

• Analyser
  Applications

Analogue applications

The basic functions of a spectrum analyser are as follows:

• Signal level measurement either by a bar display or alphanumeric characters, with frequency selection either by continuous adjustment, direct frequency entry or channel number.
• Picture display and sound monitoring.
• Spectrum display, either over a whole frequency band or over a smaller (adjustable) band.

Modern analysers also incorporate some or all of the following additional facilities:

• Audible indication of signal level (tone with variable pitch).
• Signal search.
• Sync pulse display.
• External video and audio input and output.
• Integral noise generator.
• NICAM decoder.
• Teletext decoder.
• Memory locations for preset measurement parameters.
• Data storage with a printer port to provide a written record of measurements taken.

Some terrestrial meters can generate a voltage to power a masthead preamplifier. Satellite versions can have 12/18V switching, 22KHz tone and an integral DiSEqC generator.

Digital applications

Digital spectrum analysers can be used for analogue measurements and offer some or all of the following functions for digital measurements:

• Measurement of RF parameters such as channel power (with an adjustable bandwidth) and C/N ratio.
• Spectrum display, to detect interfering signals and measure the flatness of the multiplex. A common interfering signal on satellite IF systems is from DECT phones at 1890MHz.
• Demodulation of the digital signal (this needs either a COFDM or QPSK demodulator card for terrestrial and satellite applications respectively) in order to measure the bit error ratio (both before and after "Viterbi" error correction has been applied), CSI display and give the quantity of "wrong packets" received.
• Digital picture display - this needs an MPEG2 decoder card, possibly with a card reader (if encrypted programmes are to be displayed).

Some models are offered in a basic format with an upgrade ability to add additional functions by plugging in extra modules.

An important parameter to consider when choosing a spectrum analyser is its dynamic range. This is the range of signal levels that can be resolved on the display screen. A wide dynamic range allows the user to see both strong carrier signals and much weaker noise or interfering signals on the screen at the same time.

9

Keywords

Spectrum • Display

Spectrum Display

A spectrum analyser is able to display the whole of the frequency spectrum of interest and to expand the display around a selected frequency. This gives some or all of the following specific advantages over a simple level meter:

- The ability to see and identify interfering or unwanted signals elsewhere in the band that would otherwise not be noticed.
- The ability to select the frequency at which the noise level is to be measured.
- The ability to see and measure distortions across a digital multiplex. This example illustrates the variation of signal level across a PAL I multiplex, the higher frequency signals having a greater amplitude – this is called positive slope. This could be caused by the wrong alignment of a channel amplifier or because it is being operated at more than its maximum output. A dip in the centre of the multiplex could be due to standing waves on the network.

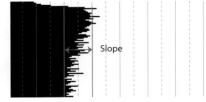

- On satellite IF networks, the ability to see signals of the opposite polarity and minimise them by adjusting the LNB skew.

This meter has an "explore" function which scans the selected frequency band, identifies each channel or multiplex found, and stores them for subsequent analysis. It also incorporates a data logger to record the signal parameters achieved for subsequent recording and archive purposes.

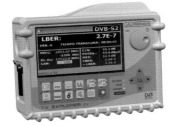

This version has two screens, both of which can display the frequency spectrum and the relevant data. Alternatively, one screen can display a picture and the other data, each providing an uncluttered display.

9

Keywords

• Astra 28°E
Spectrum
Displays

• IF Slope
Example

The IF spectrum displays for Astra @ 28°E are shown below.

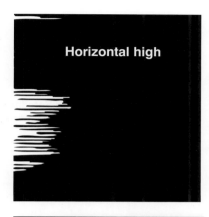

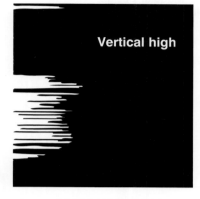

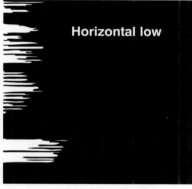

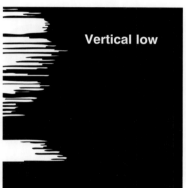

Some satellites carry both analogue and digital transponders. The analogue signals are easily recognised as shown alongside – all spectrum analysers give demodulated analogue picture displays, thus providing a positive identification of the satellite(s) being received.

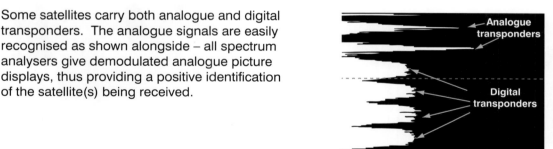

It is important to ensure that the amplitude of the multiplexes is reasonably constant across the whole IF band. If the amplitude gets smaller at the higher frequencies, this could result in missing channels, possibly caused by water in the cables or wrong adjustment of the slope control (if fitted).

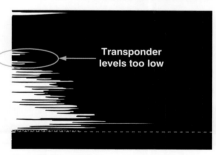

This display shows how an interfering signal at 12182MHz can cause loss of reception of the channels in the multiplex on which it is superimposed.

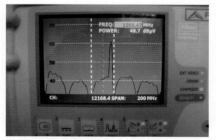

Domestic Signal Distribution

VISION®

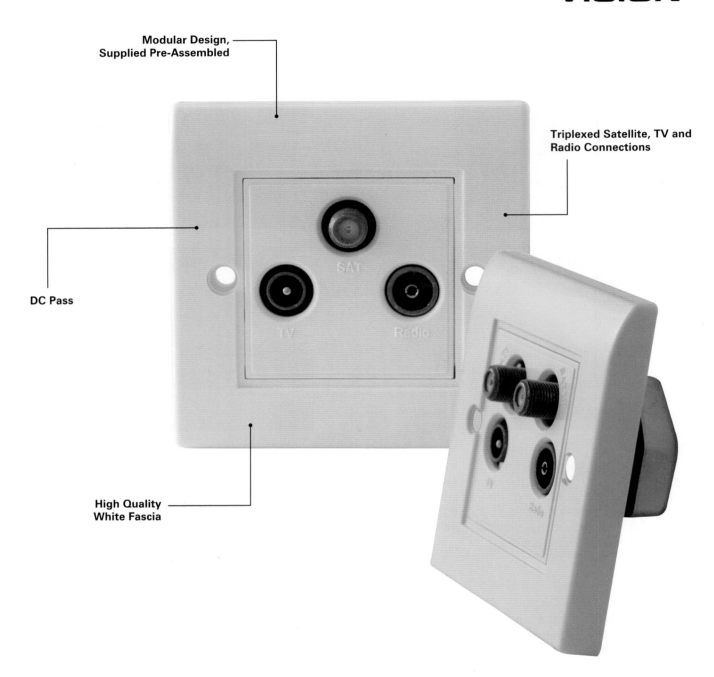

Modular Design, Supplied Pre-Assembled

Triplexed Satellite, TV and Radio Connections

DC Pass

High Quality White Fascia

SAT

TV

Radio

Features will vary across the range from model to model

Also Available In The Vision Outlet Plate Range

| F Connector Satellite Wall Plate | IEC TV Wall Plate | Diplexed TV / Radio | Triplexed SAT2 / TV / Radio | SAT / TV / Radio / Return / Telephone |

Keywords

10.1 Why Fibre?

Radio frequency signals in the VHF, UHF and satellite IF bands can be relayed using coaxial cables, but suffer from the following disadvantages:
*   Signal attenuation is high, so repeater amplifiers may be required to keep the signal levels within defined windows of operation.
*   Equalisers may have to be fitted, to compensate for the increased signal losses at higher frequencies.
*   The signals may be affected by external electrical interference.
*   Lightning strikes can damage equipment and relay cables.
*   Varying earth potentials can give rise to safety issues.

• Disadvantages
  of Cable

All these drawbacks can be minimized or even eliminated by using a beam of light as the transmission medium. The intensity of the beam can be modulated to carry the information through the air without the need for a transmitting licence, as long as there is a continuous line-of-sight path between the transmitting and receiving locations.

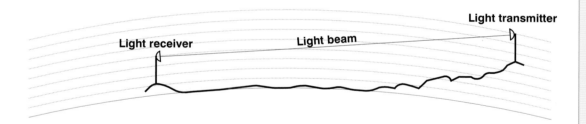

It is also possible to relay the light beam along a thin transparent "optical fibre". The beam can be amplitude-modulated to relay TV and satellite signals between two or more locations. Fibre optic networks are already used extensively as high speed data links, and recent developments have resulted in the introduction of low cost fibre systems for the TV industry that offer significant advantages over the traditional method of using coaxial cables for this purpose.

• Optical Fibre
• Fibre
  Applications

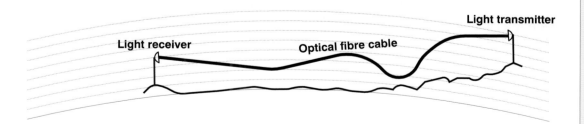

10.2 The Propagation of Light

Light waves are similar to radio waves, but have a very much higher frequency.
Visible light has a typical frequency of 1 000 000 GHz and a corresponding wavelength of 3×10^{-6} metres:

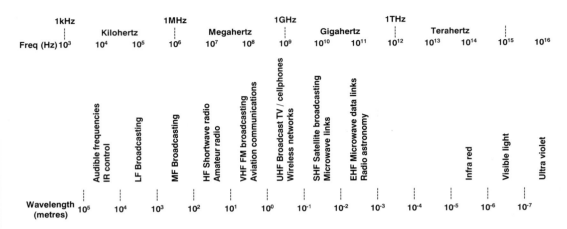

Light travels through the air, or any transparent medium. When it travels from one medium to another with a different density, two effects can occur:

- Some of the light is reflected – the transition acts like a mirror.
- Some of the light passes through the interface, but the beam is bent or "refracted".

These effects can be seen when looking into water. You can sometimes see your own reflection on the surface and a straight stick appears to be bent at the point where it enters the water.

The amount of reflection and refraction depends on the angle at which the light beam strikes the interface between the two media:

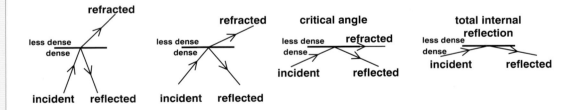

At less than a certain "critical angle", there is total internal reflection and all the light is contained within the boundaries of the medium. This is the principle of fibre optics, whereby all the light hits the interface at less than the critical angle and therefore stays within the fibre.

10

Keywords

• Fibre
  Wavelengths

10.3 Wavelengths and Types of Propagation

This diagram shows the relationship between wavelength and signal attenuation in an optical fibre.

The original fibre links in the 1970s used an optical wavelength of 800-900 nanometres (nm), with an optical fibre loss of around 10dB per Km. Subsequent advances in technology have resulted in the use of lower loss fibre cables and longer wavelengths of about 1300nm and 1600nm. Fibre optic systems currently used in the TV industry operate by amplitude modulating a single light frequency with an optical wavelength of either 1310 or 1550 nanometres.

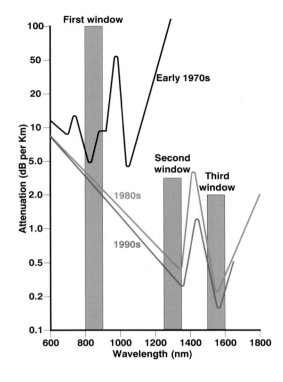

There are two types of optical fibre:

• Multimode, with a core diameter of 50-100 micrometres (10^{-6} metres), used mainly for lower bandwidth telecommunications and data communication applications.

• Multimode Fibre

A multimode 50/125 graded index fibre

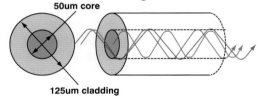

• Single mode, with a core diameter of 8^{-10} micrometres, used in the cable TV industry and for long-distance telecommunications.

• Single Mode
  Fibre

A single mode 9/125 step index fibre

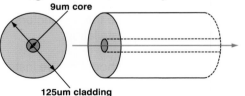

Note that multimode fibre cables cannot be used for single mode applications - they just will not work.

10

Keywords

Fibre •
Construction
Core •
Cladding •

Fibre Interface •

Fibre Buffer •

Fibre Jacket •
Kevlar Yarn •

Bendable Fibres •

10.4 Fibre Construction

In a single mode fibre, the light is confined to its core, which has a diameter of 8μm. Around this is the "cladding" which provides the reflective interface. This cladding has an overall diameter of only 125μm. Fibres are therefore very delicate and must be well protected against physical abuse.

The interface between the fibre and cladding can be "stepped" or "graded". The outer acrylic coating can be coloured to identify the particular fibre, its overall diameter being some 250 micrometres.

One or more such fibres can then be contained in a jelly-filled (non-dripping and silicon-free) buffer material. This type of "loose-tube" construction is normally used outdoors to protect the fibres during installation, or where the fibres might otherwise be crushed. An alternative "tight-buffered" form of construction is sometimes used indoors on long vertical runs where the jelly in a loose-tube cable might otherwise migrate downwards, and where there is no danger of subsequent physical damage to the cable.

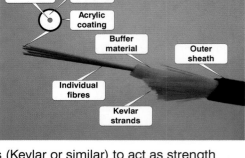

The whole assembly is contained in an outer sheath made of polythene or a fire-retardant (LSOH) material. This sometimes has a nylon outer jacket or added chemicals to act as a rodent repellent. The sheath also contains yarns (Kevlar or similar) to act as strength members (when pulling cables into ducts) and for longitudinal watertightness.

The outer jacket (polythene or similar) also contains a strengthening material such as Kevlar, so that the cable can be pulled through a duct without damage. A jacket can contain up to 12 or more fibres, all colour coded for ease of identification. The cable can be treated just like coax, although care must be taken to ensure that it does not kink.

Fibre optic cables have an expected lifetime in excess of 30 years.

Such cable can be obtained with the fibre ends already terminated, in which case the connectors are protected to avoid damage during installation.

Traditional fibre cables should not be installed with sharp bends - fibre losses increase dramatically if bend radius is less than 30mm. However, a new range of "bendable" fibre cables can have a bend radius as low as 10mm without significant loss – these are covered in a new specification ITU-T G.657(A).

A new design of bendable single fibre cable has recently been introduced for use in the TV industry. Additional mechanical protection is provided by a steel band wound around the fibre, this being contained in an overall LSOH (low smoke / zero halogen) sheath with an outer diameter of only 3mm. This cable is virtually indestructible and is available in preterminated lengths of between 1m and 200m. Such cables come with a test report showing the overall insertion loss and return loss.

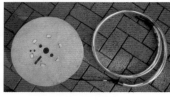

10

Keywords

• Fibre
  Connectors

• PC

• APC

• FC
• SC

• Fibre Joints

• Arc Fusion
  Splicing
• Mechanical
  Splicing

• Fibre Joints Box

• Splice Bridge

10.5 Fibre Connectors

A connector must align the two fibres with the minimum optical loss across the junction between them. There can be either an air gap, or **p**hysical **c**ontact (**PC**) between them. Various types of junction are illustrated in the diagram alongside.

Connectors for single mode propagation have the fibre ends polished with a slight curvature so that they touch only at their centres.

The **A**ngled **P**lanar **C**onnector (**APC**) is sometimes used for TV applications. The fibre faces are angled at about 8° to minimise the reflection of light back down the fibre. This means that the connector must orientate the two fibres so that they are aligned correctly – align the keyway before tightening each connector. Angled Planar Connectors always have a green "boot" for cable strain relief.

Always ensure that both connectors are of the same type (PC or APC).

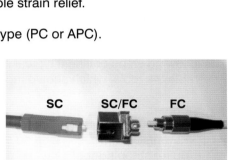

The two common types of fibre connector are the bayonet type (FC) and the push-on type (SC). Back-to-back couplers are available for both types and FC/SP adaptors are also available.

Do not remove and refit connectors more than is absolutely necessary. Constant undoing and refitting of connectors can cause damage to the fibre ends.

10.6 Fibre Jointing Techniques

Where the fibre cables are not preterminated, the installer has two options:
• To cut a preterminated patchcord in half and splice the open end of one of the resulting "pigtails" on to the incoming fibre, or
• To fit a connector directly on to the incoming fibre.

Fibre-to-fibre joints can be made using **arc fusion splicing**, which melts the fibre ends together using an electric arc, or **mechanical splicing**, using crimping techniques. Fusion splicing gives lower joint losses.

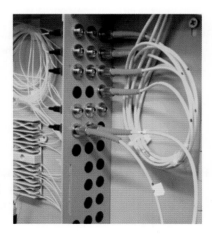

In either case, the resulting fibre joints are extremely delicate, and must be protected and supported in a suitable enclosure. The photo alongside shows a fibre joint box with the fibre joints on the left-hand side and patchcords (linking to the associated transmitters or receivers) on the right. Back-to-back couplers link the fibre pigtails to the patchcords.
The composite fibre cables enter from the bottom through a cable gland. The fibre joints are individually supported in a "splice bridge" (the grey unit on the left-hand side) and the excess fibre cable is coiled up and fixed using cable ties with stick-on bases. The cabinet is then locked – the motto should be "fit and forget".

10

Keywords

Fibre •
Cleanliness

Arc Fusion •
Splicing

Cleanliness is absolutely paramount when joining fibres or inserting connectors. Use a lint-free wipe moistened with isopropyl alcohol to clean the end of each fibre before making each joint or inserting the connector.

A special jig is used to carry out the jointing operation. The composite cable containing the individual fibres must be rigidly anchored using a suitable cable gland so as not to impose any strain on the delicate fibres – they are only one tenth the diameter of a human hair. The environment must be clean and the tails must be long enough to reach the splicing machine.

Arc Fusion Splicing
This is the preferred method, but it requires specialised equipment and training. Optical losses on a good splice are so small that they cannot even be measured!
The usual jointing sequence for standard fibre is as follows:
*   Remove the sheath and buffer material, to expose the fibre
*   Clean the fibre "until it squeaks"
*   Using a cleaving jig, score and then snap-off each fibre end
*   Use the fusion splicer to melt together the two fibre ends
*   Provide mechanical protection for the resulting fibre joint
*   House the completed joint in a protective enclosure

The following steps outline a typical installation procedure:
Assemble the tools, which should include the following:

*   Cutters
*   Stanley knife
*   Kevlar scissors
*   Buffer stripping tool
*   Cleaning alcohol and lint-free wipes
*   Fibre cleaving jig
*   "Sharps" tin for fibre offcuts
*   Fusion splicer (to include heat-shrink facility)
*   Fibre microscope

Strip off the outer jacket to expose the protected fibre and Kevlar yarn

Cut off the exposed yarn using the Kevlar scissors

Keywords

Slide the heat shrink sleeve with its integral metallic supporting strip on to one of the fibre ends

Use the buffer stripping tool (middle hole) to remove the buffer material in 5mm sections, exposing some 35mm of raw fibre

Clean the exposed fibre using iso propyl alcohol and lint-free wipes (or similar). The rule is "clean it until it squeaks"!

Again using the buffer stripping tool (small hole), strip of the acrylic coating leaving 15mm from the end of the buffer material. Then reclean the fibre end.

Clamp the fibre into the cleaving jig (using the single mode V-groove if it is a dual purpose jig) with the correct length of raw fibre between the buffer material and the fibre end (differs between manufacturers, but usually about 10mm).

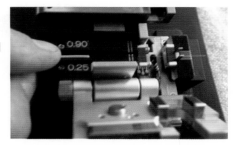

Use the jig to first score and then cleave the fibre end, carefully disposing of the fibre offcut in the "Sharps" tin

Repeat the whole procedure for the second fibre end

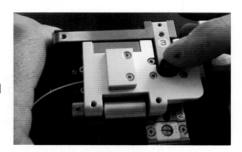

Insert both fibre ends into the fusion splicing machine and initiate the automatic fusion splicing sequence. The splicer will align the fibres and fuse the ends together. A good splice will be undetectable to the human eye, even under the microscope

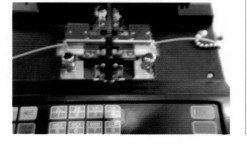

10

This photo shows how the machine aligns the two fibres before splicing them together

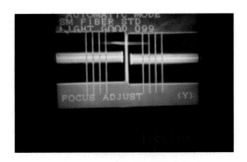

This is a good splice with the joints undetectable to the human eye.

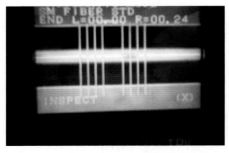

Slide the heat-shrink sleeve over the joint and apply heat to provide the necessary mechanical protection.

Fit the completed joint into a secure housing, supporting the joint so that no mechanical strain is imposed on it.

Mechanical • Splicing

Mechanical Splicing

Mechanical fibre splices are designed to be quicker and easier to install, but there is still the need for stripping, careful cleaning and precision cleaving. The fibre ends are aligned and held together by a precision-made sleeve, often using a clear index-matching gel that enhances the transmission of light across the joint. Fibres can be secured using either a quick-set adhesive or a mechanical crimp. Such joints typically have higher optical loss and are less robust than fusion splices, especially if the gel is used.
Also, the gel may deteriorate with time, if exposed to extremes of temperature.

The following procedure outlines the steps necessary to fit a single bendable fibre with a steel protection band, to a typical SC connector containing a short "stub" of fibre with the end pre-polished:

10

Keywords

Assemble the necessary tools, which should include the following:

- Cutters
- T-shaped tool (black)
- Guide tool (blue)
- Buffer stripping tool
- Fibre cleaving jig
- Boot clamp tool
- Kevlar scissors
- "Sharps" tin for fibre offcuts
- Cleaning alcohol and lint-free wipes
- Fault locator

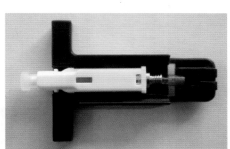

Insert the connector housing into the T-shaped tool, located so that it can slide up and down inside the tool.

Use the stripping tool to strip off the outer sheath some 65mm.

Stretch the exposed steel armour coil around a 10mm diameter mandrell

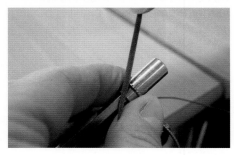

Use a needle file to make a groove in the steel coil.

10

241

Keywords

Snap off the steel armour coil, avoiding damage to the buffer cable.

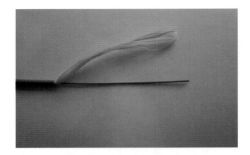

Insert the ring into a 3.0mm boot and then insert the cable into the boot until it is located in the middle of the Kevlar yarn.

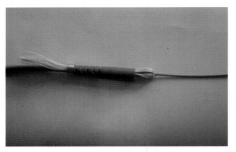

Mark the buffer material at 35mm. Use the buffer stripping tool to remove the buffer material in 10mm sections, to expose 35mm of fibre. Then carefully clean the exposed fibre with alcohol.

Place the ring (the correct way round with the tapered side inwards) over the 0,9mm buffer material. Then use the cleave jig to cleave the exposed fibre exactly 12mm from the stripped fibre side.

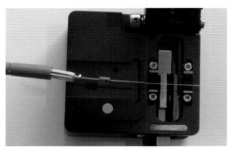

Place the cleaved fibre into the V groove of the T-shaped tool, inserting it into the frame hole until the ring reaches the end of the tool. Check that the buffer cable bends when the fibre is pushed in further (to make sure that it is butting up correctly).

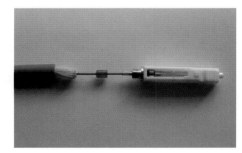

10

Keywords

Press down the connector to release the T-shaped tool and remove the protective cap. Fit a fault locator on the other end of the cable and switch on – any light coming from the sides of the connector (as shown in this photo) indicates a poor connection.

Replace the protective caps.

Push on the clamp ring until it reaches the stopper. Slide the boot over the connector and screw on 4-5 times clockwise. Cut off the protruding yarn.

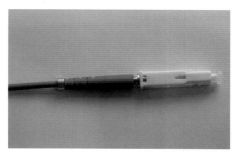

Insert the frame into the housing and tighten the boot fully by turning it clockwise.

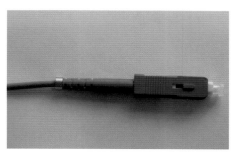

Use the boot crimp tool to crimp the fixing ring.

This completes the installation.

Another method of terminating fibres is to fit the connector directly around the end of the fibre, in which case the end of the fibre must be polished – a process that requires some training and expertise.

A typical tool for such a process is available from HUBER+SUHNER The multifunction tool cleaves the fibre, fits the connector and applies the adhesive.

An outline of the fitting procedure is as follows.

The following items are required:

*   QXA multifunction tool (includes epoxy adhexive, intergral heating element, sharps tin and cleaver)
*   QXA adhesive powder
*   QXA SC fibre connector(s)

10

243

Keywords

Insert the SC connector into the clamping head of the tool

Prepare the cable end for termination

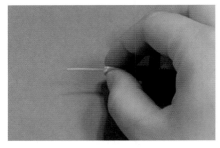

Apply dry epoxy adhesive to the fibre

Carefully fit the cable into the connector

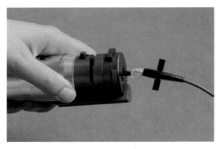

Clamp the tube and activate the adhesive using the integrated heating element

Clamp and secure the Kevlar yarn

10

Keywords

Score the fibre using the ceramic cleaver

Snap off the fibre at the score mark – the loose end will fall into the scrap container located within the tool

Prepare the fibre end face for polishing

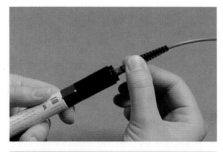

Remove the protruding fibre stub

Polish the fibre end by hand using a two stage lapping process

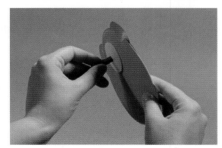

10

10.7 Fibre Hardware

An **optical transmitter** comprises either a light emitting diode or a laser diode that emits light waves at a single frequency, which are first magnified and then amplitude modulated with the information to be relayed.

An **optical receiver** consists of either a pin photodiode or an avalanche photo diode, which reconverts the signals back into the original frequency band, followed by a conventional solid-state amplifier.

An optical splitter can be created by bringing the cores of two parallel fibres so close together that light from one fibre bleeds across into the other fibre. A process similar to fusion splicing is used to permanently form the splitter. Attenuators can also be produced by offsetting the fibre ends prior to a fusion splice.

Systems are now readily available to relay the whole UHF TV spectrum on fibre optic cables over distances of several kilometers.

Satellite IF Applications

Equipment is now available to replace a complete satellite IRS installation with a single fibre optic network of up to 5Km in length, comprising the following main items of equipment:

- An "**Optical LNB**" - in effect a Quatro LNB with a 1300nm single mode optical output.
- A range of optical splitters (4way and 8way) that can be daisy-chained to produce up to 32 outputs

- A **G**ateway **T**ermination **U**nit (**GTU**) – an optical receiver that converts the optical signals back into satellite IF frequencies, to emulate either a Twin, Quatro or Quad LNB

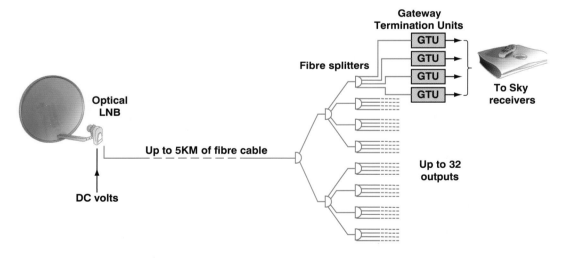

The optical LNB has an integral feedhorn and is designed for use with any 78cm offset dish with a standard 40mm diameter LNB clamp. DC power must be provided from an external supply via an F connector on the base of the unit.

Keywords

• Optical Splitter
  Losses

Optical splitters are available with the following
optical through losses:

4 way	7dB
8 way	11dB

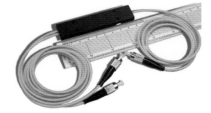

Three versions of the Gateway Termination Unit are
available, to emulate Twin, Quad and Quatro LNBs.
These are designed to be powered from a set-top box,
although they also have an auxiliary power input for
use if required.

In some instances, it may be preferable to terminate the
incoming fibre on a single gang wall outlet plate with a
patch cord connection to the gateway termination unit.

10.8 System Planning

Fibre offers the following advantages over an equivalent coaxial cable network:
• Extremely low signal loss – typically 0.5dB per Km.
• Totally unaffected by electromagnetic interference, lightning strikes and temperature /
  humidity changes.
• No equalization is required, since there is zero slope across the frequency band.
• No earthing issues.
• Smaller cables.

• Fibre
  Advantages

The typical output power of a typical fibre optic transmitter or optical LNB is between
+3 and +13dBmW. The receiver sensitivity is typically –18 to +3dBmW. The difference
between the transmitted and received power is the total allowable loss on the system,
including losses through connectors, splices and splitters.

• Optical Budget

Typical losses are as follows:

• Optical Losses

• Fibre optic cable, per Km	0.35-0.5dB
• Each connector	<0.5dB
• Each fusion splice	<0.1dB
• Two way symmetrical splitter (per leg)	3.7dB
• Four way symmetrical splitter (per leg)	7dB
• Eight way symmetrical splitter (per leg)	11dB

If the actual system losses are greater than the maximum allowed, the C/N ratio of the
UHF output channels will be correspondingly degraded. As a general rule, 1dB of optical
attenuation is equivalent to 2dB of UHF attenuation.

10

Keywords

Fibre Cable •
Installation

The satellite IF system referred to above has been designed for fibre cable lengths of up to 5Km, including splitters to feed 32 gateway termination units. The optical LNB has a launch level of +7dBmW and the GTUs have a maximum sensitivity of -18dBmW, giving a theoretical maximum allowable optical loss of 25dB.

10.9 Installation and Commissioning

Multi-fibre cable can be installed in the same way as coaxial cable, attaching the draw rope to the Kevlar string inside the fibre sheath. The connectors and splices on each end of the cable are normally protected with an outer sleeve with a pulling "eye" which is attached to a draw rope when pulling into a duct.

The new 3mm bendable fibre is even easier to install as long as the bending radius is always more than 10mm. Do not use staples to fix this type of cable. Don't try to break fibres by pulling apart with both hands - simply form the fibre into a tight bend until it snaps apart.

The following equipment will be useful when commissioning and troubleshooting a fibre optic relay system:

Laser Pen •

- Individual fibres can be identified using a **laser pen** as a light source at one end of the network, and pointing the other end towards a piece of white paper. Such a device can also be used to check the quality of a fibre joint or connector fitting – the presence of any escaping light indicates excessive optical loss at that location.

Fibre •
Microscope

- Fibre ends can be examined using a portable **fibre microscope**. The version illustrated alongisde has a magnification of 400x. Always ensure that the laser transmitter is turned off before using such instruments, although an ordinary torch can be used to make the fibre end glow.

Optical Power •
Meter

- Power levels can be measured at each receiving location using an **optical power meter**. This version is a combined satellite IF and optical signal level meter that can be used for either application. It can be used to align the satellite dish and adjust the skew using the optical LNB.

10

Keywords

• Optical Time
  Domain
  Reflectometer
  (OTDR)

• The overall performance of a fibre optic link can be assessed using an **O**ptical **T**ime **D**omain **R**eflectometer **(OTDR)**. This remarkable (and very expensive) device sends a pulse of light down the fibre and displays the time delay for any light reflected back from it. The display is calibrated in metres and it is possible to see all the imperfections on the fibre link and assess how many metres down the fibre they are occurring. It also indicates the total length of the fibre link and the

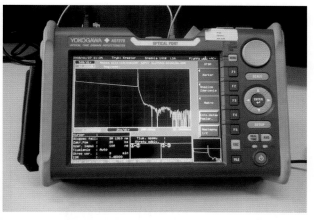

total optical loss. The display also shows the quality of each fibre joint and exactly where a fibre cable has been damaged during installation. A printer attachment enables the commissioning engineer to keep a "hard-copy" of the total link performance for record purposes. The followingf diagram shows how the insertion losses of each transition can be interpolated from the OTDR display.

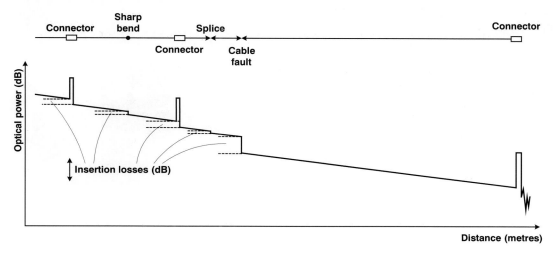

The following **safety** aspects should be considered whenever working on a fibre optic relay system:

• Fibre optic cables are made of silica glass and should be handled with care.
• Offcuts must be disposed of properly.
• Optical transmitters use lasers that produce an intense beam of invisible light which can damage the skin and eyes. The transmitter must <u>always</u> be switched off before making splices or fitting connectors. Never use a magnifying glass to inspect a live fibre!

The lasers used in the satellite IF system referred to in this section are not powerful enough to damage your skin or eyes, as long as magnifiers are not used.

• Fibre Optic
  Safety

10

Keywords

Optical •
Cleanliness

Cleanliness

It is absolutely essential that all connectors are cleaned every time before they are inserted into their mating sockets.

These truly amazing pictures taken using a microscope with 200 times magnification show the end of an optical fibre after it has been cleaned, and then after it has been lightly wiped across the back of a human hand. Imagine the increase in the optical path loss if the connector is not cleaned again!!!!

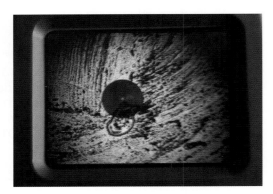

Cleaning can be achieved using either dry or wet materials. Dry cleaning can be accomplished using a spooling device containing a cleaning tape, as shown alongside. Open the sliding door to expose a small area of cleaning tape within a narrow slot. The fibre end face is then drawn across the exposed tape surface, using a twisting and turning motion.

End face contaminants including dust can be more effectively removed by wet cleaning. This is normally achieved using Iso-Propyl Alcohol (IPA) which must be at least 87% pure. IPA can be contained in a pump-action dispensing bottle or aerosol container, and applied with a lint-free cloth or wipe ("Kimwipes" or similar). Sachets of impregnated wipes are also available. A portion of the wipe is wetted and the fibre end face is drawn across the wipe from the wetted section to a dry section using a smooth unidirectional cleaning stroke. Swabs are also available to clean recessed fibre ends inside ferrules and connectors – these should be lightly moistened with IPA before use

A typical cleaning kit from ITW Chemtronics is shown alongside. This includes a patented QbE container with 200 wipes and an integral cleaning platen, an "Electro-Wash" aerosol dispenser and swabs.

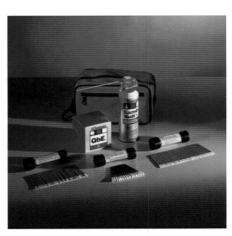

10

Keywords

• Telephony

• Telephone Components

• Handset Activation

• Telephone Communication Frequencies

• PSTN

11.1 An Introduction to Telephony

A traditional telephone handset contains the following items:

• A microphone to convert sound pressure waves to analogue electrical signals
• An earpiece to convert electrical signals back into sound pressure waves
• A "ringer" or bell to indicate that a caller is waiting

When a telephone handset is on its cradle, the microphone and earpiece are disconnected. The ringer is the only item connected to the telephone line. When a call is received, a 50V battery in the telephone exchange causes a current to flow in the telephone wires, activating the ringer. Removal of the handset from its cradle connects the microphone and handset, thus enabling a two-way conversation to take place.

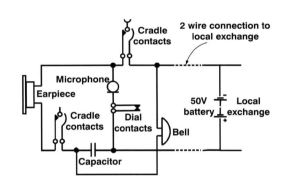

Communication between a telephone subscriber and the local telephone exchange takes place at audio frequencies. The frequency range of the human ear covers a frequency bandwidth from about 50 Hz (deep bass) to about 18 kHz (squeaky treble) – a range of some 8 octaves (going up one octave doubles the frequency). However, by international agreement, public telephone networks only cover the range 400 Hz to 3.4 kHz – this is because the sound power of the human voice is low at frequencies below 400 Hz, rising to a peak at around 3 – 4 kHz, and progressively reducing with increasing frequency. In practice, a frequency band of 4 kHz is allocated to each channel, with 3.4 kHz representing the frequency at which the power is halved.

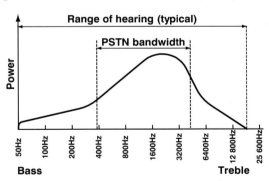

The **P**ublic **S**witched **T**elephone **N**etwork **(PSTN)** in Britain comprises some 1300 local exchanges serving about 29 million subscribers using a "star" wired network configuration. These local exchanges are in turn connected to some 80 trunk exchanges. Each trunk exchange is directly connected to all the others to ensure that there will be a maximum of two trunk exchanges between the originating and terminating local exchanges. Each trunk exchange is also directly connected to an international exchange.

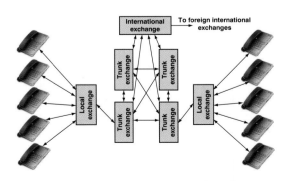

251

Keywords

Time Division •
Multiplexing
(TDM)

Connections between most exchanges is now digital uses a technique called **T**ime **D**ivision **M**ultiplexing **(TDM),** which increases the capacity of the link by allowing several telephone channels to be carried as one signal stream each of which is known as a "virtual circuit". Small slices of time are allocated to each channel, during which the full capacity of the TDM "highway" is made available to that channel. Each channel is

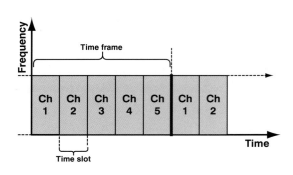

sampled sequentially at intervals of 125µs (known as the "time frame") – thus, for the five channel example shown in the drawing, the "time slot" of each channel would be 25µs wide. Where the communication is not point-to-point, derivative of TDM, known as **T**ime **D**ivision **M**ultiple **A**ccess **(TDMA)**, is used for satellite communications and GSM mobile phone networks.

Time Division •
Multiple Access
(TDMA)

Pulse Dialling •

Tone Dialling •

The removal of a handset from its cradle (known as the "off hook" condition) connects the subscriber to the exchange. The action of dialling a telephone number operates a series of selector mechanisms to establish a direct connection with the called subscriber. This used to occur by sending a series of pulses down the line to operate mechanical selector switches in

the appropriate exchanges, but this has been superseded by tone dialling, with solid state switching at each exchange. This is why tones of different frequencies can be heard when using a push button phone to dial a number.

Hybrid •
Transformers

Speech in both directions can be carried on a single pair of wires by using "hybrid transformers". This same pair can also be used as a ringing circuit, since ringing and speech occur at different times.

There is a limit to the length of telephone cable between a subscriber and the local exchange. Its electrical resistance must be less than 2000 ohms to ensure that sufficient current flows in the "off hook" condition, and so that the loudness of the call is acceptable.

Master •
Telephone
Socket

A typical domestic telephone installation as supplied by British Telecom (BT) comprises a single pair "drop" cable, terminating in a Master Socket. **These items are the property of BT, and must not be interfered with.** Everything else in the home is usually the property of the homeowner, and can be modified or extended, as long as any equipment connected to the line is BT approved. It is common practice to daisy-chain extension telephone handsets on the same line number in various locations for customer convenience.

11.2 Telephone Installations

NTE5 Socket •

Most BT installations utilise an NTE5 master socket. The top half is protected by a fixed cover, and the bottom half has a removable cover which, when removed, reveals a standard phone socket, into which the internal phone system is connected. This allows all the internal wiring to be isolated, for fault finding. Any standard phone can be plugged into the socket to check the incoming line.

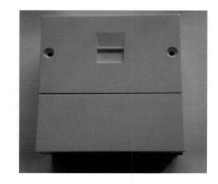

11

Keywords

The wiring of a typical master socket is shown alongside.
This converts the incoming 2 wire system to 3 wires, the third wire providing a "ring" circuit.

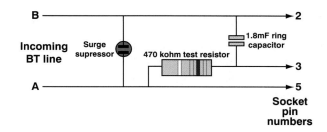

• Telephone Pin Connectors

Nearly all telephone equipment has six terminals, but pins one and six are not used in the UK. Most standard telephone cables have two twisted pairs of wires, a blue pair and an orange pair. The blue pair carries speech and the orange pair the ringing circuit. The standard pin connections are as follows:

• Telephone Cable Colour Code

Pin 1		Not used
Pin 2	Blue with white bands	Speech and ringing
Pin 3	Orange with white bands	Ringing
Pin 4	White with orange bands	Not used, but usually connected for neatness
Pin 5	White with blue bands	Speech and ringing
Pin 6		Not used

The wiring of a typical home is therefore as shown below:

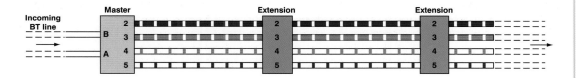

The socket that all standard UK phones plug into is known as an **RJ11**. When mounted on a wall plate, it is referred to as a Line Jack Unit **(LJU)**. There are three standard sizes of LJU socket boxes:

• Telephone Sockets

*   LJU1   55mm x 55mm x 25mm
*   LJU2   68mm x 68mm x 25mm
*   LJU3   85mm x 85mm

RJ11 sockets can be obtained with screw connectors, but the most common types have **I**nsulation **D**isplacement **C**onnectors **(IDC)**. When inserting a wire into an IDC terminal, do use the correct punch down insertion tool (known in the trade as a **"Krone"** tool). This can be an inexpensive plastic one (which wears out after about six insertions) or a more expensive metal version – this normally comes with a hook for removing surplus wire and a flat headed screwdriver for unscrewing the socket plates. Do <u>not</u> use a flat blade screwdriver – this pushes the connector apart and does not make a good connection with the wire.

• Insulation Displacement Connectors (IDC)
• Krone Tool

There is no need to strip the insulation from each wire – the connector has sharp blades that bite through the insulation. Lay the wire over the connector, then place the Krone tool over the connector with the wire cutter (normally black) on the opposite side to the wire entry, and gently push downwards until a click is heard from the tool.

Keywords

Phone •
Extension
Installation
Sequence

The following tools will be required in order to terminate a two pair telephone cable on to an LJU socket:

- Cable cutters
- A suitable cable stripper
- An insulation displacement connector (Krone) tool

The installation procedure is as follows:

1. Unplug the extension telephone cable at the master socket – this is because, whenever a telephone is ringing, a 50V voltage is present across the wires, which can cause an electrical shock

2. Fit the back box on to the wall using rawlplugs and dome-headed screws (if surface mounted) and route the telephone cable through the side of the box.

3. Cut the cable to the required length and use the cable stripper to remove approximately 50mm of the outer cable sheath, revealing the two twisted pairs of wires.

4. Lay each wire above its appropriate connector on the rear of the plate as follows:
   - Pin 2 Blue with white bands
   - Pin 3 Orange with white bands
   - Pin 4 White with orange bands
   - Pin 5 White with blue bands
   (Do <u>not</u> strip the outer insulation from each wire).

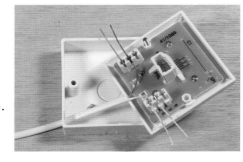

Keywords

5. Use the Krone tool to connect each wire in turn. The IDC module knives cut through the insulation and makes tight contact with the wire, guaranteeing a reliable connection. The tool cuts off the surplus wire at the same time.

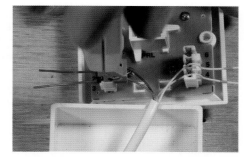

6. Remove the surplus wires. This is a top view of a fully wired LJU socket.

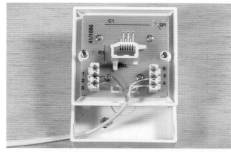

7. Fit the face plate on to the back box and reconnect the extension cable at the master socket.

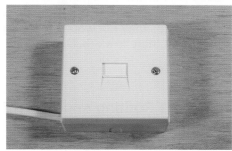

Sky digital satellite receivers are usually connected to an analogue telephone line, but they only make outgoing calls – they do not receive incoming calls. It is therefore not strictly necessary to connect the orange (ringing) wires. However, these are usually connected at the same time, in case the user wishes to plug a telephone handset into the same socket using a telephone double adaptor.

The ringing current from the telephone exchange is limited for safety reasons and, if too many telephone handsets are connected to the same incoming line, there will be insufficient current to make any of them ring, so the customer will not know that they have an incoming call, even though a two-way telephone conversation can still take place.

• Ringing Current

Each piece of equipment connected to a telephone line puts a load across it – this is called the **R**inger **E**quivalence **N**umber **(REN)**. Each telephone handset normally has a REN of 1 whereas a fax or acoustic modem can have a REN of 2. If the total RENs across a telephone line exceeds 4, there is a possibility that the phone(s) may not ring when an incoming call occurs. It is therefore most important to check that the phones still ring after the installation has been completed – if not, a REN amplifier must be fitted to increase the ringing current available.

• Ringer Equivalence Number (REN)

The following basic principles should be adhered to when installing telephone extensions:

- There should not be more than 50m of cabling between the master socket and the furthest extension.
- Telephone cables must be kept at least 75mm from mains electrical cables and long runs parallel to mains cables should be avoided. Telephone cables should cross a mains cable at right angles.
- Sockets should be located at least 50mm away from mains electrical outlets and must

11

Keywords

not share wall fixings or back boxes with electrical outlets.
- Extension sockets should be mounted vertically, not horizontally on window sills.
- When installing telephone cables on the exterior of buildings, it is essential that outdoor cable with ultra violet protection is used – indoor telephone cables are <u>not</u> suitable for outdoor use.
- Telephone extension cables must <u>not</u> be left trailing across the floor, but must be clipped (usually to the skirting board) using cable clips or staples.

Typical Phone Faults •

If the newly completed telephone extension does not operate correctly, check that the previous wiring was installed using the correct colour codes. Typical faults are as follows:

- Phone ringing continuously – terminals 2 and 5 swapped between sockets
- No ringing – terminal 3 not connected.
- Ringing but no speech (or very poor speech) and can't dial out – wires between terminals 2 or 5 broken.
- Very poor speech quality and possibly poor ringing – terminals 3 and 2 or 3 and 5 transposed..

Wireless Phone Extensions •

It is possible to use a wireless telephone extension kit to provide a phone link to another location in the same building. Some versions utilise the existing mains power wiring to relay the speech and ringing signals. Check the phone connection on completion since these devices may not work if the power sockets are on different phases of the mains supply, or if there is an RCD in circuit.

11.3 Data Routing and Switching

Data can differ from audio and video in the following ways:

Data Parameters •

- It <u>may</u> be tolerant to delays and may therefore be sent out of sequence, and reassembled at the receiving location.
- Data can be transmitted at variable speeds, depending on the network conditions
- There are various ways of organising the data – these are called "protocols"
- Data can be resent automatically.

Data Packets •

Rather than sending a stream of data down a dedicated continuous circuit between the sender and receiver, it is usually much more efficient to divide it into **"packets"** these being relayed over an optimum route, and to reassemble it at the receiving location.

Each packet needs some form of destination address attached to it, so that it can be routed and reassembled in the correct sequence. A data packet therefore comprises a payload

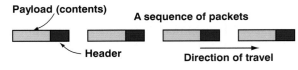

Payload (contents)   A sequence of packets   Header   Direction of travel

Data Headers •

together with a "header" which identifies its source and destination – this can also include additional information such as its priority, its sequence in the data stream (of time stamp for real time data), the size of the payload and a "checksum" (used for error correction). It can then be interleaved with data from other sources and separated out whenever required.

Data can be relayed on a carrier network in two ways:

Data Virtual Path •

- By establishing a specific path (known as a virtual path) for all the relevant data to follow – this is known as the connection orientated packet mode which is established at the start of a transmission and cleared down at the end.

11

Keywords

- By allowing the data to be routed over various paths, depending on the condition and loading of the network – this is called the connectionless packet mode, the most well known example being the Internet Protocol (IP).

A standard protocol called **A**synchronous **T**ransfer **M**ode **(ATM)** is used by telecommunication operators in Europe. This has been developed primarily for connection orientated transmission systems. All types of data are allocated to a set of fixed size 53 byte packets (48 bytes of data and

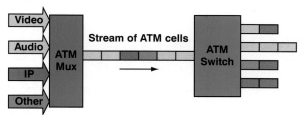

a 5 byte routing header), known as ATM cells. As soon as each cell becomes available, it joins the queue for despatch. An ATM switch then feeds these cells on to the ATM highway, following the virtual path established at the start of transmission. Various levels of priority can be applied to each virtual path, depending on the class of service required.

The **O**pen **S**ystem **I**nterconnection **(OSI)** model is a widely accepted way of defining the functions to be performed by a communication system. It is divided into seven layers, each of which performs functions for the layer above and is in turn supported by the services provided by the layer below. Interactions between functions on the same layer are governed by a set of rules or protocols. Control is passed from one layer to the next, starting at the application layer at one location, proceeding down to the bottom layer, over the channel to the next location, and back up the hierarchy. Each layer is self contained and its functions can be implemented independently, allowing protocols to be changed in one layer without affecting the other layers.

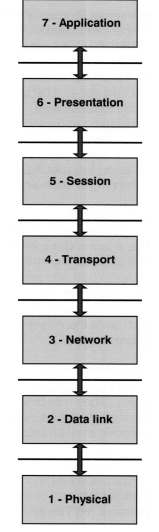

Layer 1 - Physical: This covers the transmission of data over the wires and defines the functions of each connector pin and the nature of the electrical waveform.

Layer 2 – Data link: This defines the formatting of the data into packets or cells that consist of groups of bits that can be identified at the receiving end, and an acknowledgement returned - it specifies how a computer gains access to the data. It responds to requests from the network layer and issues service requests to the physical layer. It also covers the protocols for error detection. RS232, 10BASE-T, Ethernet and ATM are protocols dealing with this layer.

Layer 3 – Network: This layer deals with routing and switching technologies to create a virtual path. Internet Protocols are also covered. It is responsible for end-to-end packet delivery.

Layer 4 – Transport: This covers end-to-end data transfer. It includes the allocation of the data into numbered packets, sequencing received packets into the correct order and retransmission requests.

Layer 5 – Session: This establishes, manages and terminates connections between applications and provides for the proper handover between computers.

Layer 6 – Presentation: This transforms data into a form that the application layer can accept. It also deals with encryption and decryption.

Keywords:
- Asynchronous Transfer Mode (ATM)
- OSI Model
- Physical Layer
- Data Link
- Network Layer
- Transport Layer
- Session Layer
- Presentation Layer

11

Keywords

Application • Layer

Layer 7 – Application: This defines the actual application being executed. Examples include the protocols for sending and receiving emails, data file transfer and accessing an internet web page.

11.4 The Internet

Internet • Protocol (IP)

World Wide • Web (www)

The "Internet" is a worldwide publicly accessible series of interconnected computer networks that transmit data by packet switching using the standard **I**nternet **P**rotocol **(IP)**. The internet "network" comprises millions of domestic, academic, business and government networks, which together carry information and services such as video and voice traffic, electronic mail, online chat, file transfer, web pages and all the other resources of the **W**orld **W**ide **W**eb **(WWW)**. It is now an absolutely fundamental part of business, with many companies relying on it as their primary form of communication.

The Internet is always defined in layers of protocols:

Internet • Message Control Protocol (IMCP)

Transmission • Control Protocol (TCP)

User Diagram • Protocol (UDP)

- Internet Protocol (IP) is at the OSI level 3 and defines the "datagrams" or data packets that carry blocks of data from one node to another. **I**nternet **M**essage **C**ontrol **P**rotocol **(IMCP)** also resides at level 3 and is used to provide control, signalling and error reporting procedures.
- **T**ransmission **C**ontrol **P**rotocol **(TCP)** and **U**ser **D**atagram **P**rotocol **(UDP)** exist at the OSI layer 4. TCP makes a "virtual connection" with interactivity so that lost packets are retransmitted. UDP is a "best effort" connectionless transport protocol used for real-time applications such as voice messages (see section 11.6) – data lost in transit is not resent.
- The application protocols which reside at layers 5, 6 and 7 of the OSI model. These define the specific message and data formats sent and understood by the applications running at each end of the link. Examples of these protocols are HTTP, FTP and SMTP.

These protocols are described in more detail on the following pages.

ICANN •

IPv4 •

IPv6 •

The **I**nternet **C**orporation for **A**ssigned **N**ames and **N**umbers **(ICANN)** assigns unique identifiers on the Internet, including domain names, Internet Protocol (IP) addresses and protocol port and parameter numbers. IP addresses currently consist of 32 bits (4 bytes), known as IPv4. With the astonishing growth of internet users, these available numbers are running out, and future users will have to change to 128 bit addresses known as IPv6 once the infrastructure of the internet has been upgraded to handle these longer addresses.

E-mail •

The concept of relaying text messages over the internet is known as **E-mail.** These are usually unencrypted and travel via networks and equipment outside the control of the users. They may therefore be read and even tampered with by third parties. By contrast, internal or intranet mail (where the information never leaves the corporate or organisation's network) may be much more secure.

Universal • Resolve Location (URL)

HTTP •

The World Wide Web (WWW) is a set of interlinked documents, images and other resources linked by hyperlinks and **U**niversal **R**esource **L**ocators **(URL**s**)**. These allow web servers and other sources to deliver the data as required using the **H**yper**T**ext **T**ransfer **P**rotocol **(HTTP)**, or its more secure version – **HTTPS**.

Web Browsers •

Internet Explorer and other such programs (known as web browsers) are software products used to access the resources of the web, allowing users to navigate between web sites. Web documents can contain any combination of computer data such as graphics, sound, text, video, multimedia and other active content including games and office applications.

11

Keywords

• Search Engines

• Shopping Sites

• Social Network Services

• Streaming Video

• Anti-Virus Software
• Firewall

• Internet Access Requirements

• IPv4

• Time to Live

• Routers

Search engines such as Yahoo! And Google allow instant access to a vast and diverse amount of online information by using keywords to find the relevant web sites. Shopping sites such as Amazon and eBay provide users with the ability to buy and sell products from the comfort of their home. Many individuals and companies use "web logs" or blogs as online diaries. Social network services such as Facebook and MySpace are also widely used.

Many radio and TV broadcasters provide internet feeds of the audio and video streams, either live or on a time shift basis. Streaming video sites such as YouTube allow free access and download facilities.

Because it is unregulated, the internet provides the opportunity for malicious intruders to access an internet terminal device to interrogate its data contents and install viruses to take control of or corrupt its operation. It is therefore essential install anti-virus software and also to use a "firewall" to prevent such activities. Since computer hackers are constantly improving their techniques, it is also essential that such protection software is continuously updated.

The following are required in order to access the internet:

• A communications link (telephone or data). This can be a standard fixed line or a mobile.phone. A broadband connection is much preferred to a standard dial up service, its increased bandwidth providing a much faster service.
• A relationship or contract with an internet service provider (ISP).
• A terminal device such as a computer, mobile phone or set top box, with a modem or router as required.
• Anti-virus and firewall software.

As previously described, a header is attached to each payload of data to identify its source and destination address (layer 3 of the OSI model). The Internet Protocol (**IP**) defines the contents of this packet.

An IPv4 packet comprises a fixed header of 20 bytes, followed by a payload of up to 64 Kbytes. Each header contains the following information:

• 4 byte (32 bit) source and destination addresses
• The lengths of the overall packet and the header, plus the IP version number (IPv4 in this case)
• A type of service indicator
• A "time to live" indicator to set the maximum number of hops between routers before the packet is discarded – this prevents the clogging of routers (described below) by unsuccessfully delivered packets continuously circulating around the network.

The route to be taken by an IP packet is controlled by **"routers"**. Packets arriving at the input to a router are queued and each header is examined in turn. A "first choice" outgoing path to the next router is obtained from a look-up routeing table using the destination IP address. The packets then join a queue to leave at the appropriate output port.

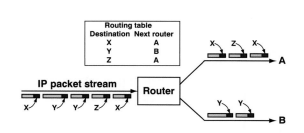

Keywords

Each router can discover the status of neighbouring routers on their network (e.g. if they are busy or out of service or if new routers have come on stream) by sending exploratory packets many times a day. They can then build up a picture of the best route to the packet's destination, and modify the routeing table accordingly.

TCP •

UDP •

An IP packet payload is encapsulated in another packet with a separate header operating at level 4 of the OSI model to manage the flow of IP packets. There are two alternative types of management. Transmission Control Protocol (TCP) is used where complete accuracy of data transmission is required and the time taken to deliver the data is not so important. The alternative User Datagram Protocol (UDP) is applicable for time sensitive applications (such as speech and streaming video) where some loss of accuracy of the data can be tolerated.

TCP Procedures •

TCP uses the connection orientated packet mode where a connection route is set-up. The first data packet is then transmitted and an acknowledgement received before the next one is sent. The receiving location checks the sequence of the received packets and requests the retransmission of any that are missing.

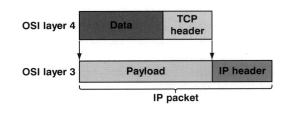

UDP Procedures •

UDP uses the connectionless packet mode, whereby data is routed over various paths, depending on the loading of the network. Its disadvantage is that packets may arrive out of order, appear duplicated, or go missing. Avoiding the need to check that every packet has arrived makes UDP faster and more efficient.

The upper layers (5 to 7) of the OSI model define the type of application and relevant protocols to be used. One example is the use of Hyper Text Transfer Protocol (**HTTP**) to request a web page. HTTP uses TCP to ensure that the data is received satisfactorily.

HTTP •

The drawing below shows how the various protocols already described are combined into a single data stream to relay information over a data network.

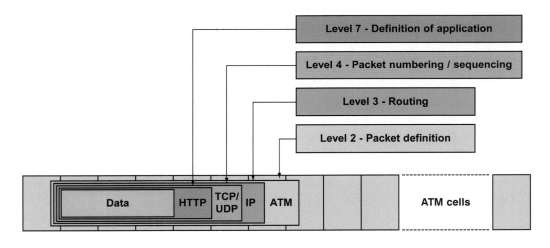

Layer 2 defines the overall packet size.
Layer 3 contains the routing information
Layer 4 is concerned with the numbering and sequencing of the packets
Layers 5-7 define the application to be carried out.

11

Keywords

• PSTN

• ISDN

• ISDN Speeds

• ASDL

• DSLAM
• ISP

• ASDL Speeds

• VSDL

11.5 Broadband Internet Connections

Most internet users utilise a computer and telephone line to gain access to the internet. The **P**ublic **S**witched **T**elephone **N**etwork (**PSTN**) was designed to relay speech traffic. It is an analogue service and signal degradations accumulate as the signals pass along the network. Data is converted into audible tones and relayed as if it were speech. The maximum data bandwidth is typically between 33kb/s and 50kb/s.

The **I**ntegrated **S**ervices **D**igital **N**etwork (**ISDN**) is an enhancement of the PSTN service, designed to relay data in its original digital state. Digital signals can be reconstituted as noise-free information at each point of regeneration along the route.

A basic rate ISDN line provides two channels simultaneously, each having a data bandwidth of 64kb/s in both directions – these can be combined to give a speed of 128kb/s. Speech traffic must be converted into digital signals before being relayed. ISDN is a dial-up service and users are charged on a time basis.

By contrast, an **A**symmetrical **D**igital **S**ubscriber **L**ine (**ADSL**) is an "always on" broadband service with a greatly increased bandwidth. ADSL uses a "microfilter" at each end of the "local loop" (the telephone line linking a subscriber to the local telephone network) to extract the standard voice signals, thus providing a simultaneous telephone service. The data can be relayed on the existing telephone cables to the local telephone exchange,

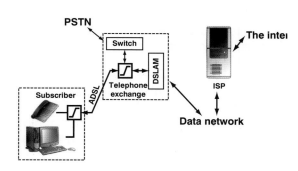

where it is routed via a **D**igital **S**ubscriber **L**ine **A**ccess **M**ultiplexer (**DSLAM**) and a data network, to the **I**nternet **S**ervice **P**rovider (**ISP**), and hence to the internet.

ADSL provides for simultaneous transmission in both directions (known as "duplex working) over a single pair copper line by using separate frequency bands for the upstream and downstream data. The drawing alongside shows the frequency spectrum of ADSL in the United Kingdom. The downstream speed is higher than the

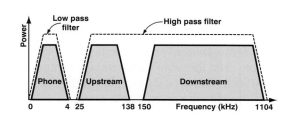

upstream speed, hence the term " asymmetric". Under ideal conditions, downstream data rates of more than 2 Mbit/s can be achieved over a 5Km local loop, and even higher rates over shorter distances – these speeds will increase as the local networks are upgraded.

Very high bit rate **D**igital **S**ubscriber **L**ine (**VDSL**) systems are a derivative of ADSL which use short links to a street cabinet and a fibre optic cable between the cabinet and the local telephone exchange. A hybrid system of this type can provide data rates of 52Mbit/s over some 300m of local loop copper cable.

British Telecom have installed most of the local telephone networks in the United Kingdom. The British government has introduced legislation requiring that these networks should be made available to other network operators (such as Sky) who can then install their own ADSL equipment at the local exchanges (a process known as "unbundling") and their own networks between exchanges.

Satellite links can also be used to provide broadband data facilities in either a single (downlink) direction, or in both directions. Both Eutelsat and Astra offer such links.

Keywords

It is possible to link together all the computers within a Company or building to a data network with a single common interface to the internet over a broadband link. Such a configuration is known as a **L**ocal **A**rea **N**etwork, or **LAN**.

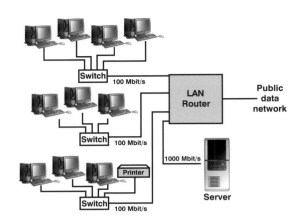

The interlinking network can be installed using twisted pair, coaxial or fibre optic cable. It can be configured as a single data bus or a set of buses in a tree-and-branch, star or ring layout. Most networks comprise clusters of terminals connected in a star formation to a "switch", these being interconnected via a LAN router.

Local Area Network (LAN) •

IEEE Ethernet •

The **I**nstitution of **E**lectrical and **E**lectronic **E**ngineers (**IEEE**) have issued a range of standard protocols for LANs, the most popular of which is the **Ethernet** standard (IEEE 802.3). The Ethernet protocols operate at OSI layer 2 to establish a path, and then at OSI layer 3 using the internet protocol. Switched ethernet allows simultaneous communication between computers without interference between them (ie collision avoidance).

The format of an Ethernet packet is shown alongside. The data packet includes the source and destination addresses and a checksum (for error correction). The padding bits ensure that the frame is at least 64 bytes in length.

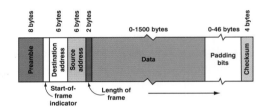

WLANs •
Wi-Fi •

Another group of IEEE specifications (802.11) cover **W**ireless **L**ocal **A**rea **N**etworks (**WLANs**), or "**Wi Fi**". These use unregulated parts of the frequency spectrum in the 2.4GHz band and do not therefore require licensing, the low power (maximum 0.1W) and short coverage distance (typically 10-20m) giving less chance of interference with other radio users.

Wi Fi "hot spots" can now be found in bars, shopping centres, airport lounges and other public areas (and even whole towns), giving broadband data access to anyone with a portable data terminal with a network interface card, such as a **P**ersonal **D**igital **A**ssistant (**PDA**), cell phone or laptop computer. Wi Fi can also be used in the home to interlink a computer, music server, game console, MP3 player etc.

PDA •

One problem with Wi Fi is the inherent lack of security. Wi Fi access points typically default to an open (encryption-free) mode. Users must reconfigure their device to provide security, usually using a router with a software "**G**raphical **U**ser **I**nterface" (**GUI**).

GUI •

Access Point •

The network interface card in each computer (or other terminal device) communicates via an antenna to a centrally located hub or "**Access Point**". Because all these computers share the available wireless capacity on an access point, larger capacities can be achieved by having more than one access point, each operating on a different wireless frequency. Each network interface card compares the relative signal strengths of

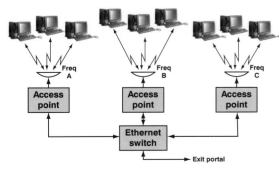

the various carrier frequencies in order to decide which one it should communicate with. The access points are then linked via an Ethernet switch to the broadband data network.

11

Keywords

A simplified illustration of the packet format for IEEE 802.11 WLANs is shown alongside. This is similar to the Ethernet frame on the previous page, and has additional fields to indicate the speed of transmission. A **M**edia **A**ccess **C**ontrol (**MAC**) protocol is utilised to identify the correct outgoing ports.

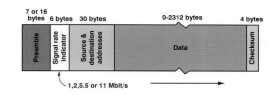

The most popular Wi Fi standard is IEEE 802.11g, providing a typical user data rate of up to 54 Mbit/s over a line of sight range of several hundred metres, depending on the environment. More recent versions of this standard (eg 802.11n) can provide significantly improved data rates.

The IEEE 802.15 standard covers wireless systems known as "Bluetooth". This is used to link data equipment over short distances (up to 30m). A typical application would be to link data terminals in the office or home – it is now being introduced in motor vehicles, so that a cell phone automatically logs on to a "hands-free" service when you enter the vehicle.

Another IEEE standard (802.16) known as WiMax covers fixed broadband wireless links between a stationary user and a stationary server. A typical application would be to create a wireless link between a central exchange and a LAN in a building using an aerial on the roof, where a broadband local loop connection is not available. Both licensed and unlicensed parts of the frequency spectrum can be used, depending on the application and reliability of performance required.

The cable TV industry also offers broadband internet connections using an international standard known as "**D**ata **O**ver **C**able **S**ervice **I**nterface **S**pecification" (**DOCSIS**). The original DOCSIS 1.0 specification allowed for data speeds of 50 and 9 Mb/s for the downstream and upstream paths respectively, and more recent versions cater for downlink speeds in excess of 400 Mb/s. A cable modem at the subscriber's premises connects to a computer, and a **C**able **M**odem **T**ermination **S**ystem (**CMTS**) at the head end location provides the interface to the internet.

11.6 Voice over IP (VoIP)

The relay of speech over the internet has been available for many years. The original method was to use a telephone

The internet

handset connected to a computer and connected via the internet to the recipient who would need similar equipment. A "vocoder" converts the analogue audio to and from a digital format, compresses the encoded audio and decompresses the reconstituted audio. The data generated is split into protocol packets in the required format by a Windows network interface card, which frames the data and sends it to the network.

Both parties need to be logged on to the internet with an e-mail pathway established between them before the conversation can take place. Even international calls do not incur any additional cost because internet subscriptions do not charge per gigabyte in most service agreements.

The speech quality is very dependent on the internet. Data transmission must occur in real time and delays can cause significant disruption to the traffic. Delays in the system may mean that the packets arrive in the wrong sequence or with varying gaps between them. Packets may even disappear, resulting in missing information - lost packets are not retransmitted, resulting in broken speech.

* MAC

* Wi-Fi Standards

* Bluetooth

* WiMax

* DOCSIS

* CMTS

* Voice Over IP (VoIP)

* Vocoder

Keywords

Broadband •
Data Links

Skype •
Vonage •

The introduction of broadband access over ADSL gives two major advantages:

- A wider bandwidth (typically 2 Mbit/sec downstream and 256 kbit/s upstream).

- An "always on" capability.

The ability for speech to be treated as packets of data over an IP network has been exploited by companies such as Skype and Vonage, who now offer VoIP services, often at no cost to the user. The speech quality is often exceptional, unless other data downloads cause loss of data packets.

Calls are only possible when both users have their computers (or VoIP phones) online and are logged on to a VoIP service. Some service providers generate a display screen to show which users are logged on to the service.

Voice communication between users A and B is achieved by setting the IP addresses in the IP packet headers, and an interchange of "ring" and "answer" message packets, followed by an exchange of data packets to convey the speech. This is called "peer-to-peer" communication, since there is no intermediate server involved in setting up the communication path.

Packets being relayed on a private data network can be assigned as various classes of service and can thereby be given the necessary priority. Since VoIP is a real-time application, these packets are assigned to a higher quality of service.

If a VoIP user wishes to communicate with a non-VoIP user, the call is routed via a gateway (in the country being called) to the local public switched telephone network. Such calls are chargeable but the rates are extremely competitive – usually equating to the cost of a local call in the country concerned.

National telephone carriers such as British Telecom have long since converted their services to carry all voice traffic as data packets. Since internet routers do not recognise the class-of-service identifier, they are installing their own IP infrastructure to provide the required standards of service for both real-time and non-real time applications. Customers will not know whether their calls are being carried using circuit switched technology, or as data packets (when quality of service in ensured)!

IPTV •

11.7 IPTV

The concept of VoIP can be equally well applied to the relay of TV signals using data packets. This technique is called **I**nternet **P**rotocol **T**elevision, or **IPTV**. Any number of video sources can be accessed from remote locations via the internet. These sources could be live streamed video from a satellite dish, TV aerial or CCTV camera, or programmes stored on disc and made available on an "on demand" basis. Any number of viewers can watch a single programme simultaneously without affecting the performance of the server or network backbone delivery bandwidth.

Each video source can be given its own internet address and each viewing location will need some means of programme selection – this could be a computer or a custom-designed device such as a handset / transmitter capable of generating internet addresses. IPTV is an extension of the audio/video switching system shown in the diagram alongside. This is designed for use in a single building. The four A/V sources feed the 4 x 4 switching matrix (or server, using computer terminology). Multipair data cables relay the selected programme to each monitor where programme selection is achieved using a handset and remote "eye".

IPTV uses the same concept, except that the source selection is achieved using internet addresses and the signals are distributed as internet data packets. For large systems, the internet can be used instead of a CAT5 cable network, as long as a broadband data port is available at each viewing location.

The performance of IPTV is limited by the bandwidth of the weakest link in the chain. Standard definition pictures require a bandwidth of at least 2 Mbit/sec. Most broadband connections are "asynchronous" (ie. different uplink and downlink speeds). Whilst a typical ADSL broadband connection has a minimum downlink bandwidth of 2 Mbit/sec or more, uplink bandwidths are usually much less than this – 256kbit/sec or even less. This will severely degrade the resultant picture quality, especially on fast-moving images. The uplink speed generally determines the overall performance of the system. The available bandwidth will also be reduced if a broadband connection is shared between several users.

VoIP service providers such as Skype often provide TV images so that the users can see each other. Even if both parties have an ADSL connection, the limited uplink bandwidth of 256 Kb/s results in poor quality pictures that freeze momentarily every time that either party moves their head. The performance of a CCTV security system (where an intruder can be monitored from another location using the internet) is limited in the same way.

This table summarises the typical performances achieved using the various technologies:

Technology	Uplink Speed (typical)	Downlink Speed (typical)	Always on?
PSTN (analogue)	50 Kb/s	50 Kb/s	No
ISDN	2x64 Kb/s	2x64 Kb/s	No
ADSL	256 Kb/s	2 Mb/s	Yes
Wi Fi	54 Mb/s	54 Mb/s	Yes
VDSL	50 Mb/s	50 Mb/s	Yes
LAN (CAT 5e)	100 Mb/s	100 Mb/s	Yes
Fibre Optic LAN	1000 Mb/s	1000 Mb/s	Yes

There is a growing market for relaying TV programmes over data networks to displays in large complexes such as airports, hotels and racecourses. Standard ADSL will not provide a good enough picture quality for these applications. The overall data bandwidth necessary for such applications must be at least 2 Mb/s and preferably more – high quality MPEG2 video needs about 6 Mb/s for good results. This can only be achieved by the use of high bit rate services such as VDSL between networks, or by installing a LAN within a single complex, using multipair or fibre optic cables. However, recent improvements in compression techniques (MPEG4) have resulted in high quality video being achieved at 2 Mb/s – the top end of typical current ADSL performance (as long as the uplink is of sufficient quality).

Keywords

- IPTV Bandwidth

- Technology Data Speeds

- MPEG2

- MPEG4

11

Filter & Signal

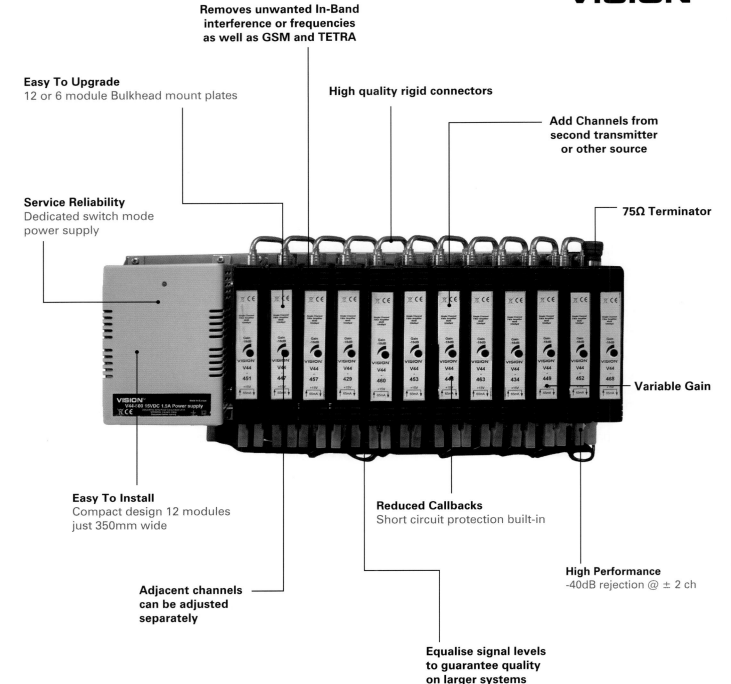

VISION®

Removes unwanted In-Band interference or frequencies as well as GSM and TETRA

High quality rigid connectors

Add Channels from second transmitter or other source

Easy To Upgrade
12 or 6 module Bulkhead mount plates

75Ω Terminator

Service Reliability
Dedicated switch mode power supply

Variable Gain

Easy To Install
Compact design 12 modules just 350mm wide

Reduced Callbacks
Short circuit protection built-in

High Performance
-40dB rejection @ ± 2 ch

Adjacent channels can be adjusted separately

Equalise signal levels to guarantee quality on larger systems

Also Available In The Vision Filter & Signal Range

Single Channel Radio

Single Channel Satellite

Single Channel UHF

Superfilter™

Varifilter™

www.vision-products.co.uk

Part Twelve - Structured Cable Networks

Keywords

• Structured
  Cable Networks

12.1 Network Concepts

This section deals with multipair cable networks using the Ethernet standards referred to in section 11.5. Typical applications are as follows:

In the home

• To communicate between data terminals.
• To share a broadband connection.

In a commercial environment

• To create a data network.
• To create a TV distribution system where programmes can be accessed from any location on the network.

In contrast to a TV coaxial cable network where the number of programmes is restricted by the UHF bandwidth, the programme capacity of a structured cable network is not limited at all by the cable (since each viewer has his own circuit), only by the capacity of the head end equipment supplying the service.

The most fundamental structured cable network links several computers together. The original method used Microsoft Internet Connection Sharing - a software

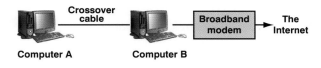

package included in operating systems from Windows 98SE onwards. It enabled two computers to share a single broadband connection if each has a network interface card. The computers were linked together with an Ethernet "crossover" cable as described in section 12.2. A broadband modem is like a telephone modem, except that it connects to the broadband service instead of the dial-up service.

• Computer
  Networks

The current technique to link several computers is by using a **L**ocal **A**rea **N**etwork (**LAN**), the interconnection point being called a **Hub**. A hub contains multiple **ports** and has no intelligence – data received on one port is simply broadcast to all the other ports. A hub operates at ISO level 1 and shares its available frequency bandwidth between all its ports - its performance will therefore be degraded when several computers are broadcasting simultaneously.

• Local Area
  Network (LAN)
• Hub
• Ports

A network **Switch** is essentially an intelligent hub. It operates at ISO level 2 and learns the "**MAC**" addresses of each device attached to it. By examining the incoming data packets, it can then switch each packet only to the device it is destined for (as opposed to broadcasting to the whole network). By providing communication between two relevant points, it reduces the overall bandwidth requirement on the network. The bandwidth of a switch is not reduced as the number of ports is increased.

• Switch
• MAC Address

A **Router** is even more intelligent. It operates at ISO level 3 and examines the destination address of each data packet received, decides on the best route to that destination, and forwards the packet in the appropriate direction. Routers use special protocols such as

• Router

Keywords

ICMP •

Firewall •
Proxy Server •

ICMP to communicate with each other and to configure the best route between any two hosts. They also provide a degree of network security – other computers on the internet can only see the router; they cannot gain access to an individual computer. Many routers also incorporate a **Firewall** to limit access to and from specific network addresses. Another type of firewall, called a **proxy server**, restricts access to specific data contained within a packet. The latest devices combine the functions of a switch/router/firewall and wireless access point into a single unit.

Three or more computers can share a broadband connection using standard straight-through Ethernet cables instead of the crossover versions. In this case, the computers must be interlinked with a hub or switch with cables not longer than 100m. The gateway computer (computer A in the drawing) must be turned on for the others to access the internet.

The more usual way is to use a dedicated broadband router which usually incorporates a switch and broadband modem. It must have one port for each computer connected to it. Each computer can then connect directly to the internet by using the router as a gateway. The router is normally switched on permanently – it is low voltage, silent and has no moving parts.

IPTV Applications •

Video Server •

IPTV applications within a single complex can use the same type of structured cable network. This drawing shows a typical system for a streaming TV or video-on-demand services in a hotel or airport terminal. The picture sources are connected to a video server using a suitable interface, the server being under the control of a computer which controls access at each viewing location to specific channels. Each viewer has an IPTV receiver to select the programme for viewing on a suitable display. One server may feed the whole network, or for large systems, several servers may be required, linked together by a fibre optic data bus.

The service can be extended to include remote control of other services such as interior lighting, security and access control. IPTV can also be integrated with other services on an existing broadband structured cable network.

The same type of multipair structured cable network can be used to select and relay video and audio programmes at their baseband frequencies (or even at UHF over short distances). Such signals are relayed over any of the pairs of wires by using a balance- to unbalanced transformer (Balun) at each end of the connection to match the unbalanced coaxial signals to the balanced pair cable network. Video equalisers are required if the cable runs are long. The baluns can be powered over a separate pair of wires in the overall cable sheath.

Keywords

• Video / Audio Switching Matrix

• RS232 Control

• UTP

• CAT5

• Krone Frames

• CAT5e

• CAT6
• CAT7

• RJ45

A typical application would be the use of a 16x16 video/audio switching matrix to provide a choice of 16 programmes over a cable network to 16 viewing locations. In its simplest form, channel selection can be achieved by relaying an infrared signal from a handset at the viewing location to an LED device attached to the front of the input source.

More sophisticated applications utilise IP addressing with the switching matrix configured as a hub and RS232 control from a laptop computer. The number of users can be increased in multiples of 16, each connected to a hub with its own IP address

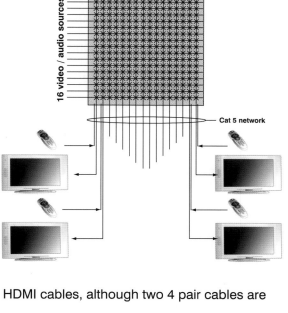

Uncompressed high definition TV signals can also be relayed on multipair cables over much longer distances than on HDMI cables, although two 4 pair cables are normally required for such applications.

Most data networks and IPTV systems utilise 100 ohm Unshielded Twisted Pair (**UTP**) cables which are identified by their category rating. Category 5 cables (known in the trade as "**Cat 5**") consist of four twisted pairs in a single cable jacket. The use of balanced pairs of wires helps to preserve a good signal-to-noise ratio despite interference from both external sources and other pairs. The inner conductors are solid for backbone cables and stranded for patch cables. These cables often terminate on patch panels or "Krone frames" for ease of cross-connecting and testing. Each pair is twisted by a different amount to minimise crosstalk between the pairs, although this is only effective up to about 30 MHz. Cat 5 cable typically has three twists per inch of each pair of 24 gauge copper wire within the cable. The outer insulation is typically pvc or LSOH. Cat 5 cable is normally supplied on 1000 ft drums.

12.2 Network Cables and Connectors

There are various grades of UTP cable:

• **Cat 5** cables have a bandwidth of up to 100 MHz for cable lengths not exceeding 100m. Typical losses for Cat 5 cables are shown alongside. Cat 5 cable networks are always star-wired.
• **Cat 5e** is an improved version of Cat 5 with an increased bandwidth of 155 MHz.
• **Cat 6** is specified up to 200 MHz bandwidth.
• **Cat 7** is a recent cable specification for Screened Twisted Pair (STP) cables, where each of the four pairs is individually screened – this can give a bandwidth of up to 600MHz.

Cat 5 cables are nearly always terminated by 8P8C modular 8 pin connectors, known in the trade as RJ45. These would normally be mounted on a Krone frame at the launch location, and on a single gang flush plate flush plate at each outlet location. Such plates can incorporate either one or two RJ45 sockets, and RJ45 modules are available for

12

Keywords

multi-service outlet plates. The socket incorporates Krone connectors and an insulation displacement tool is required to connect the cables. The mating plug has a latch, to prevent it from being accidentally disengaged.

The most common data applications for Cat 5 cable utilise the following pin connections:

- Pin 1   Tx+ (transmit data +)
- Pin 2   Tx- (transmit data -)
- Pin 3   Rx+ (receive data +)
- Pin 6   Rx- (receive data -)

CAT5 •
Connections

The four pairs of wires in a Cat 5 cable are colour coded as follows:
- Blue, and white with a blue stripe
- Orange, and white with an orange stripe
- Green and white with a green stripe
- Brown and white with a brown stripe

CAT5 Colour •
Code
T568A •
T568B •

Cat 5 cable lengths are limited to 100m. The cable is terminated using either the **T568A** scheme or the **T568B** scheme. It does not matter which is used, since they are both straight through (pin 1 to pin 1, pin 2 to pin 2 etc). T568A is normally used for installed wiring and T568B for patch cables. The pin assignments are as follows:

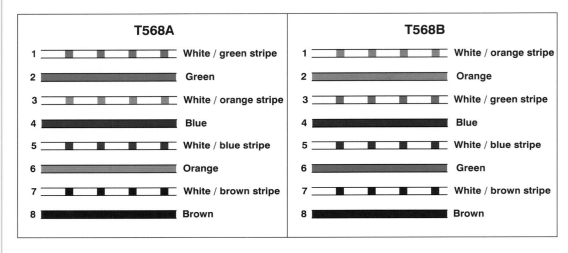

T568A	T568B
1 — White / green stripe	1 — White / orange stripe
2 — Green	2 — Orange
3 — White / orange stripe	3 — White / green stripe
4 — Blue	4 — Blue
5 — White / blue stripe	5 — White / blue stripe
6 — Orange	6 — Green
7 — White / brown stripe	7 — White / brown stripe
8 — Brown	8 — Brown

These assignments obviously apply to **both** ends of the cable. The only difference between the two methods of wiring is that the orange and green pairs are reversed.

Crossover Cable •

Some interconnections require the use of a **crossover** cable (normally identified with a red heat shrink collar at each end). The interconnections for crossover cables are follows:

12

Keywords

T568A	T568B
1 1	1 1
2 2	2 2
3 3	3 3
4 4	4 4
5 5	5 5
6 6	6 6
7 7	7 7
8 8	8 8

Crossover cables are used to connect PCs to one another, or to connect a hub to another hub. The connection between a PC and a hub uses a straight cable.

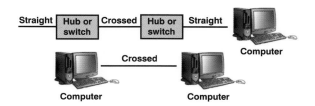

12.3 Installation Techniques

This section describes the procedure to connect an RJ45 socket at one end of a Cat 5e cable and a Krone frame at the other end, using T568B pin assignments. It also covers the fitting of an RJ45 plug.

The following should be available:

- An insulation displacement connector (Krone) tool
- A suitable cable stripper
- Cable cutters
- Pliers
- Cable markers
- A specialist crimp tool for RJ45 plugs

• RJ45 Socket Connection

As a general principle, the twists of each pair of wires in a Cat 5 cable should be maintained as close as possible to the connector pins in order to reduce the crosstalk and interference between the wires – do not unwind each pair more than is absolutely necessary.

To connect to an RJ45 socket to a Cat 5 cable:

1. Slide on the appropriate cable markers

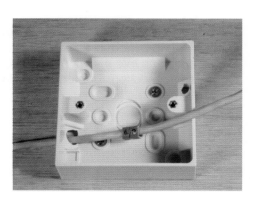

Keywords

2. Use a proper stripping tool for twisted pair cables

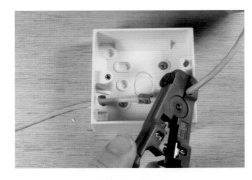

3. Remove approximately 50mm of the outer cable sheath

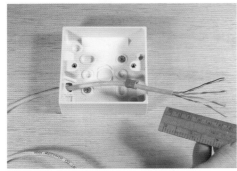

4. Lay out the pairs using the colour code on the side of the connector and according to T568A or T568B

5. Arrange the twisted pairs on the module knives keeping the integrity of the twists of each pair. Do not strip the outer insulation of each wire.

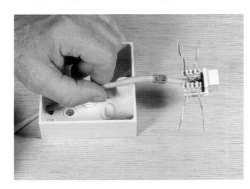

6. Use a Krone tool to connect each wire in turn. The IDC module knives cuts through the insulation and into the wire, guaranteeing a reliable connection. The tool cuts off the surplus wire at the same time.

12

Keywords

This is a top view of the socket fully wired.

To connect an RJ45 plug to a Cat 6 cable:

1. Cat 6 cables usually incorporate an x-shaped plastic spacer in the middle to position each pair for minimum interference – this must be removed with a pair of cutters when the outer sheath is stripped back.

2. They incorporate a metal screening foil under the outer pvc sheath. This also has a silk thread (or rip cord) under the pvc. Pulling the thread will make a longitudinal cut in the jacket. The cut should be about 50mm in length.

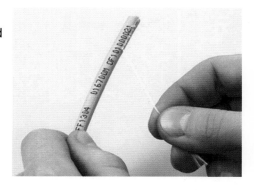

3. Use a skinning tool tool to cut right round the cable.

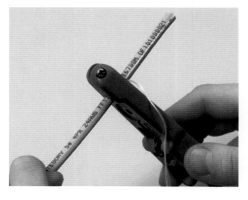

12

4. Remove 50mm of the outer pvc covering.

This prevents damage to the screening foil under the outer sheath.

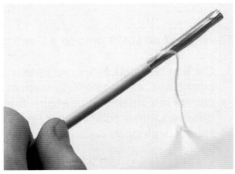

5. Unwrap the foil and fold it back over the outer sheath.

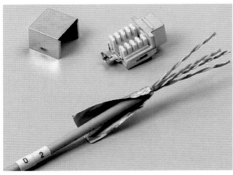

6. Cut off the end of the foil, leaving 15mm folded back.

There is a tinned copper drain wire contained within the foil

12

Keywords

7. Wrap the drain wire around the foil

8. Use pliers to fix the cable in the earth clamp of the connector, ensuring that the drain wire and foil make good contact.

9. Arrange the twisted pairs on the module knives keeping the integrity of the twists of each pair.

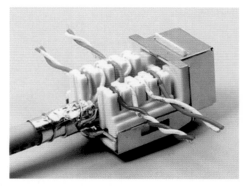

10. Use a Krone tool to connect each wire in turn.

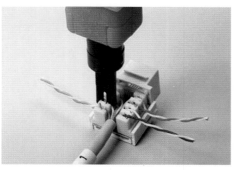

This is a top view of the socket fully wired.

Keywords

11. Fix the screening can over the module to complete the connection

Krone Frame •
Connection

To connect to a Krone frame:

Slide on the appropriate marker and lay out the wires from each cable over their appropriate connectors, maintaining the twist in each pair.

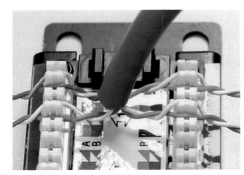

Most frames are colour coded for both T568A and T568B

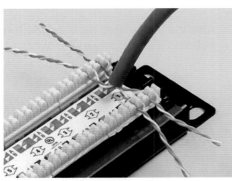

Punch down the pairs using a Krone tool.

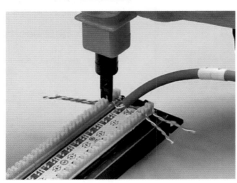

Note that each cable is made off in a uniform manner

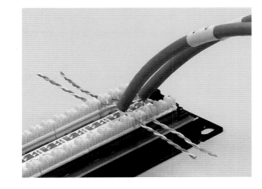

12

Keywords

Remove the surplus wire that is cut off by the Krone tool.

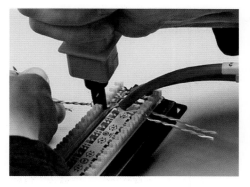

Note how the pairs are presented to the patch panel.

See how uniform the nearly finished frame looks.

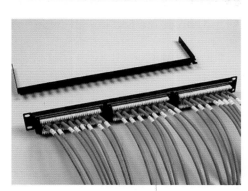

This is an alternative type of frame with a screening continuity strip. Note how each foil is folded back for screening continuity.

This shows the shield and cable clamps used in a screened twisted pair network patch panel.

12

Keywords

Note how each cable is tied to the cable management bar.

This is the completed frame prior to being mounted in the 19" rack.

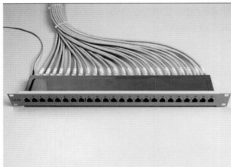

All the cables are tied-in with cable ties

This is now ready for installation.

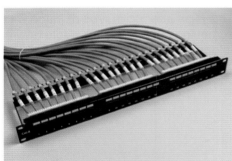

The patch panel is now mounted in the rack with the cables tied to management trays.

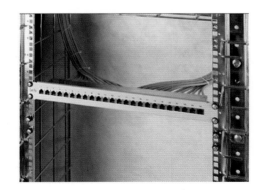

12

Keywords

Another installation, also very neat and tidy.

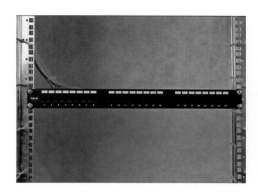

Some general comments on Cat 5 cable networks:

• Maintaining the twist of each pair of wires and not stripping away more of the outer sheath than is necessary all helps to maximise the frequency bandwidth and minimise crosstalk between cable opairs
• Use connector boots if supplied, to act as strain relief and give protection to the rear of the connector
• Do not install Cat 5 cables in parallel with or near to mains power cable, especially those carrying large currents.
• Don't use cable clips

To connect to an RJ45 plug:

This drawing shows the wiring sequence for a T568B assignment:

• RJ45 Plug Connection

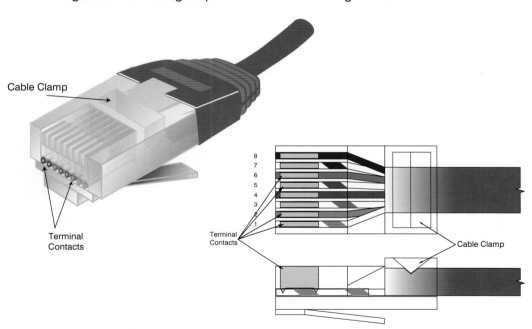

1. Slide on the appropriate cable markers (if required).

2. Remove 25mm of the outer cable sheath using a proper stripping tool.

3. Untwist each pair and straighten each wire, placing the wires in the correct order for T568A or T568B as applicable.

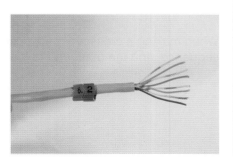

12

Keywords

4. Bring all the wires together so that they touch, keeping them in the correct sequence and cut them to a perfect 90° angle, possibly using a pair of scissors (this is very critical – if they are not all the same length, they may not all make contact).

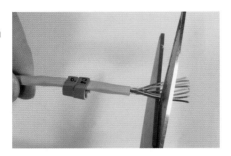

5. The free length of each wire should be 12mm from the end of the cable sheath.

6. Insert the wires into the connector with the pins facing upwards.

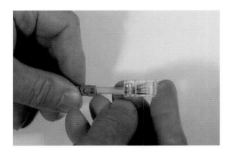

7. Push moderately hard to ensure that each wire has reached the end of the connector

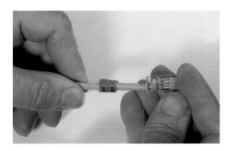

8. Place the connector into the crimp tool and squeeze hard so that the handle reaches the limit of its travel.

9. Use a cable tester to check for proper continuity.

When making a crossover patch cable, ensure that one end is wired to the T568A sequence, and the other end to the 568B sequence.

12

Working on Building Sites

Building sites invariably have a nominated Health and Safety Officer to whom all sub contractors must report when they first visit the site. Many such officers insist on seeing the Company's Health and Safety Policy before commencing any work, and for all personnel on site to undergo formal training - this usually consists of watching a Health and Safety videotape and discussing what procedures are to be undertaken and how the risks involved will be minimized.

All personnel on site must wear a "Hard hat" and steel capped boots. They may also be required to wear a face mask when other contractors are carrying out specific activities which cause dust or pollute the surrounding air.
230V AC mains operated equipment may **not** be used on any building site. Most sites provide a 110V AC mains supply via isolating transformers when required. The use of battery powered drills etc. is normally permitted.
The use of "walkie talkies" may not be permitted unless the operator can produce a licence to prove that he is legally entitled to use such equipment.

Personnel may not erect, change or tamper with any scaffolding unless they have the appropriate qualification to do so. Staff must not use any scaffolding which they consider to be unsafe without prior discussion with the site Health and Safety officer.

Operators of hoists, fork lift trucks, cranes and mobile scaffold towers must be properly trained to do so.
On installation sites, staff must be vigilant as to the activities of others which can increase the risk of slipping, particularly whilst carrying heavy loads which obstruct the field of view.

Appropriate ear defenders must be worn on any site where the level of noise and vibration, however caused, could otherwise affect their health.

Construction, Design and Maintenance (CDM)

The introduction of CDM regulations in 1994 places new responsibilities on clients, planners, supervisors, designers and contractors. Appointed designers and contractors must be competent and have adequate resources for Health and Safety.

CDM applies when either:

- The work lasts more than 30 days, or
- Involves more than 500 person days, or
- Involves 5 or more people on site, or
- There is any design work, no matter how long or however many people.

CDM does not apply if the work is carried out for a domestic householder or is minor construction work.

CDM is intended to minimise risks associated with all aspects of the construction industry not only through the construction stages but also through refurbishment and maintenance.

Keywords

- Building Sites

- CDM

Keywords

All personnel and companies have assigned responsibilities and a summary of these duties is as follows:-

Contractors and the self-employed:
- Provide a Health and Safety plan that identifies and manages risks.
- Manage work to comply with Health and Safety.
- Provide information for the Health and Safety file.
- Provide information to the employer.
- Provide method statements and risk analyses for each task.

Designers:
- Alert clients of risks and prepare a risk analysis.
- Design to avoid or reduce risks.
- Pass on information to the planning supervisor.
- Manage the on-site risks.

Method Statements and Risk Analyses

The risks associated with each activity undertaken by the company should be considered in detail. Such considerations should include the following:

- The methods and procedures to be followed;
- The extent of the risks involved;
- Whether there is a safer way of doing the job;
- What precautions can be taken to minimise the risks.

If activities are to be undertaken that are not specifically covered by the general Health and Safety policy, it may be necessary to document each of these activities and the method by which the associated risks are minimised.

All staff must be made aware of, and abide by, any method statements applicable to the tasks being performed.
They are also duty bound to inform the site Health and Safety officer of any condition on site that they consider to be unsafe.

The following section illustrates a method statement for the installation of a TV aerial on a chimney. A risk assessment must be prepared for each task and a sample assessment is also included.

Method • Statement

Method Statement

- Company name.
- Contract detail: Title, number, etc.
- Statement prepared by: and signed by:
- Contents – refer to sections, paragraphs and page numbers.
- Preface or forward – explain here the basis on which the plan is prepared ie. Construction Design and Management Regulations 1994 and related to the Health and Safety at Work Act 1974.
- Key to parameters:-

Severity:	Low	May cause minor injury.
	Medium	Short term disability.
	High	Major injury resulting in long term disability or fatality.

Probability:	Low	Very slight chance.
	Medium	Quite possible
	High	Frequent occurrence.

Keywords

- Project Description. *The replacement of a TV aerial and down lead on an office block with a pitched roof and tiles. The aerial is to be installed on a chimney using a lashing kit. The down lead will lay on the tiles and be clipped down the wall to the first floor and then routed through a hole drilled through the wall and terminated on the existing earth bar at the head end location.*
- Client
- Planning by
- Nature of existing structure. *The building is a two storey office block constructed around 1960.......*
- Time scale   Contract start and finish dates.
- Environment Description
- Restrictions
- Noise, nuisance problems.
- Protection or proximity of gas, water, electricity.
- Traffic access
- Parking issues.
- Material storage
- Existing H & S precautions
- Work sequence
- Material requirements   Any hazardous materials
- Site rules   ID, hard hat site
- Names list   For liaison and emergency communication

Work sequence:

1. Materials and tools will arrive by van which will be parked outside the building in the road.
2. A ladder will be lent against the front of the building extending above the gutter line.
3. A roof ladder will be laid across the roof from the ladder position to the chimney.
4. A chinmey lashing kit will be secured to the chimney and a 2M mast with a ten element aerial mounted on it.
5. A coaxial cable will be connected to the aerial and secured to the mast using insulation tape.
6. The cable will be laid on the surface of the roof tiles and fixed in position at every fourth tile.
7. The cable will be routed under the gutter and be cable clipped to the gutter board and down the brick wall to the first floor window.
8. A hole will be drilled through the wall using a 10mm masonry bit.
9. The coaxial cable will pass through the hole and terminate on the existing earth bar at the head end location
10. The hole will be sealed to prevent water ingress.

Tasks: Risk assessment attached
1. Erection and use of a ladder.   [X]
2. Erection and use of a roof ladder.   [X]
3. Installation of a lashing kit and aerial.   [X]
4. Routing and clipping of cable.   [X]
5. Drilling of wall entry.   [X]
6. Fixing of coaxial cable to earth bars.   [X]

Plant:
1. Ladder, 3 extension, 9M maximum.
2. Roof ladder, 4M.
3. Battery powered drill.
4. Small tools

Keywords

Risk •
Analysis

Risk Analysis

Task: Erection and use of a ladder

Risk: Falls from height
Falling Materials
Damage caused by ladder falling over

Risk Assessment:

	Severity				Probability of Occurance	
Low	Medium	High [X]		Low	Medium [X]	High

People Affected

Installers/Staff/Operatives [X]   Tenants [X]   Visitors [X]   General Public [X]

Control Measures:

- Consider if the ladder will be a safe working platform.
- Ladder must be of adequate strength.
- Ladder must be inspected prior to use.
- Short ladders carried by one person, long ladders carried horizontally by two.
- Ladder must be placed on a firm, level base.
- Ladders over 3m in length must be footed or the base secured.
- Top of ladder must preferably be secured.
- Ladders must be set at 4:1 angle.
- Ladder sections must overlap by at least three rungs.
- Don't over reach.
- Don't overbalance.
- Don't overload the ladder.
- Don't use the top step.
- The ladder must extend at least 1.05M above the landing place unless another suitable handhold is provided.
- Only one person on the ladder at a time.
- Always face the ladder and use both hands when climbing or descending.
- Place signs/warning bollards underneath when working over public thoroughfares.

Personal Protection Equipment

Installation and service staff can only be as safe as their Company equips them to be!
Each person will need some or all of the following, depending on the nature of the tasks to be performed:

- A first aid kit (usually kept on the vehicle)
- A helmet with chinstrap to standard BS EN 397
- Steel capped boots to standard BS EN 345
- Eye protection to standard BS EN 166, 167, 168
- A high visibility vest, face mask and gloves to standard BS EN 471
- Hearing protection to standard BS EN 352-2
- An eye bolt and ratchet strap (for fixing ladders)
- A ladder safety rope
- A safety harness and rope grab
- A safety barrier and bollards
- A ladder stabiliser, stand-off device and levelling device

Keywords

Ladder standards are defined in standard BS EN 131. There are three classes as follows:

Class 1	Industrial	Maximum static vertical load 175Kg
Class 2	Light trade	Maximum static vertical load 150Kg
Class 3	Domestic	Maximum static vertical load 125Kg

Always ensure that the correct grade of ladder is used – domestic ladders are not suitable for trade use.

Review of Health and Safety Requirements

There are three aspects to be considered:

- Mechanical safety
- Electrical safety
- Installer safety

Mechanical safety

Location

When a system is designed, consider both the aesthetic and the safety aspects. Try not to locate a dish or aerial above a public thoroughfare. Brackets and other structures installed below head height must be visibly marked.

Cables between buildings must be supported by catenary wires.

Don't position a receiver or amplifier where it might get wet or overheat.

Don't specify the use of polythene cables indoors.

Locate roof mounted equipment where it is accessible for maintenance without exposing the technician to undue risks.

Corrosion

It is preferred that masts are made of a non-ferrous metal. All steel structures must be hot-dip galvanized to ensure that components are protected internally and externally. Care must be taken that no water can be trapped inside the mast. All assembly nuts and bolts must be made of stainless steel or plated to the appropriate standards.

Ensure that all waveguide joints will have the appropriate sealing ring and that all external cable joints will be sealed to prevent the ingress of moisture.

Some plasters and cements have a corrosive effect on metals and precautions against this may be necessary where cables or conduits are installed in damp situations.

Consider the effects of electrolytic corrosion between two dissimilar metals. In particular, copper / aluminium joints must be avoided.

- Mechanical Safety

- Corrosion

Keywords

Ventilation •

Supporting •
Structures

Safety of •
General Public

Ventilation

All equipment must be located in an accessible well ventilated location to prevent the risk of overheating. Fans must be fitted in poorly ventilated areas or where the ambient temperature is likely to exceed 50°C.

When locating cables in vertical risers, ensure that there will be a fire seal between floors. For multiple cable runs in vertical ducts, consider the use of low smoke zero halogen (LSOH) cables to minimise the fire risk.

Rigidity of Supporting Structures

Antenna systems must be designed to withstand wind speeds of 162 Km/h (100 mph). Consider the strength of the materials being used. The Code of Practice covers many such aspects including the wind loading of aerials, the need for mast guy wires and spacing between wall brackets. Mast diameter alone is no indication of the mast strength - the wall thickness must be adequate. For mast brackets, continuous welds are preferable to spot welds.

Consider also the rigidity of the fixings and the strength of the wall or roof to which the equipment is to be fixed. Avoid the use of expansion bolts if rawlplugs will suffice, especially into bricks. Never fix into the mortar between bricks. Don't wall mount dishes greater than 1,2m diameter. If the bricks are soft, specify the use of chemical fixings.

Before using a chimney as a support, check its rigidity. Avoid the use of the top three courses of brickwork and ensure that corner plates are fitted.

For exceptionally weak walls, specify additional supports or other measures to spread the loading over a large area.

Specify that all nuts will be spanner tightened (but not overtightened, to prevent distortion of the mast).

Holes must be drilled to the correct diameter and depth for the particular fastener.

Cables must be adequately fixed. Those with a diameter greater than 10mm must be fixed at a lesser spacing than as shown below:

- On masts   230mm
- On other vertical runs   750mm
- On horizontal runs   460mm

Safety of the General Public

Installation and service staff must at all times be alert to the need to avoid creating hazards to others working on the site and to the general public. Barriers and/or warning notices must be used where appropriate. Guy wires and trailing cables must be visibly marked.

When an aerial or dish is transported in an open trailer or externally on a vehicle, it must be located so as to minimize the aerofoil effect consistent with the speed of the vehicle. Due care and attention must be exercised when transporting open trailer mounted aerials and other equipment notwithstanding current legislation on the towing of trailers. When poles and ladders overhang the ends of a vehicle, the appropriate warning symbols must be attached.

Keywords

• Installer Safety

Electrical safety

This has already been covered in detail earlier in this publication.

Installer safety

The CAI have issued a document entitled "Guidelines on Safe Operating Procedures for the Aerial and Satellite Industry". This deals mainly with the risks associated with working above ground level. Three aspects are of prime importance:

1. Consider if a ladder will be a safe working platform
2. Securely fix a ladder so that it cannot slip outwards or sideways
3. Always maintain 3 points of contact with the ladder

The way that a ladder should be fixed depends on the site conditions. Possible solutions include the following;

• Using a "Laddermate" stabiliser
• Positioning the foot of the ladder against the wheel of a vehicle
• Tying the ladder to a stack pipe using a rope
• Fixing an eyebolt into the wall and using a ratchet strap
• Tying the ladder to a roof ladder
• Having a colleague to "foot" the ladder

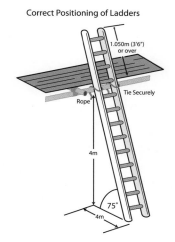

Correct Positioning of Ladders

The three points of contact with the ladder are normally two feet and one hand. Where both hands are needed to do the work, the installer should fit a safety rope to the ladder and wear a safety harness attached to the rope with a rope grab.

Keywords

These pictures show how **<u>not</u>** to do it!

The Digital Television Group Ltd. (DTG):   Tel. 020 75014300
    Installing Digital Television 1 – Basic Domestic Systems
    Installing Digital Television 2 – Domestic Systems
    Installing Digital Television 3 – MATV Systems
    Installing Digital Television 4 – Integrated Reception Systems
    High Definition TV – The Essential Guide for TV Professionals

The Office of Communications (Ofcom):   Tel. 08456 505050
    Guidelines for Improving Television and Radio Reception

Web-sites:

Astra:	ses-astra.com
BBC:	bbc.co.uk
British Sky Broadcasting	sky.com
Department of Trade and Industry (DTI)	dti.gov.uk
Digital UK	digitaluk.co.uk
Eutelsat:	eutelsat.org
Freesat	freesat.co.uk
National Grid Wireless	nationalgridwireless.com
Ofcom	ofcom.org.uk
Registered Digital Installer Licensing Body	rdi-lb.tv

Satellite programme information is available from the following web-sites:
    Satcodx.com
    lyngsat.com/dig/skyuk/shtml

Appendix C - Abbreviations and Glossary of Terms

22KHz tone	The signal generated by a satellite receiver and relayed to an LNB to select the "high" local oscillator.
A/D	Analogue-to-Digital (conversion)
ADSL	"Asynchronous Digital Subscriber Line". The method used to provide broadband services to UK telephone subscribers,
Amplifier	A circuit that increases the power or voltage of a signal.
Amplitude	The strength or magnitude of a signal
Amplitude modulation	A transmission system in which the modulating waveform is made to vary the carrier amplitude.
Analogue	A mode of transmission of information. An analogue waveform has a physical similarity with the quantity it represents.
Antenna (aerial)	A device used to transmit or receive radio waves.
AP	Access point (on a Wi Fi wireless LAN)
API	Application Programming Interface. A software interface for data networks.
ARP	Address Resolution Protocol.
Arpanet	The US defence department project that created the Internet.
Aspect ratio	The ratio of width to height for a TV screen.
Astra	The "trade" name for satellites operated by SES ("Societe Europeenne des Satellites").
ATM	Asynchronous Transfer Mode. A data service using packet switching.
Attenuator	A passive device that decreases signal power.
Azimuth	A compass bearing east or west of true south
Balun	A balance-to-unbalance transformer (sometimes an integral part of an aerial) used to match an unbalanced coaxial cable to a balanced device such as an aerial dipole or receiver input.
Bandpass filter	A circuit that passes a restricted band of frequencies. Unwanted lower and upper frequencies are attenuated.
Bandwidth	The total range of frequencies occupied by a signal. It is normally measured between half-power points.
Baseband	The band of frequencies containing information after demodulation.
Beamwidth	An aerial acceptance angle measured between half-power points.
Bit	A binary digit (a "1" or "0").

Bit error ratio (BER)	A ratio of the number of errors in a data stream to the total number of data bits.
Bit rate	The number of digital bits transmitted per second.
Boltzmann's constant	The relationship between the energy of a particle and its motion is related to its absolute temperature multiplied by Boltzmann's constant, which has the value of -228.6dB. This very small factor exerts a powerful influence on the effects of noise and thus on quality.
Boresight	The principle centre axis of an aerial or dish antenna.
Bouquet	A number of programmes grouped within a multiplex.
BSkyB	British Sky Broadcasting.
BSS (Bus. Satellite Services)	The band of frequencies 11.7-12.5GHz
Byte	A group of 8 digital "bits".
C120 flange	A standard mating flange for circular Ku band waveguides.
CAM	"Conditional Access Module". Normally fits into the PCMCIA socket of a satellite receiver, to hold a viewing card.
Capacitance	A energy storage device that is formed wherever an insulator separates two conductors between which a voltage difference exists. Capacitance is measured in "Farads".
Carrier-to-noise (C/N) ratio	A ratio of the received carrier power to the noise power in a given bandwidth, in dBs.
Cascade amplifier	A line-powered amplifier that also passes the powering voltage to its input terminals.
Cassegrain	A dish with a paraboloid prime focus main reflector and a convex sub-reflector.
Catenary wire	A supporting wire for an overhead coaxial cable between buildings or structures.
Cathode ray tube (CRT)	An evacuated glass vessel in which an electron beam produces a luminous image on a fluorescent screen.
CATV	Community (Cable) Antenna Television.
C band	The band of frequencies 3.6-4.2GHz.
CCIR	"International Radio Consultative Committee".
CCIR impairment scale	A 5 point scale of subjective analogue picture quality.
CCTV	"Closed Circuit TeleVision"
CDM (construction/design/maint)	Regulations concerning activities on a building site that must be complied with in certain circumstances.
CDMA	Code Division Multiple Access. A method of allocating frequencies for a cellphone service.
Ceefax	The teletext service provided by the BBC.
CEPT	"European Conference of Postal and Telecommunications Administrations".
Channel	The frequency band over which information (data, audio TV) is relayed.
Characteristic impedance	The impedance in ohms of a device in the path of a communications signal

Circuit protective conductor	A cable used to earth a mains power socket.
Circular polarity	Electromagnetic waves whose electric field uniformly rotates along the signal path. Facing an incoming wave, clockwise rotation is called Right-Hand Circular (RHCP) and anti-clockwise rotation is called Left-Hand Circular Polarisation (LHCP).
Chrominance	The hue and saturation of a colour. A chrominance signal carries the colour information.
Cinemascope	A widescreen TV picture format, usually 16:9.
Cladding	The outer coating of a glass fibre which provides a reflective surface.
Clarke belt	The circular orbital belt 35 786Km above the equator, at which all satellites appear to be stationary.
Cliff effect	The effect of a digital picture suddenly blocking or freezing when the signal parameters degrade below a certain level.
Cluster amplifiers	A series of filters/channel amplifiers tuned to amplify and pass a single cluster of analogue and/or digital terrestrial TV channels.
Cluster filter	A series of filters, each tuned to attenuate a single cluster of analogue and/or digital terrestrial TV channels.
Coaxial cable	An internal conductor surrounded by an insulating dielectric and one or two outer conducting screens.
Co-channel interference	Interference on a single terrestrial TV channel resulting from signals on the same TV channel.
COFDM	"Coded Orthogonal Frequency Division Multiplex". The method of modulation used for digital terrestrial broadcasts in Britain.
Common interface (CI)	A DVB standard that defines the software and hardware standards for conditional access systems.
Composite baseband	The raw demodulator analogue output before filtering, clamping and decoding.
Composite video	A complete video signal, including luminance, sync. and colour information but not audio or data sub-carriers.
Conditional access	A system used by service providers to control subscribers' access to certain services, programmes and events.
Constellation diagram	A representation of the amplitude and phase of each bit of information in a digital symbol.
COS	Class Of Service.
CPU	Central Processing Unit.
Cross colour	A TV picture defect that results in swirling coloured patterns.
Cross luminance	A TV picture defect that results in brightness variations and colour changes.
Cross modulation	A form of interference caused by the modulation of one or more carriers affecting that of another signal. It can be caused by non-linearity or the overloading of an amplifier, or signal imbalances.

Cross-polarisation	Signals of the opposite polarity to those being received.
Cross-polar discrimination	The ratio of the amplitude of the wanted polarity to the unwanted one.
Cross talk	Interference between two or more video or audio baseband signals.
CSMA/CA	Carrier Sense Multiple Access / Collision Avoidance. A media access control protocol used on Wi Fi networks.
CSMA/CD	Carrier Sense Multiple Access / Collision Detection. The method of collision control used on Ethernet LANs.
DAB	"Digital Audio Broadcasting". A standard to define the method of transmitting digital audio signals.
dBi	The gain of an aerial relative to an isotropic source. This is normally 2.15dB more than the gain relative to that of a half-wave dipole.
dBm	dB power relative to a 1 milliwatt standard.
DBS (Direct Broadcast Satellite)	The band of frequencies 11.7-12.5GHz
dBw	dB power relative to 1 watt.
DC pass	The ability of a circuit element (usually a splitter, diplexer or outlet plate) to pass dc voltages – this is necessary to power a masthead amplifier or LNB, or to pass remote control signals.
DCT (Discrete Cosine Transform)	An MPEG technique that converts pixel values from the time domain to the frequency domain and "quantises" the values to compress the data bandwidth.
Decibel (dB)	The logarithmic ratio of voltage or power levels, used to indicate the gains or losses of signals.
Declination offset	The adjustment angle of a polar mount between the polar axis and the plane of a satellite dish used to aim at the geosynchronous arc. Increases from zero with latitude away from the equator.
Decoder	A unit that is connected to a satellite receiver to unscramble an encrypted programme.
DECT	"Digital Enhanced Cordless Technology". A system standard for cordless telephones over a short range (normally indoors).
De-emphasis	A reduction of the higher frequency parts of a signal to neutralise the effect of pre-emphasis.
Demodulator	A device that extracts the baseband signal from a transmitted carrier wave.
Depolarisation	The twisting of the polarisation of a radio wave as it travels through the atmosphere.
Deviation	The maximum amount the carrier frequency is shifted by the modulating signal.
DHCP	Dynamic Host Configuration Protocol. An Internet protocol used to route data within a sub-network.
Dielectric	Insulating material used to separate the conductors of a coaxial cable or the conducting circuits of a capacitor.
Dielectric plate	A device for insertion into a feedhorn to convert circularly polarised signals to a linear polarity.
Digibox	A generic name for a satellite or terrestrial digital receiver.

Diplexer	A frequency-conscious device for combining or splitting signals in different frequency bands. A diplexer has a lower insertion loss than the equivalent splitter.
Dipole	Normally a single aerial element half a wavelength long with cable connections at its centre point.
Director element	An element mounted on an aerial boom in front of the dipole that modifies the aerial characteristics.
Discriminator	A type of circuit used to demodulate an FM signal.
DiSEqC	"Digital Satellite Equipment Control". An extension of the 22KHz concept to provide control of multiple devices.
DLP	Digital Light Processing. A flat panel display technique using rotating mirrors, developed by Toshiba.
DNS	Domain Name System. A directory service to relate an Internet address to its equivalent binary code.
DOCSIS	Data Over Cable Service Interface Specification.An interface standard for two way data communication over a cable TV network.
Down conductor	A conductive link to an earth termination to provide lightning protection.
Down-conversion	A reduction of a band of high frequencies to a lower band.
Downlink	The transmission path from an orbiting satellite to a receiving dish.
DP	Distribution Point.
Drip loop	A loop formed in a coaxial cable so that water will drip off instead of penetrating apparatus or a structure.
Drop-in cable	A coaxial cable linking each dwelling unit to the signal distribution network.
DSB (Double SideBand)	A form of amplitude modulation where both the upper and lower sidebands (which result from modulation of the carrier by the signal) are transmitted.
DTH (Direct-to-home)	Satellite transmissions intended for reception in homes.
DTT	Digital Terrestrial Television.
DVB (Digital Video Broadcast)	A broadcast standard for digital radio and TV using MPEG2 compression.
DVI	An audio/video multipin connector used in the computer industry.
Earth bonding	The connection of a system to an earth point
Earth station	A ground-based transmitting or receiving satellite installation.
EBU	European Broadcasting Union.
EIRP	The power of a transmitter with reference to that of a point (isotropic) source.
EIT (Event Information Table)	Programme data relating to events occurring within a digital multiplex.
Electromagnetic wave	The technical name for a radio wave, so called because it comprises electric and magnetic fields moving in unison.

Elevation	The vertical angle measured from the horizon up to a target satellite.
Encoding	Converting a message to code eg when characters are stored in binary code. Often used to describe a process in which the form of an electronic signal is changed.
Encryption	The process of hiding information or keys needed to unlock scrambled signals.
Energy dispersal	A low frequency signal added to the baseband signal before modulation. Used to reduce the peak power per unit of bandwidth of an FM signal to reduce its interference potential.
EPG (Electronic Prog. Guide)	A compilation of all the programmes available.
ESA	"European Space Agency".
ETSI	"European Telecommunications Standards Institute".
Eutelsat	European Telecommunications Satellite Organisation.
FDMA	Frequency Division Multiplex Access. A method of allocating frequencies for a cellphone service.
F/D ratio	A ratio of the focal length to the diameter of a dish.
FEC (Forward Error Correction)	A technique for improving the accuracy of data transmission. Excess bits are included in the outgoing data stream so that error correction can be applied by the receiver,
Feeder cable	The main coaxial cable emanating from the head end equipment and connected to one or more spur distribution cables.
Feedhorn	A device that collects microwave signals from the surface of a dish (located at the focal point).
Ferrite	A magnetic polarotor.
Fibre optics	The relay of signals on glass fibres using light waves.
Field	One half of a complete TV picture or frame. There are 50 fields per second in a PAL system.
FTP	"File Transfer Protocol". Used for internet file transfers.
Filter	A device used to pass or reject a specified range of frequencies. This normally comprises one or more tuned circuits.
Filter/leveller	A series of filters with adjustable attenuation, each tuned to a single analogue terrestrial TV channel.
Flat screen display	A TV screen using LCD or plasma display techniques instead of a cathode ray tube.
Flylead	A plug-in lead to link together two domestic satellite or TV products.
FOB (Flush Outlet Box)	A TV or satellite outlet designed for flush mounting on to a flush conduit or surface pattress box.
Focal length	The distance from the reflective surface of a parabola to its focal point.
Focal point	A point in front of a satellite dish to which all the reflected energy is focussed.
Folded dipole	Two half-wave dipoles connected in parallel in order to modify the centre impedance.

Footprint	The geographical area towards which a satellite downlink signal is directed. The contours indicate lines of equal signal strength.
Frame	One complete TV picture, composed of two fields
Frequency	The number of oscillations per second of an electrical or electromagnetic signal, expressed in cycles/sec or Hertz
Frequency modulation (FM)	A transmission system in which the modulating waveform is made to vary the carrier frequency.
Freznel zones	Circular regions of an electromagnetic wave where the signals are in the same phase
Front-to-back ratio	The ratio of the gain of an aerial in the forward direction to that in the reverse direction.
FSK	Frequency Shift Keying. A type of modulation where the output frequencies represent the incoming signals.
FSS (Fixed Satellite Service)	The band of frequencies 10.7-11.7GHz
FTP	File transfer Protocol.
Fused spur	A mains electrical power supply outlet comprising a fuse and captive mains cable (but not including a power socket).
Fusion splice	The low-loss glass fibre jointing technique using heat to join two fibres together.
Gain	The amplification of input to output power in dBs.
Geostationary orbit	The circular orbital belt 35 786Km above the equator. Satellites in this belt appear to be stationary.
Galvanic isolator	An in-line device to improve lightning protection and electrical safety by providing dc isolation between different parts of a cable network.
GTU	Gateway Termination Unit. A fibre-to-copper converter unit.
Ghosting	Multiple TV images usually caused by the reception of a signal via two different paths.
GPRS	"General Packet Radio Service". An enhanced version of GSM mobile phone technology with data rates of up to 200Kbits/sec.
Gregorian	A dish with a parabolic offset main reflector and a concave sub-reflector.
Grid aerial	A series of stacked "X" arrays with a grid reflector, to give a high front to-back ratio.
GSM	"Global System for Mobile Communications". The original digital mobile phone technology with a data rate of 9,6Kbits/sec.
G/T (Gain/noise Temperature)	The figure of merit of a dish and LNB. The higher the G/T ratio, the better its reception capabilities.
Half power beamwidth	The beamwidth angle of a transmitting antenna that produces a beam footprint contour on which the signal power is 3dB lower than the maximum value.
Half transponder	A compromise method of broadcasting two signals through one transponder.

Harmonic	A component of a wave having a frequency an integral number of times that of the basic (fundamental) frequency eg if the fundamental frequency is fHz, then the harmonics are 2f, 3f, 4f etc.
HDTV (High Definition TV)	A TV format with enhanced picture resolution and viewing quality.
Head-end equipment	The portion of an MATV system where all the signals are received and processed prior to distribution.
Hertz (Hz)	An abbreviation for the frequency measurement of one cycle per second.
HFC	Hybrid Fibre-Coax.
High-pass filter	A circuit that passes signals above a designated frequency.
Home gateway	An STB interface between the delivery platform and appliances or systems throughout the home.
Horizontal polarisation	A radio wave where the electrical field is horizontal and the magnetic field is vertical.
HTTP	Hyper-Text Transfer Protocol. An OSI level 2 protocol used on the Internet.
Impedance	The resistance to alternating current flow in an electrical circuit.
Impulse noise	External interference from terrestrial sources such as thermostats, fridges etc, that can cause a DTT receiver to block or freeze.
Inclinometer	An instrument used to measure the angle of elevation to a satellite from the surface of the earth.
Inductance	The effect of a magnetic flux created by a current flowing in an electrical circuit. An inductor is normally a coil of wire mounted on a former. Inductance is measured in "Henries".
Insertion loss or through loss	The signal loss in dB caused by inserting a splitter or insert into a communications line.
Interframe (temporal) compression	An MPEG compression technique transmitting only changes between frames.
Interlaced scanning	A technique to minimise picture flicker whilst conserving channel bandwidth. Even and odd-numbered lines are scanned in separate fields to make one complete frame.
Intermediate frequency (IF)	A middle frequency range generated after down-conversion in an LNB or receiver.
Intermodulation	A form of interference caused by the modulation of one carrier affecting that of another signal in the same frequency band. It can be caused by non-linearity or the overloading of an amplifier.
Intraframe (spatial) compression	An MPEG compression technique eliminating repitition.
Ionosphere	A layer of the atmosphere that refracts or reflects electromagnetic radio waves,
IP	"Internet Protocol".
IRD	"Integrated Receiver-Decoder".
IRS	"Integrated Reception System".

ISDN	"Integrated Services Digital Network". A dial-up service to relay data in its original state over a telephone line.
ISO	International Standards Organisation.
ISP	Internet Service Provider.
Isotropic	Ideally, a point source that transmits signals of equal power in all directions.
ITU	International Telecommunications Union.
JPEG	An image compression standard which removes information.
Ka band	A band of frequencies 20-30GHz.
Kelvin	A degree of temperature in degrees Celcius or Centigrade. The Kelvin scale starts at absolute zero so O° Celsius is equivalent to 273° Kelvin.
Krone tool	A specialist tool for connecting telephone wires to phone sockets using the insulation displacement technique.
Ka band	The band of frequencies 20-30GHz.
Ku band	The band of frequencies 10.7-18GHz.
Ladder styles	The vertical part of a ladder to which the rungs are attached.
LAN (Local Area Network)	A cable network that links computer terminals together.
Laser diode	A device used in an fibre-optic transmitter that emits light waves at a single frequency.
Latitude	The measurement of a position on the surface of the earth north or south of the equator, in degrees of angle.
L band	A band of frequencies at 1.7GHz
Letterbox	A format for viewing widescreen pictures on a 4 x 3 TV screen.
Lightning protection	A system to minimise the effects of a lightning strike.
Link budget	An overall calculation of power gains and losses from transmission to reception.
Linear polarisation	Horizontally or vertically polarisation (as opposed to circular polarisation).
LNB	"Low Noise Block downconverter". A low noise microwave amplifier and converter that downconverts a block or range of frequencies to an IF range.
LNBF	An LNB with an integral feedhorn.
Local oscillator	A device used to supply a stable frequency to a down-converter. The local oscillator signal is mixed with the carrier wave to change its frequency.
Loft box	A unit containing all the devices commonly needed for the reception and distribution of terrestrial and satellite services within the home.
Log-periodic aerial	A wideband TV aerial with elements of different lengths.
Longitude	A distance in degrees east or west of the Greenwich meridian
Loop-wired network	An MATV network (no longer recommended) where the cable loops from room to room between padded outlet plates

299

Low pass filter	A circuit that only passes signals lower than a designated frequency.
LSOH (Low smoke/zero halogen)	A type of cable specified for use in public buildings to minimise the fire risk.
Luminance	The part of a TV waveform that contains the brightness information.
MAC	Medium Access Control.
Macro block	A defined group of pixels used in MPEG compression.
Magnetic north	The earth can be considered as a huge magnet having north and south magnetic poles. The line joining these poles is inclined slightly to the axis of rotation, hence true north and magnetic north do not coincide. A compass points to magnetic north.
Magnetic variation (or deviation)	The difference between true north and the north indication on a compass.
MATV	Master Antenna Television System
Method statement	A statement of the method to be used to carry out tasks.
Microwave	The frequency range from 1-30GHz and above.
Mini DiSEqC	A simple version of DiSEqC with only two states.
Mixer	A device used to combine signals together.
Modem (modulator/demodulator)	A telephone interface used in computers and digital TV receivers
Modulation	A process by which information is added or encoded on to a carrier wave
Modulation error ratio (MER)	A form of S/N ratio measurement, the noise being measured within the active channel.
Modulation index	The ratio of peak deviation to the highest modulating frequency.
Modulator	A device that modulates a video signal or MPEG2 transport stream onto a radio frequency carrier.
Monochrome	A black and white TV picture
Motor feedback	Information fed back to a motorised satellite receiver concerning the orientation of the dish
MP3	MPEG-1 Audio Layer 3. A high-quality audio compression standard.
MPEG	"Moving Picture Experts Group".
MPEG2	A set of digital TV compression standards.
MPEG4	A new compression standard that is "object-based".
Multicrypt	A digital scrambling system that uses a common PCMCIA interface. Several CAMs can be daisy-chained in a single receiver.
Multimode	A low-bandwidth mode of fibre-optic transmission using more than one light frequency. Used predominantly for telecommunication applications.
Multiplex (mux)	The simultaneous transmission of several signals or programmes over a single communication channel.
Multiple dwelling unit (MDU)	A group of homes, sometimes within the same building.

Multiswitch	An IF switching unit to enable any satellite receiver to access either polarity or band using voltage and 22KHz tone commands. Some versions relay terrestrial signals and allow access to multiple satellites using DiSEqC control signals.
Mutual isolation	The isolation in dBs between drop-in cables connected to the same network tee insert.
NIC	Network Interface Card. A PC interface with a wireless network.
NICAM	"Near Instantaneous Companded Audio Multiplex. Terrestrial transmitters broadcast sound channels using NICAM for improved sound quality in stereo.
NIT (Network Information Table)	A table that describes the transport medium for services on the currently demodulated and other multiplexes.
Noise	An unwanted signal that interferes with reception of the desired information. It is usually expressed in °K or dB.
Noise figure	A ratio of the actual noise power generated at the input of an amplifier to that which would be generated in an ideal resistor. The lower the noise figure, the better the performance.
Noise temperature	A measure of the amount of thermal noise present in a system or device. The lower the noise temperature, the better the performance. Expressed in (degrees) Kelvin.
NTSC	The National Television Standards Committee. The analogue system standard for TV broadcasts in the USA and Japan. 525 lines, 60Hz, 4MHz video bandwidth and 6MHz channel spacing.
Offset angle	The adjustment angle of a polar mount between the polar axis and the plane of a satellite dish used to aim at the geosynchronous arc. Increases from zero with latitude away from the equator.
Offset dish	A dish with a reflector that forms only part of a paraboloid of revolution, usually excluding the pole or apex, such that a front feed causes no aperture blockage.
Offset feed	A feed that is offset from the centre of a dish antenna. This configuration does not block the dish aperture.
Ohms law	The most fundamental relationship in the theory of electrical circuits is that relating potential difference, current and resistance, known as Ohm's Law ($V=IxR$).
OMT (OrthoMode Transducer)	A waveguide splitter. The input port is a circular C120 waveguide. The two output ports can be either circular or rectangular (WR75).
Orthogonal	At right angles to each other.
OSI model	Open Systems Interconnection model. A seven layer model that defines data communication protocols.
Output derating	The action of reducing the maximum output level of each of several amplifiers in cascade or of a single amplifier relaying several TV channels, to compensate for the overall increase in distortion levels.
PABX	Private Automatic Branch Exchange. A privately owned telephone network.

PAL (Phase Alternate Line)	The analogue TV broadcasting format used in some parts of Europe. 625 lines, 50Hz with 8MHz channel spacing
PAL G	The UHF analogue TV broadcasting standard used in Germany. The vision/sound carrier spacing is 5.5MHz
PAL I	The analogue TV broadcasting standard used in Britain and South Africa. The vision/sound carrier spacing is 6MHz
Panel or grid aerial	A series of stacked "X" arrays with a grid reflector, to give a high front-to-back ratio.
Parabola	A geometric shape that has the property of reflecting all signals parallel to its axis to a single focal point.
Parity bit (check sum)	Error correction data that is added to a data stream to make the bit values total either an odd or even number.
Path loss	The attenuation of a signal when travelling over a path between two points. Path loss varies inversely as the square of the distance travelled.
Pattress (pattra) box	An adaptor used to surface-mount a flush outlet plate.
PCM	Pulse Code Modulation.
Peritel connector	An alternative name for a SCART connector.
Phase	A measure of the relative position of a signal relative to a reference, in degrees.
Phase modulation	A transmission system in which the modulating signal is made to vary the carrier phase.
Phase shift keying (PSK)	A transmission system in which the modulating signal is made to vary the carrier phase.
PID (Programme Ident. Data)	A series of 4 character hexadecimal video and audio codes to distinguish between digital SCPC signals that are close together.
Pixel	An element of a digital picture.
Plasma display	A flat TV screen using light modulators or emitters to reproduce a TV picture.
PLL (Phase-Locked Loop)	A technique used to accurately lock oscillator frequencies.
PME (Primary Multiple Earth)	The main earth in a building, to which a cable distribution system must be bonded.
Polar diagram	A plot of the relative gain of an aerial or dish in various directions.
Polar mount	A dish mount that allows all satellites in geostationary orbit to be received with the movement of only one axis.
Polarisation	The plane of propagation of an electromagnetic wave. There are 4 states – horizontal, vertical, left-hand circular and right-hand circular.
Polarotor	A polarity-selection device with "skew" adjustment.
Polykit	A kit of all the parts needed to fix a lashing bracket to a chimney.
Polythene (polyethylene)	A waterproof material used as the outer sheath for outdoor cables. Not to be used internally.
POP	Point Of Presence.

POTS	Plain Old Telephone Service.
Pre-emphasis	A technique to increase the higher frequency. components of a signal before transmission to compensate for the greater cable loss, thereby improving the signal-to-noise ratio.
Prime focus dish	A parabolic dish with its focal point on its centre axis directly in front of the dish.
Progressive scanning	A TV sequential scanning process where the lines are scanned in numerical order.
PSK (Phase-Shift Keying)	A type of digital modulation.
PSTN	"Public Switched Telecommunications Network".
PVC (PolyVinyl Chloride)	A material used for the outer sheath of coaxial cables.
QAM	"Quadrature Amplitude Modulation".
QOS	Quality Of Service.
QPSK	"Quadrature Phase Shift Keying". A modulation technique used on satellite transmissions that uses phase shifts of a carrier wave to relay 4 symbols per cycle.
Quantising	Rounding up or down to the nearest whole number.
Radian	The angle at the centre of a circle subtended by an arc equal in length to its radius. It is equivalent to 57.3°.
Rain degradation	A reduction in C/N ratio due to rainfall.
Rain outage	Loss of a Ku band signal due to absorption and thermal noise accompanying heavy rainfall.
Raster	A pattern of scanning lines on a TV screen.
RCD (Residual Current Device)	An electrical safety device designed to disconnect mains power in the event of an earth current.
Reed Solomon	An MPEG error correction technique using "outer coding" to minimise burst errors.
Reed switch	A mechanical switch operated by a rotating magnet to count the revolutions of a motor-actuator.
Refraction	The deflection of a radio wave or light wave as it passes between two mediums of different densities.
Reflection	The rebounding of a radio or light wave from a surface or junction of two different materials with different densities.
Reflector plate or element	The rear element of an aerial mounted behind the dipole that modifies the aerial characteristics.
REN (ringer equivalence number)	The loading factor of a unit connected to a phone line.
RF	Radio Frequency.
RGB (red/green/blue)	The three primary colours used in colour television.
RHCP	Right-Hand Circular Polarisation.
Risk assessment	An assessment of the risks involved in carrying out a task, and how they will be minimised.
RS232	An interface standard for serial data.
Satellite IF	The band of frequencies eminating from an LNB that are relayed via a coaxial cable to the IF input of an amplifier, multiswitch or satellite receiver.

S band	A band of frequencies at 2.5GHz
Scalar feed	A wide-flare corrugated dish feed.
Scalar rings	A corrugated concentric surround to a prime focus feed to improve its impedance-matching characteristics.
Scanning	A moving electron beam to reproduce an entire picture as a sequence of horizontal lines.
SCART	"Syndicat des Constructeurs d'Appareils Radio recepteurs et Televisieurs". A European 20 pin standard connector used to interlink video/audio circuits between domestic audio and TV products. Also known as a "Peritel" connector.
SCPC (Single Carrier per Chan.)	A satellite transmission system that uses a separate carrier for each channel (compared with frequency division multiplexing which combines several channels on to a single carrier).
SDT (Service Description Table)	Data relating to the services contained within a digital multiplex.
SECAM	"SEquential Couleur A Memoire". The French analogue TV standard.
SES	"Societe Europeenne des Satellites". Astra is the trademark of SES.
Shadowmask tube	A CRT employing 3 electron guns to reproduce the red, green and blue components of a colour TV picture.
Side lobe	A parameter used to describe the ability of an aerial or dish to receive off-axis signals. The larger the side lobes, the more noise and interference that is received.
Side loss	The signal loss in dB of a network tee insert, between the input coaxial cable and the drop-in cable
Signal level meter	A frequency selective heterodyne receiver capable of tuning to the frequency band of interest, with an indicating meter showing the magnitude of the input voltage at a specific frequency.
Signal to noise (S/N) ratio	A ratio in dBs of the peak voltage of the signal of interest to the root-mean-square (rms) voltage of the noise in that signal.
Simulcrypt	A digital scrambling system where some of the functionality is built into the receiver itself.
Single mode	A high-bandwidth mode of fibre-optic transmission using a single light frequency.
SIP	Session Initiation Protocol. A procedure using URL addresses to convey messages on an IP network.
Skew	Adjustment of an LNB to minimise reception of the unwanted polarity.
Slices	A group of digital macro blocks.
Slope	The uneven attenuation of a broadband signal across its frequency band as it travels along a coaxial cable
SMATV	"Satellite Master Antenna Television". A system intended to receive and distribute radio, TV and satellite programmes to multi-dwelling units.
Snow	Video noise caused by a insufficient S/N ratio.

SOB (surface outlet box)	A TV or satellite outlet designed for surface mounting on a window frame or skirting board.
Software download	The action of upgrading a software operating system in a digital satellite receiver.
Source switching	The use of 12V on pin 8 of a SCART connector to switch between the aerial socket and SCART inputs of a TV receiver.
Sparklies	Small black and/or white horizontal dashes in an analogue TV picture caused by an insufficient S/N ratio.
Spatial (intraframe) compression	An MPEG compression technique eliminating repitition.
Spectrum analyser	A scanning receiver with a display that shows a plot of frequency versus amplitude of the signals being measured.
Splitter	A device used to split radio signals on a coaxial cable.
Spot beam	A circular or eliptical beam covering some defined region of the earth's surface.
Spur cable	A coaxial cable feeding drop-in cables via tee inserts.
Spur insert	A device that transfers a specific amount of energy from a main feeder cable to one or more spur cables.
Stacking combiner	A matching device to combine the outputs of several identical aerials on to one coaxial downlead.
Standing wave	Peaks and troughs of signal on a cable due to forward and reflected signals being either in-phase or out-of-phase.
Star-wired network	An MATV network with separate drop-in cables linking each dwelling to a multiswitch at a central "node".
STB	"Set-Top Box".
Stream	The digital signal received from a satellite transponder that contains video signals plus the additional information needed to process the received signal correctly.
Sub carrier	An information-carrying wave that in turn modulates the main carrier in a communications system.
S-VHS	A method of video/audio interconnection that relays the brightness, colour and audio information separately.
Synchronising (sync.) pulses	Pulses imposed on a video signal to keep the TV picture scanning synchronised with that of the picture source.
Tap loss	The signal loss in dB of a network tee insert, between the input coaxial cable and the drop-in cable.
TDMA	Time Division Multiple Access. A protocol used to allocate services to the frequencies available.
TCP	"Transfer Control Protocol". An OSI level four protocol to manage the flow of IP data
TDT (Time and Date Table)	Digital data received to synchronise the IRD clock.
Tee insert (tap)	A device that transfers a specific amount of energy from the main distribution system to a secondary outlet.
Telecom band	The band of frequencies 12.5-12.75GHz
Telephone connection	The connection of an interactive digital receiver modem to a telephone line.

Teletext	Separate information transmitted with a TV picture signal that can be displayed on the screen in place of the normal picture. This service is called CEEFAX by the BBC and ORACLE by the ITV companies
Temporal (interframe) compression	An MPEG compression technique transmitting only changes between frames.
Terminating resistor	A 75ohm matching resistor fitted across the end of an unterminated coaxial cable to prevent the creation of standing waves
TETRA	TErrestrial Trunked RAdio. A standard used by the UK emergency services to provide secure voice and data communications.
Threshold	The minimum S/N input required to allow a satellite receiver to produce a picture.
Through loss or insertion loss	The signal loss in dB caused by inserting a splitter or insert into a communications line
Tilt	The uneven attenuation of a broadband signal across its frequency band as it travels along a coaxial cable.
Triad	A group of three dots representing the red, green and blue content of a single picture element on a TV screen.
Transformer	A device to link two rf circuits together, comprising two or more coils of wire. Used to provide voltage and impedance matching and/or galvanic isolation.
Transponder	One circuit on a satellite that receives and retransmits an uplinked signal.
Transport stream	An MPEG2 multiplex with short, fixed-length packets carrying programmes intended for general broadcast.
Tree-and-branch network	An MATV network with spur cables connected to individual "drop-in" cables using tee inserts.
Tree-and-bush network	An extension of the "tree-and-branch" MATV network concept where the with spur cables are connected via "nodes" to individual drop-in cables feeding each viewing location.
Tuned circuit (filter)	A device used to pass or reject a specified range of frequencies.
TV plug or Belling plug	A standard UK TV connector to specification IEC95.
TVRO	A TV Receive-Only earth station designed to receive (but not transmit) satellite communications.
UDP	User Datagram Protocol. An OSI level four protocol to manage the flow of IP data
UHF (ultra-high frequency)	The frequency spectrum 300MHz-3GHz. Terrestrial UHF broadcast TV occupies the band 470-860MHz.
Universal LNB	A Ku band LNB with 9.75/10.6GHz local oscillators, that uses voltage and tone switching to select polarity and band respectively.
Uplink	The earth station electronics and aerial that transmit information to a communications satellite.
URL	Uniform Resource Locator.
USB	An external computer interface for serial data. Units can be "daisy-chained" to this port.

UTMS	"Universal Mobile Telecommunications System". The "third-generation" of digital mobile phone technology that provides higher data speeds and advanced features.
VDSL	Very high bit rate Digital Subscriber Line. A high speed version of ADSL.
Vector	A voltage that varies with time in a sinusoidal manner.
Viterbi	An MPEG error correction technique using a variable amount of "inner coding", known as FEC. This is also called "convolutional error correction".
VNOD	"Video nearly on demand". A multi-channel service broadcasting copies of a film with staggered start times so that a complete film is always available to the viewer within a short waiting period.
VOIP	Voice Over IP. The relay of speech over the Internet.
VSB	"Vestigial SideBand" transmission. Used for TV broadcasting. Double sideband transmission is used for low video frequencies, and single sideband transmission for higher video frequencies.
VSWR	Voltage Standing wave Ratio. The ratio between the minimum and maximum voltage on a coaxial cable. The ideal VSWR is 1.0. Ghosting can result as the VSWR increases. It is also a measure of the reflected power to the total power at any point on the system.
WAN	Wide Area Network.
WAP	"Wireless Application Protocol". An open global specification that defines a set of hardware and software interfaces to allow mobile phones to send and receive email messages and to browse the internet.
WARC	"World Administrative Radio Conference".
Waveguide	Usually a hollow copper tube of such rectangular or circular dimensions that it will propagate electromagnetic waves of a given frequency. Used for relaying super high frequency waves, or microwaves.
Wavelength	The length of one complete cycle of an electromagnetic wave. Wavelength decreases as the signal frequency increases.
Wegener	A proprietary system for subcarrier stereo transmission. It uses discrete low level companded subcarriers.
Weighting	The correction of S/N ratio measurements to take into account such factors as bandwidth and annoyance value.
White noise	Noise having a constant energy per unit bandwidth over a particular frequency band.
Widescreen	A "cinemascope" TV picture format, usually 16:9.
Window of operation	A range of minimum and maximum parameters required for the satisfactory performance of a system.
WLAN	Wireless Local area Network.
WR75 flange	A standard mating flange for rectangular Ku band waveguides.
WWW	World Wide Web.
X band	The frequency band 7-8GHz.

X-type aerial	A type of high gain TV aerial design with several elements connected at each point on the support boom, to give increased overall gain whilst minimising the overall length of the aerial.
Yagi	A common type of aerial design comprising a dipole with a rear reflector and several front director elements.
Zone 1 / zone 2 dishes	Standard offset dishes used for BSkyB installations
Zone beam	A beam pattern (usually a shaped beam intermediate between hemispheric and spot beams.

Binary prefixes

Name	Symbol	Factor	Power of 2
Kilo	k	1 024	2^{10}
Mega	M	1 048 576	2^{20}
Giga	G	1 073 741 824	2^{30}
Tera	T	1 099 511 627776	2^{40}

Metric prefixes

Name	Symbol	Factor	Power of 10
Milli	m	0.001 (one thousandth)	10^{-3}
Micro	μ	0.000 001 (one millionth)	10^{-6}
Nano	n	0.000 000 001 (one billionth)	10^{-9}
Pico	p	0.000 000 000 001 (one trillionth)	10^{-12}
Kilo	k	1 000	10^{3}
Mega	M	1 000 000	10^{6}
Giga	G	1 000 000 000	10^{9}
Tera	T	1 000 000 000 000	10^{12}

GET THIS BOOK FREE

Thank you for purchasing this book. Vision Products (Europe) Ltd hope that it will prove invaluable when you plan and install professional TV, satellite, AV and fibre systems over the coming years.

Vision manufacture an industry leading range of high-quality equipment to make your installs faster, better value and more powerful. We know that installers who try Vision like it and buy again. So as a thank you for buying this book, we would like to refund the £29.99 cover price when you try Vision for the first time before 31st May 2010.

Here's how to get a cheque for £29.99 sent to you

1) Visit **www.vision-products.co.uk** to find an approved Vision wholesaler

2) Purchase at least £350 worth of Vision goods on a single invoice

3) Fill in the voucher below with your details

4) Send a copy of the invoice with the voucher to Vision at the address below

5) We'll do the rest and send your cheque back to you

Terms & Conditions

Original vouchers only accepted. A qualifying invoice may be used once only with this offer and only one voucher can be claimed per invoice. Invoice must clearly show a purchase date between June 2009 and May 2010, wholesaler purchased from, individual purchase prices and business address of purchaser. Invoice must show at least £350 of Vision branded goods ex VAT, ex CP&I. Cheques for £29.99 will be drawn on a UK bank and will be made payable to individual or organisation shown on invoice. Proof of postage not accepted as proof of delivery. Offer subject to availability and may be withdrawn without notice. We reserve the right to reject any application in order to prevent fraud. Errors and omissions excepted. Check www.vision-products.co.uk for fully updated terms.

YES!! I want to claim my £29.99

I have attached an invoice showing I have bought £350 of Vision goods.
My details are on the back. Please send me my cheque.

Send to:-

GET THIS BOOK FREE!!
Vision Products (Europe) Ltd
Unit 1 Redbourne Park
Liliput Road
Brackmills
Northampton
NN4 7DT

Please send my cheque back to my business address below

Payable to:

Address:

Postcode:

Telephone: **Email:**

Terms & Conditions

Original vouchers only accepted. A qualifying invoice may be used once only with this offer and only one voucher can be claimed per invoice. Invoice must clearly show a purchase date between June 2009 and May 2010, wholesaler purchased from, individual purchase prices and business address of purchaser. Invoice must show at least £350 of Vision branded goods ex VAT, ex CP&I. Cheques for £29.99 will be drawn on a UK bank and will be made payable to individual or organisation shown on invoice. Proof of postage not accepted as proof of delivery. Offer subject to availability and may be withdrawn without notice. We reserve the right to reject any application in order to prevent fraud. Errors and omissions excepted. Check www.vision-products.co.uk for fully updated terms.

Index

Access Point 262

Aerial
Alignment 93
Balun 108
Bow Tie 71
Choice 92
Colour Code 70
Combiners 94
Diplexed 93
Director Elements 68
Front-to-Back Ratio 95
Gain 94
Ghosting 95
Grid 71
Grouped 70
Location 89, 192
Log Periodic 72
Multi Boom 72
Multiple Arrays 93
Parameters 69, 73
Performance 73
Siting 92
X type 71
Yagi 71

Amplifier 14
Cascade 79
Derating 78, 125
Indoor 80
Location 18, 74, 211
Masthead 77, 79
Noise 125
Set-Back 80
Specifications 124
Split Band 125

Analogue
Digital Conversion 25
Formats 21
Interconnections 43
Level Windows 74
Reference 62
Signal Level 74, 221
TV Interference 103
TV Troubleshooting 102

Analyser Applications 229
APC 237
Application Layer 258
Arthur C Clarke 139
Aspect Ratio 22
Asynchronous Transfer Mode 257

Attenuators 80
Types 81

Audio
Dolby Pro-Logic 43
Sources 35
AV Sources 35

Azimuth 146
B Frames 28

Backbone
4 Cable 211
5 Cable 187
9 Cable 188
17 Cable 189, 207

Backlash 175

Band
BSS 142
C 142, 167
DBS 142
FSS 142
Guard 66
Ka 142
Ku 142
L 142
S 142
VHF TV 135

Bandwidth 69
Multiplex 62
Transponder 62
Benchmark Standards 72

BER 32, 77
Limit 225
Locations 225
Measurement 225

Bluetooth 263
BluRay 42
Boresight 139

Brackets 84
T&K 86, 89
Wall 86

Brightness Levels 25
BSB 139
Building Sites 283

Cable
Backbone 215
Benchmarking 110
CAT5 269
CAT5 Colour Code 270
CAT5 Connections 270
CAT5e 269
CAT6 269
CAT7 269
Coaxial 109
Composite 110, 215
Crossover 44, 270
Dielectric 109
Disadvantages 233
Ducts 109
External IRS Routes 212
External Vertical 216
Feeder 127
Fixing 96
Flat Roofs 216
Internal IRS Routes 212
Joint Sealing 96
Losses 111
LSNH 109
LSOH 109, 197
Management 96
Routing 96
Screens 109-110
Sheath 109, 196
Spur 120, 127
Terminators 112
UTP 269

Capacitor 56
Carrier Offsets 136
Carrier to Noise Ratio 74, 77, 224
Carrier Wave 51
Cassegrain 144
Catenary Wire 97
CBER 225
CCIR Impairment Scale 75
CDM 283
CEC 46
Channel Transposition 138
Characteristic Impedance 57, 68,
Characteristic Impedance 110
Chimney Installation 100
Chimney Stability 90
Chrominance 23
Cinemascope Widescreen 22
Cladding 236
Class 1 Equipment 195
Class 2 Equipment 195
Cliff Effect 32, 75
CMTS 263
Code of Practice 194

COFDM 62
Colour Code 215
Combiners 81
Compass 146
Component Video DVD Players 43
Composite Triple Beat 136

Compression
Digital 26
MPEG 26
Spatial Intraframe 26
Statistical 27-28
Temporal Interframe 27

Conditional Access 155-156, 165

Connectors
D-Sub 45
DVI 45
HDCP 46
HDMI 47
IEC95 112
Insulation Displacement 253
RGB SCART 44
RJ45 269, 271, 279
SCART 22, 43-44, 117
TV 112

Constellation Diagram 60, 224,
Constellation Diagram 226
Copper Conductors 196
Core 236
Corotor 167
Corrosion 287
Coverage Area 137
Cross Modulation Distortion 126
Cross-Polar Discrimination 151
CTB 196
Current 13

Data
Address Byte 171
Binary 24
Bit Rates 25
Bits and Bytes 24
Broadband Links 264
Command Byte 171
Errors 31
Headers 256
Link 257
Packets 29, 256
Parameters 256
Parity Bits 32
Technology Speeds 265
Virtual Path 256

dB 17
Microvolts 17
Millivolts 17
Signal Levels 18

DC Pass 82
DDC 46
Declination Angle 172
Declination Offsets 173
Deep Colour 47
Derating Rules 78
Dielectric Plate 148, 166

Digital
Switchover 66
Advantages of 23
Errors 224
Light Processing 39
Signal Levels 75
TV Troubleshooting 105

Diplexer 83
TV/Satellite 163

Diploe, Folded 69

Dipole, Half Wavelength 67
Discrete Cosine Tansform 30

DiSEqC 170
DiSEqC 1 171
DiSEqC 2 171
Full 170
Mini 170
Tone Burst Generator 207

Dish
Alignment 174
Antennas 143
Assembly 178
Camouflage 157
Design 143
Location 145
Materials 143
Mountings 177
Painting 143
Prime Focus 166
Size 141, 145, 152
Types 144

Display
16QAM 61, 223
256QAM 61
Cathode Ray Tube 37
Flat Panel 38
Liquid Crystal 38
Plasma 38
Spectrum 230

DOCSIS 263
Down Conductor 88
Downlink 139
Drilling through Walls 97
Drip Loop 96
Drop-in Cable 127
Drop-in Cable Containment 193
DSLAM 261

DTT 61, 66
Carrier to Noise Limits 224
Demodulator 123
Level Limits 222
Level Measurements 220
Meters 227
Multiplex 66, 82
Power Levels 62
Signal Levels 76

DVB 62
DVB-S 62
DVB-S2 63
DVB-T 62
DVB-T2 63

Earthing
Bars 217
Lugs 217
Mains 120
Mat 196

EDID 47
Electric Field 54
Elevation 146
Encryption Types 165
Equalisation Slope 132
Equipment Cabinets 214, 218
Equipment Potential Bonding 195
Error Correction 155
Eye Mask 48
Eye Pattern Testing 48
Farads 56
FC 237
FEC 34, 141, 155
Feedhorn 143, 147

Fibre-Optic
Advantages 247

Applications	233	Troubleshooting	49	Krone Frames	269
Bendable Fibres	236	**Head End**		Krone Tool	253
Buffer	236	Equipment	127	Laser Pen	248
Cable Installation	248	Equipment Location	192	Lashing Splices	90
Cleanliness	238	Henries	56	Lattitude	139
Connectors	237	Hertz	51	LBER	225
Construction	236	Hi-Fi	35	Levellers	84
Distribution	190	Home Cinema	35	LHCP	166
Interface	236	Home Distribution	116	**Light**	
Jacket	236	Hub	267	Emitters	38
Joints	237	Hybrid Transformers	252	Frequencies	234
Joints Box	237	I Frames	28	Modulators	38
Links	196	I2C Bus	47	Reflection	234
Microscope	248	ICANN	258	Refraction	234
Multimode	235	ICMP	268	**LNB**	**147**
Single Mode	235	IEEE Ethernet	262	Block Down Conversion	147-148
Wavelengths	235	IF Slope Example	231	C120 Flange	166
Filter	**56, 83**	IF Stacker	189	Enhanced	150
Cluster	84, 121	Impedance	138	Location	148
Leveller	121	Impulse Noise	107, 124	Multiple Installations	169
Programmable Cluster	122	Inclinometer	146	Noise Figure	151
Terrestrial	196	Inductor	56	Noise Temperature	152
Types	57	In-Phase	53	Octo	185
Fixings		Insert Values	128	Optical	246
Cavity	40	Insertion Losses	82	Quad	185
Chimney	85, 90	**Installation**		Quattro	186
Guy Wire	87	Aesthetic Consideration	157	States	185
Loft	87	BSkyB	156	Switching	169
Roof	86	Freesat	156	Twin	185
Spring Toggle	40	Multiple Sky	184	Universal	150
Tile	92	Planning Permission	137, 191	Voltages	148
Types	89	Planning Permission	198	Lobe	68
U Bolt	85	Site Survey	191	Local Oscillator Frequencies	149
Umbrella	40	Integration	220	Loft Box	183, 214
V Bolt	85	Interfaced Scanning	21	Longitude	139
Wall	89	**Interference**		Luminance	23
Flyleads	99	Adjacent Channel	76	MAC Address	263, 267
FOB	99	Co-channel	55, 76	Macro Block	30
Focal Point	143	External	102	Magnetic Deviation	146
Forward Error Correction	33	Microwave	152	Magnetic Field	54
Framing Byte	171	Interlaced Scanning	41	Main Operating Windows	121
Frequencies Shifter	149	Interleaving	33	**Mast**	
Frequency	**51, 56, 67**	Intermediate Frequency	147	Clamps	87
Bands	52	Intermodulation Distortion	126	Couplers	87
Modulation	58	Intermodulation Distortion	135	Diameter	86
Freznel Zones	54, 137	Internet Access Requirements	259	Wall Thickness	86
Full HD	42	Internet Message		**MATV**	**119**
Fused Spur	98	Control Protocol	258	Cable Losses	128
G/T Ratio	151	Interpolation	220	Losses	129
Gap Fillers	136	Interstage Gain Control	80	Planning	127
Gateway Termination Unit	246	Ionosphere	55	System Concepts	121
Geostationary Orbit	139	IP Rating	214	MER Limits	227
Ghosting	55	**IPTV**	**264**	MET	195
Gregorian	145	Applications	268	Metallic Stud Locator	40
Groups of Pictures	27	Bandwidth	265	Meteosat	167
GUI	262	IPv4	258-259	**Modulation**	**51, 131**
Handset Activation	251	IPv6	258	Amplitude	58
HD		**IRS**		DSB	131
1080i	41	**187**		Error Ratio	227
720p	41	Cables	196	Phase	58, 60
HDTV	38, 41	Layout Concepts	191	VSB	131
HD by DTT	63	Planning	196-197	**Motor**	
HD Ready	42	Outlet Plates	188	Actuator	175
HDMI	**45**	Services	192	Feedback	175
Alternatives	49	Specifications	190	H to H	175
Data Speeds	47	Terrestrial Input	187	Limit Switches	175
Distribution	49	ISDN	261	Systems	172
Equaliser	49	ISP	261	**Mount**	
Long Cables	49	Kevlar Yarn	236	Non-Penetrating Roof	217
Over CAT5	49	Krone Frame Connection	276	Polar	172
Remote Control	49			Wall	39
Standards	47			**MPEG**	**26, 60**
Timing Error	48			MPEG2	265

MPEG4	63
MPEG4	265
Multicrypt	156
Multi-Dwelling Units	119
Multimeter	14
Multiple Remote Eyes	183
Multiswitch	**186**
Capacity	187
Locations	193
Mounting	215
Powering	187
Network	
Computer	267
Gains and Losses	197
Isolation	127
Layer	257
Layout	192
Local Area	262, 267
Loop Wired	119
Star Wired	120, 186
Structured Cable	267
Tree-and-Branch	119
Tree-and-Bush	119
WLAN	262
New Buildings	118
Noise	**73**
Accumulation	125
Distortion Effects	223
Generation	73
Levels	75
Margin	227
Measurements	224
Reference	125
Removal	32
Sources	125
Temperature	151-152
NTE5 Socket	252
Ofcom	136
Offset	145
Offset Angles	166
Ohms	15
Ohm's Law	16
Optical	
Attenuator	246
Budget	247
Cleanliness	250
Feedback	176
Fibre	233
Losses	247
Power Meter	248
Receiver	246
Splitter Losses	247
Time Domain Reflectometer	249
Transmitter	246
Organic Light Emitting Diode	39
Oscilloscope	22
Outer Coding	33
Outlet	
Diplexed	99, 188
Frames	188
Isolated	83
Modular	99
Multiservice	188
Plates	99, 127
Quad	188
Screened	83
Signal Levels	198
Triplexed	188
Out-of-Phase	53
P Clips	215
P Frames	28
Parabolic	143
Pattress Box	99

PC 237
PDA 262
PET Strapping 85
Phase 51
Physical Layer 257
Picture
  Blocking 32
  Displays 36
  Formats 41
  Letterbox 22
  Widescreen 22
PID 168
Pixels 23, 38
  Block 23, 30
  Slice 23
Plumb-Bob 146
PME 195
Polar Diagram 68, 138
Polarisation 54
  Circular 148, 166
  Selection 148
Polarotor 166, 175
  Magnetic 177
  Mechanical 176
Poles 84
Polyethylene 109
Polykit 85
Polythene Sheath 196
Ports 267
Power 16, 141
  Lofts 98
  Power Line 127
  Power Supply Unit 79
Pre-Emphasis 130
Prefixes 51
Presentation Layer 257
Prime Focus Type 144
Programmable Filter/Amplifier 122
Programme Languages 165
Programme Multiplexing 28
Progressive Scanning 21, 41
Projector Screen 36
Propagation Charts 137
Protection, Lightning 88, 137, 195
Proxy Server 268
PSK 60
PSTN 251, 261
PVC 109
PVR 156
Q Factor 56, 69
QAM 61
QEF 225
QSI Model 257
QSPK 61, 155
Quantising 30
Radio
  AM/FM 59
  FM Troubleshooting 102
  Paths 53
  Waves 51-52
Rain Degradation 153
Reception, Multi-Satellite 165
Red / Green / Blue 37
Reed Feedback 176
Reed Solomon 33
Reflection 55
Reflector Plate 68
Refraction 55
Relay Sites 137

Remote Control
  AV 81
  Other Equipment 182
  VCR 100
Remote Eye 181
Repeater Amplifiers 127
Resequencing 33
Resistance 13
  Colour Code 15
Resolution 42
Resonant Circuit 57
RHCP 166
Ringing Current 255
Risk Analysis 286
Rotating Vector 51
Router 259, 267
RS232 Control 269
Run Length Coding 27
Safety
  CE Marking 81
  Electrical 54, 126, 194
  Fibre-Optic 249
  General Public 288
  Health and Safety 89
  Installer 289
  Ladder 89
  Mechanical 287
  Method Statement 284
Sampling 25
Satellite
  22kHZ Tone Switching 150
  Amplifiers 211
  Astra 139-140, 231
  BER 154
  Carrier to Noise Ratios 153
  CTH 139
  Digital Level Measurements 220
  Digital Meters 228
  Eutelsat 140-142
  Footprints 140
  Frequency Bands 142
  Fibre Applications 246
  Receiver Connections 168
  Receivers 155
  Remodulator 123
  Search Parameters 168
  Signal Measurements 154
  Troubleshooting 163
SC 237
SCPC 168
SDS Drill Bits 89
SDs Sockets 90
Services Relayed 186
Session Layer 257
Shadow Mask 37
Shopping Sites 259
Side Loss 127
Signal Measurements 219
Simulcrypt 156
Single Cable Router 189
Skew Adjustment 151
Sky
  Azimuth Elevation 158
  Card Activation 161
  Dish Alignment 159
  Dish Sizes 156
  Handing Over 163
  Handset Programming 161
  Installation Sequence 158
  Interactive Services 162
  Meter Display 159
  Multiroom 184

Receiver Installation 160
SCART Connections 161
Skew Adjustment 159-160
Sky+ 156
Sky+ / Sky+ HD Integration 184
Sky+ HD 161
Telephone Charges 161-162
TV Distribution 181
UHF Output 161
Skype 264
Slicing 32
SMATV 131
SOB 99
Social Network Services 259
Software
  Anti-Virus 259
  Download 161
  e-Mail 258
  Firewall 49, 259, 268
  HTTP 258, 260
  Internet Protocol 258
  Search Engines 259
  URL 258
  Web Browsers 258
Sparklies 154
Spectrum Analysers 228
Splicing
  Arc Fusion 237-238
  Bridge 237
  Mechanical 237
Splitter 81
  Asymmetrical 82
  Losses 19
  Optical 246
Spur Inserts 127
Stacking Combiners 94
Standing Waves 112
Strainers 87
Subscriber Insert 127
Subscriber Taps 127
Supporting Structures 288
Surge Arrestors 214
Switch 267
Symbol 60
Sync Pulse 22
T568B 270
Tall Buildings 214
TCP 258, 260
Telephone
  ASDL 261
  Cable Colour Code 253
  Communication Frequencies 251
  Components 251
  Extension Installation 254
  Line Check 158
  Master Socket 252
  Pin Connectors 253
  Pulse Dialling 252
  Ringer Equivalence Number 255
  Sockets 194, 253
  Telephony 251
  Tone Dialling 252
  Typical Faults 256
  Wireless Extensions 256
Teletext 21
Tensioners 87
Terminating Resistors 127
Terminators 15
TETRA 83, 108
Thatched Roof 196
Through Loss 127
Time Division Multiplexing 26, 252

Time to Live 259
TMDS 46
Torodial 145, 169
Total Internal Reflection 234
Transformer 57, 69
Transport Layer 257
Triad 37
Troughs / Nuts 68
Tuned Circuit 56
TV Link Plus 182
TV Projector 36
TVRO 151
UDP 260
UHF
  Amplifiers 78, 122, 124
  Bandwidth 65
  Choice 133
  Channel Selection 133
  Channels 221
  Crystal Palace 219
  Frequencies 65
  Modulator 116
  PAL I Channel 219
  Signal Levels 123
  Single Channel Amplifiers 124
  Spectrum PAL I 65
  Window of Operation 123
Uplink 139
User Diagram Protocol 258
Variable Length Coding 27
VBER 225
Ventilation 288
Video
  Audio Switching 269
  Video Frequencies 58
  Composite 43
  Inversion 167
  Server 268
  Streaming 259
  S-VHS 43
  Test Signal 21
  VGA 45
  Waveform 21
Viera Link 49
Viterbi 33
Vocoder 263
Voice Over IP 263
Voltage 13-14
  Hazardous 194
  Prefixes 16
  Switching LNB 148
Vonage 264
VSDL 261
Wall Mounted Installation 101
Wall Panels 218
WARC 139
Waveform, Sawtooth 25
Wavefront 52
Waveguide 147
  Noise Temperature 152
  WR75 166
Wavelength 51, 67, 56
  Frequency 94
  Wavelets 52
Wi-Fi 262-263
WiMax 263
World Wide Web 258